D0810008

SELECTED ENGLISH CLASSICS

General Editor: A. H. R. Ball, M.A.

CHAUCER
THE PROLOGUE & THREE TALES

Chaucer

THE PROLOGUE & THREE TALES

THE PROLOGUE TO THE CANTERBURY TALES
THE PRIORESS'S TALE
THE NUN'S PRIEST'S TALE
THE PARDONER'S TALE

Edited by
GEORGE H. COWLING, M.A.

GINN AND COMPANY LTD.
QUEEN SQUARE, LONDON, W.C.1

GINN AND COMPANY LTD.

COPYRIGHT

First published 1934
Fifth impression 1946
054612

PRINTED IN GREAT BRITAIN
BY R. & R. CLARK, LIMITED, EDINBURGH

PREFACE

THESE selections from Chaucer's *Canterbury Tales* have been prepared for those who are going to read Chaucer for the first time. I have endeavoured, therefore, to normalize the text, as far as it can be normalized without " show of violence." For the confirmed reader of Chaucer this is unnecessary, but on the other hand I am certain that normalization is helpful to beginners. The introduction and notes are made as short as is consistent with lucidity. On the other hand, the glossary, which is essential to the study of Chaucer's meaning, is as full, except for obvious words, as I could make it ; but rightly or wrongly I have not thought it worth while to give line-references to the meanings of words.

In these labours I have owed everything to the work of my predecessors : to Skeat, Pollard, Manly, Sisam, Koch, and Kaluza, and to them I gratefully acknowledge my debt. My thanks also I should like to give to the numerous scholars from whom I have garnered such knowledge as I possess about Chaucer and his works. Finally, I should like to thank most cordially Mr W. T. Price, who has read the proofs and made many valuable suggestions.

G. H. COWLING

MELBOURNE, 1934

v

PREFACE

These selections from Chaucer's *Canterbury Tales* have been prepared for those who are going to read Chaucer for the first time. ...

... C. H. COWLING

MELBOURNE, 1916

CONTENTS

	PAGE
PREFACE	V
ENGLAND IN CHAUCER'S DAY	ix
THE CANTERBURY TALES	xxvi
THE LANGUAGE AND METRE OF CHAUCER	xxxviii
THE PROLOGUE TO THE CANTERBURY TALES	1
THE PRIORESS'S TALE	67
THE MERRY WORDS OF THE HOST TO CHAUCER	80
THE NUN'S PRIEST'S TALE	82
THE PARDONER'S TALE	124
GLOSSARY	159

ENGLAND IN CHAUCER'S DAY

I

In the fourteenth century England was a small nation. Its population is not exactly known, but it is estimated to have been in 1377 about two and a quarter millions. London had a population of about 45,000. York had 13,500 souls. Bristol was a little riverside port of some 12,000, and no other town or city had more than ten thousand inhabitants. The chief industry of the country was agriculture, a miserably unfruitful system of grazing and cultivation of unenclosed fields, conducted partly by the lord of the manor or his bailiff, and partly by the tenants and labourers; for every manor was an agricultural unit. Chaucer's Plowman was one of these peasants, who tilled strips of the arable field with painful toil (in their ignorance of effective fertilization and machinery) for an average production of from four to eight bushels of corn per acre; and who kept pigs and sheep under the oversight of a herdsman on the common pastures. The alternative to this unproductive and unenterprising system of agriculture was sheep-farming, which, encouraged by the profitable example of the various communities of Cistercian monks, had increased largely after 1349. There was a steady demand from the looms of Flanders for English wool, and the king's customary duty on its exportation was one of the greatest sources of income to the royal exchequer. Chaucer's merchant was perhaps engaged in the wool trade with Flanders.

London was a crowded city, closely confined by its great wall, more than two miles long, which extended from Blackfriars—around by way of Ludgate, Aldersgate, Bishopsgate, and Aldgate—to the Tower. The chief thoroughfares were, with the exception of Chepe, narrow ; and the inhabitants were for the most part herded away in houses built of wood and plaster facing alleys and courts which led off from the main streets. Here and there in the city were the great stone houses of the nobility and of the richest merchants, built, as a rule, foursquare around a courtyard, each with its hall for dining and entertainment, its offices, and its servants' quarters. The city was divided for civic purposes into wards, and every ward bristled with the spires and towers of the city churches, of which there were all told about one hundred, the most magnificent of all being the cathedral church of London, St Paul's, a Gothic building which in many respects resembled Winchester Cathedral. Spanning the river, stood, on its twenty arches, old London Bridge, with its chapel and its great houses. Outside the walls were the great religious houses : the new Charterhouse, the foundation of Sir Walter Manny, in the field beyond Aldersgate ; the house of the Carmelites, or Whitefriars, south of Fleet Street ; and the house of the Dominicans, or Blackfriars, in Chancery Lane. And south of the Strand, which was the highway to the King's palace and Westminster Hall, and to the Benedictine Abbey of Westminster, stood the Savoy, the palace of John of Gaunt. Everywhere the narrow streets were unpaved and unclean ; sanitation was most primitive, and household water had to be carried from the nearest well or from the conduit in Chepe. It was a comfortless age, when knighthood was in flower. Men who could rivet themselves up in hard steel could endure almost anything. Coal-fires, cushions and carpets, were things of the future. A glass window was a luxury.

Let us look at these hardy men of London Town. There were the clergy (including the schoolmasters), the lawyers, the physicians, and the higher officials of the retinues of the nobles. The guildsmen were the merchants and tradesmen of the city, all—whether rich or poor, whether engaged in seaborne ventures or in shopkeeping, or in the smallest industrial workshop—united in the several guilds or companies of their craft or trade. The guilds and companies of the city possessed a monopoly of their own particular business. They tolerated neither individual eccentricity nor outside competition. None was admitted to the rights of membership unless he had served his apprenticeship; and none was permitted to exercise his trade or occupation within the city, nor was eligible as alderman, sheriff or mayor, unless he were a guildsman, free of the city. The guildsmen were proud and jealous of their civic rights and liberties, and no noble or cleric residing in the city was permitted to share their honours, unless he became admitted to the honorary fellowship of one of the guilds or companies. The rest of the inhabitants simply were not citizens. Perhaps, if they had influence, they joined, like young Geoffrey Chaucer, the retinue of a noble; if they were of the clergy they lived, we may hope, for the good of Holy Church, and sought no base advancement nor worldly wealth; but otherwise the fortunes of the unskilled were bound up with those of their masters, and the best that old age could look forward to was a place in one of the ecclesiastical hospitals, or a room in an almshouse.

II

What was the mental condition of a man of Chaucer's age? Let us attempt to reconstruct it. We think to-day of the state as the supreme authority in the nation, and of the law of England, whether administered in one of the great courts of Westminster or in the remotest country town, as a unity, protected, and in part created, by the state. In the

Middle Ages men had recognized two states, the temporal and the spiritual ; the one secular and governed by the King, the other religious and presided over by the Pope. The one was originally a military organization, a system of subordination descending from the immediate feudatories of the King— dukes and earls—down to the knights and squires who were the lords of single manors—a feudal system in which rank and power depended (in the absence of exceptional personal ability) upon the number of men, or the amount of money, which the vassal could furnish in time of war. The other was an international institution covering Western Europe for the maintenance of the faith and rites of medieval Christianity, organized with a similar subordination to its head, professed by all its officers, from the highest archbishop down to the meanest acolyte. Church and State had each its own law, and as the subject of the King was also a member of the Church, he owed obedience both to the statute law administered by the sheriff and the justices, and also to the canon law administered by the archdeacon. Likewise the churl who lived as a villein on a manor was similarly subject to the regulations and customs of the manor, and to the customs of the parish in which the manor lay. This feudal organization permeated every department of life. Apprentice, journeyman, master ; deacon, priest, bishop ; squire, knight, earl—every free man of every degree fitted into a graduated system of subordination, each grade with its own rights and its corresponding duties ; and at the bottom of the social ladder, unenfranchised and enslaved, crowded the vast uneducated populace of churls and villeins—" Laboreres that have no land to live on, but hire handes," as Langland called them.

In Chaucer's age, 1340–1400, this dual empire was visibly cracked and askew from top to bottom. The pitcher had gone to the well for a long age, but soon it was to go no

longer. The papal head of the spiritual estate was, owing to
the development of English national consciousness, regarded
as a holy foreigner, who, by a mischance during the reign of
King John for which Englishmen of the fourteenth century
could hardly be held responsible, happened to have a nominal
claim for a large annual tribute of dearly-won English gold.
This claim for tribute was repudiated by Edward III ; but
the Pope exercised the right of appointing foreign clerics
to English benefices, which hurt nationalist sentiment and
aroused feelings of anger or regret. Parliament strove in
vain for the rejection of Roman patronage to vacant benefices,
and against legal appeals to papal courts. It repeatedly
urged that the ministers of the Crown should be laymen and
not clerics. Amongst the commons of England the anti-
clerical teachings of Wycliffe were tending, on the one hand,
to the individualist piety of the Lollards ; and, on the other,
to the racial idealism of the author of *Piers Plowman,* or to
the revolutionary spirit of John Ball. The friars—papal
clergy—were unpopular. Alien priories were suppressed by
the King and their incomes appropriated. All was not well
with Holy Church. The feudal system was even more
strained. The obligations of vavasours to perform military
service for their liege-lords had been, or was being, commuted
into rent. Peasants were becoming tenants. At the same
time the order of knighthood was being degraded. Knight-
hoods were still earned on the field of battle : they were also
sold to raise gold for kings. A knight was probably a lord
of a manor and a vassal of an earl or a duke ; but he might
be a bandit-captain of a troop of mercenaries, or (how
modern it seems !) a London patrician, who dealt in prisoners,
wardships, and wool.

III

It was an age of discontent and disillusion. The age of enlightenment was still to come. And as yet there was no conscious goal for reformers to struggle towards ; for that which was to come was not seen even darkly. If they thought about progress at all, it was with regret. Their conviction was that the golden age of men—Chaucer's *Aetas Prima*, the " former age,"—lay in the dim, distant past ; and that the state of man was slowly but steadily growing worse. The only compensation was that if morals had deteriorated, the present comforts of life were better worth than the husks and cold water of primitive simplicity. And, after all, human life was very short and fleeting, and eternity was long,—long and uncommonly important. What mattered a little discomfort or even a little injustice in this earthly inn, provided that one made sure of the future joys of heaven—angelic music, courtly pomp, and the deep-spread vision from the battlements ?

Nevertheless the " lewd lossels " who formed the mass of the population found little consolation in this beautiful thought. The villeins were seething with discontent at their burden of duties without rights. They had to cultivate wheat and barley in the arable demesne under direction of the reeve or the bailiff of their overlord. They must perform their task-work for their lords on stated days, according to the custom of the manor. Theirs it was to furnish archers and pikemen for the small troop of their overlord, which, joined with other similar troops, made the feudal army of an earl, which, assembled with other similar armies, made an expedition to ravage the pleasant land of France. Bitter were the wounds, deadly were the famine and the plague, small was the wages or the possibility of advancement, and there was no ransom for the rank and file. In war as in peace, only the grades of the feudal order counted. The poor were, for the most part, uneducated and without economic or political power. Here and there a boy might obtain some schooling as a chorister, or might be educated to take orders in the Church at the cost of some patron; but, as a rule, John Miller and Piers Plowman were ignorant and superstitious.

The position of women was even worse; but, perhaps fortunately, they were unsophisticated and did not notice it. Despite the doctrine of the Wife of Bath, the wisdom of the Church agreed with the wisdom of the world that women, both by their physical weakness and their natural disposition, were unfit to have dominion. The women of the peasant class occupied a place in life somewhat between that of a Red Indian squaw and an Italian *contadina*. Then, as now, the women of the labouring and artisan classes worked much harder than their husbands and sons. They were field-labourers and housewives too. They hoed and they harvested; they tended sheep, milked cows, and churned butter; and in their spare time they baked and brewed, and clothed themselves and their families by spinning, weaving, and sewing for them. Small wonder that the wandering friars found their supporters amongst this class, for what time had these women on their hands to go to church for confession, or to waste a precious hour listening to sermons about the evils of luxury, gluttony, or sloth? If the women of the churls and villeins had no position at all, the women of noble birth enjoyed rank only by marriage. By law they could, it is true, inherit a manor or an estate, but they could not defend it. If they were not yet of age, they were awarded as a regal favour to some perhaps benevolent guardian, who took as a reward for his services ten per cent of their dues and rentals, and finally married them off at the price of a fee. Girls might wish, like Chaucer's Emily in *The Knight's Tale*, to remain a maid, and to walk in the wild woods alone;

but the alternative to marriage was a place in a nunnery. Hence amongst the upper classes girls were married not so much for love, as for sound practical reasons. A good marriage added castle to castle, and found a husband to administer and defend them. Amongst the burgher class too, the dowry system prevailed, and marriages were either arranged by thoughtful parents or by well-meaning friends. In the Middle Ages romantic love was rarely the golden hour of youth and maiden free to choose: usually it implied a slightly scandalous if not illicit *liaison*—the secret love of a noble which, for some reason, might not openly be pursued ; and the heroine is usually either a Dulcinea del Toboso, like Arnaut Daniel's lady, or Petrarch's Laura ; or one out of the hero's reach, like Aucassin's Nicolette, or the Chatelaine de Vergi, or Tristram's Iseult.

IV

Within the dual realm of Church and State stood, like islands here and there, the communities of the monastery and the borough. They had, as it were, contracted out of the feudal system by means of a charter from pope or king. Their charter was their dispensation, their title to freedom. It endowed them with a sort of republican character, constituting them brotherhoods of equals in law, with the right to elect their own officers (possibly subject to papal or to royal approval), and their respective heads, the abbot and the mayor. Their charter gave them certain local rights of taxation. It gave them power to hold their own courts, in which their officers administered justice between members of the community, and legally dealt with the misdemeanours of those unenfranchised churls who were attached to their lands and lived within the verge of their jurisdiction. The chartered communities enjoyed also the manorial rights of their region with its peculiar system of fees and fines, and had the privilege of holding fairs. In this freedom they exercised their business of either the contemplative life, or of the active life of trade and affairs.

Education, whose presiding genius was the grammar-schoolmaster and his fescue and birch-stick, existed for the franchised—for the sons of the gentry, franklins and burghers, and for those sons of the poorer classes who intended to make the ministry of the Church their vocation or profession. School was designed for boys : girls entered the educational world only indirectly as inmates or as pupils of nunneries, or as the little victims of ladylike governesses who possibly knew how to read and write French and English. The grammar-schools connected with cathedrals and parish churches were designed for the sons of those freemen who were not rich enough to engage a priest or a friar as a private tutor. From these the ambitious scholar might pass, like Chaucer's Clerk, to Oxford or Cambridge, there to crown his studies with the queen of sciences, theology. For the humbler classes the only roads to learning were the choir-schools of the parish churches and monasteries, in which boy-choristers were taught—like the " litel clergeoun " of *The Prioress's Tale*—to read and to sing the services of the church. The average education of those who were lucky enough to be birched for it was Latin grammar (memorized), the construing of Latin into French or English, together possibly with a certain amount of arithmetic and logic, and enough " astronomy " to enable them to understand the mystery of reckoning time and the calendar of Holy Church. The language of teaching was, until about 1350, Anglo-Norman. In the latter half of the fourteenth century, owing to the popularity, if not to the necessity, of an innovation made first at Merton College School by the headmaster, Master John Cornwall, the language into which the Latin texts read in schools were translated gradually became English.

V

The ideals of the age were, one imagines, derived by general consent from the practical needs of the social system rather than from the doctors of the schools. The manly ideal was the " verray, parfit, gentil knight," who was, in his excellence, prowess and truth personified. Physically, he should possess the military virtues which alone could enable him to bear his fortune in the chase, in the lists, and in war : he should be a man of courage, fortitude, patience and good temper. Morally, he should be a true knight, a man of honour, loyal to his liege-lord, one who never perpetrated an unjust deed or found delight in wanton cruelty, a man who never broke his plighted word. But goodness, such as that of Chaucer's Poure Persoun, scarcely entered into this conception of nobility. Goodness was an ideal of the Church. Purity and humility were part of the ascetic ideal. Fasting monk and anæmic nun might wrestle with original sin, and observe the foiled devil depart leaving a foul stench in his traces ; but the only moral restraint upon the tyranny of the noble, apart of course from the blunt or muttered condemnation of public opinion, was his personal conception of his honour, *noblesse oblige.* As the beauty of holiness was almost entirely a religious ideal, so also the artistic beauty of the age—the tranquil beauty of perpendicular architecture, the wonder of stained glass, the splendour of ecclesiastical pomp and ritual, the charm of allegory and mystery play—belonged at least originally to the Church. Poet and musician were still as much in the service of the Church as they were in the retinue of the world.

The complete contrast between the respective outlooks of cleric and noble is to be seen in their estimation of women. The unthinking never troubled to define their attitude : most men, one imagines, regarded woman in the abstract as, with luck, a good wife with a useful dowry; sharp of tongue, perhaps, at times—but then how otherwise than by marriage could the state of man subsist? But, to the clerical mind, woman was an evil, or at least a temptation and a snare. Was not woman a shrew, a tale-bearer and scandal-monger? Through woman first sin and death came into the world, as witnessed Eve and Pandora. Regarding woman as man's inferior, his weaker vessel in strength and reason, less patient, more quarrelsome and prone to petty pride, a trickster and liar at heart, the clerical poets with Jean de Meung at their head never tired of scoring points against women; and their philosophic instruction was improved upon by the popular minstrels and *diseurs* who regaled sniggering circles of bucolic faces with satirical histories and fabliaux, which ever exemplified and conclusively proved the folly of trusting a woman. On the other hand, woman by the courtly poets was exalted and regarded as a queen of beauty and love—a prize for the faithful service of her true knight. Love became a kind of religion. A semi-religious terminology was selected or invented, with which to worship feminine tenderness personified and enshrined. The lady of the courtly lover's dreams became his soveran lady, almost his deity. He considered her feudally, and with a vassal's heart offered her such poems as Chaucer's *Complaint to Pity*, and *To his Lady*. He regarded her as effulgent beauty which, transmitted by love to him, became the inspiring influence upon his courtesy and valour. He professed that, overcome by love-longing, he dared not confess his love. He complained of her pitiless cruelty. Yet in the poems sent to her, he addressed her in a diction of conceit and hyperbole which was almost identical with the medieval language of religious devotion to the mother of Our Lord, who in the feudal age was regarded as the queen of Heaven.

VI

The learning of the age was treasured almost exclusively in the minds of ecclesiastical teachers, and its truth was sanctified by the authority of the Church. Indeed, the Church held a complete monopoly of the knowledge of God. Science and philosophy were firmly wedded to theology. Most men had little or no curiosity as to the meaning of the facts of the external world. They did not even care to make sure of the facts. Their books of travel and of natural history, their pious biographies too, indicate that they were much more attracted by fiction than by fact. Formal logic, rather than correspondence to fact, was their criterion of truth. The schoolmen elaborated their *Quaestiones* and their *Summae* out of the contents of the Vulgate Bible, from one difficult dialogue of Plato's (the *Timaeus* in a Latin translation), and from a few treatises of Aristotle done into Latin, first from the Arabic commentaries of Avicenna and Averroes, and later from the texts by the Flemish Dominican, William of Moerbeke.

Indeed, the present world was regarded as a very little thing in comparison with eternity ; and to avoid the torments of Hell and to reach the seven joys of Heaven was universally regarded as the chief end of man. The interpreter of this chief end, the guide of the way, and the commander of the faithful, was the Church. Human society was founded in it. Its mystical, sacramental system, supported both by custom and authority, accompanied learned and lewd, cleric and layman—by the instrumentality of baptism, confirmation, orders or marriage, and extreme unction—from the cradle to the grave. Its religious festivals, its saints' days and its pilgrimages were the only popular holidays in a world of war and toil. Its doctrines of penance for sin, and of the treasury of saintly merit bountifully but thriftily stored by the Fountain of all good from the supererogatory works of the religious, which could be dispensed papally and episcopally to the penitent by means of pardoners and their indulgences, were the basis of the plain man's theory of morality, —if he had one. The Church was the sole authority for knowledge. Its theology, as expressed by its "angelic" doctor, Thomas Aquinas (1226-74), in his *Summa Theologiae*, was also the orthodox philosophy of the age. To point out weaknesses in the papal panoply, to seek or to accept other spiritual values, and different ways of attaining them, was heresy—the almost unpardonable sin.

The accepted opinion was that Heaven was originally inhabited by God and nine (according to some, ten) orders of angels, until Lucifer, for pride, was cast with his followers into Hell. The depleted seats of Heaven were being filled since the death of Our Lord by the souls of the faithful dead, chief amongst whom, because of their faith and works, were the saints. The saints were regarded almost as demi-gods, accessible to prayer, and intervening to protect or to bring success to their devotees. Relics were potent workers of miracles. Every trade and profession had its patron saint. There was a fitting saint to invoke in every occupation, and to swear by in every circumstance of life. It was the merits of the saints which were offered as indulgences to the sinner. It was to shrines containing the bodies or relics of saints that the troops of pilgrims went—

> Pilgrimes and palmers plighted hem togidere
> To seke Seynt James and seyntes in Rome.
> They went forth in hire way with many wise tales,
> And hadde leve to lye al hire lyf after.
> Heremites on an heep with hoked staves
> Wenten to Walsingham, and hire wenches after,

in search of temporal and spiritual blessings. Chaucer accepted the faith and rites of the Church, and appears to

have studied to some extent the philosophy and theology of
the schools ; but like the rest of his fellow-men he accepted
the popular belief in the miraculous workings of devil and
saint.   To say this is not to condemn either his faith or his
additional beliefs.   His faith was both rational and logical,
and though we may not agree with it, it was derived from the
most spiritual religion and the noblest instrument of morality
that man had so far attained.   We mention these beliefs
because they explain why Chaucer wrote the Prologue to the
Pardoner's Tale, or the *Friar's Tale* of the Summoner and the
fiend, a sincere and pointed anecdote which could only be
rewritten to-day in the vein of the *Ingoldsby Legends* ; or
because they account for the pious edification which he or his
readers found in the *Prioress's Tale* of the little chorister, or
in the Second Nun's *Life of St Cecile.*

VII

Passing from the supernatural to the physical world, we
should find Chaucer's notions equally foreign.   The physical
universe was thought to be a huge sphere of unknown size,
inside which the stars were fixed, and whose centre was the
centre of the earth.   Within this outer sphere of the fixed
stars, each in its own more or less concentric sphere, were the
seven planets (including the sun and moon) revolving around
the earth in circular paths, for it was an unquestioned belief
that all heavenly motion was perfectly circular.   Beyond the
eighth sphere of the fixed stars, the *primum mobile*—the first
movement, itself unmoved—energized and maintained the
motions of the spheres.   Between the sphere of the moon
and the earth, in the sub-lunar sphere, resided the four
elements—fire above air, air above water, water upon earth.
Hence in *Troilus and Criseyde,* V, 1807, when the soul of
Troilus passes from the place where Achilles slew him, it rises

naturally above the grosser elements of the sphere of the earth.

> His lighte goost full blisfully is went
> Up to the holwnesse of the eighte sphere,
> In converse leting everich element.
> And there he saugh with ful avisement
> Th'erratik sterres, herkning harmonye
> With sounes full of hevenissh melodye.

And the harmony which he heard was the musical chord produced by the continual humming of the planets as they revolved—"the music of the spheres." This geocentric system of astronomy was derived ultimately from the speculations of the Greek astronomers.

The daily rising and setting of all the heavenly bodies (the effect of the earth's daily rotation) was regarded as the incredibly swift daily motion of the eight spheres together about the central earth. The erratic wanderings of the planets (the effect of their and of the earth's revolution around the sun) was regarded as a series of unequal but comparatively slow rotations of their spheres about the earth, in which each planet, except the sun, made a minor rotation —"wheels within wheels"—comparable to a torch whirled round and round his head by a man running round a circular path. As the sun, moon, and planets are seen from earth projected against a broad belt of constellations of fixed stars known as the Zodiac, the Zodiac was (and had been from the dawn of history) divided into twelve parts or "signs" corresponding to months; and in Chaucer's time the astronomical year began at the moment when the sun entered the sign of Aries (the Ram) on 12th March. One month later the sun passed into Taurus, as we may gather from the *Complaint of Mars*, and so onwards every month through the twelve signs of the Zodiac. Similarly the other planets passed through the Zodiac, but in longer or shorter revolutions than that of the sun. Sometimes two planets were seen together in the sky in one sign of the Zodiac. They were then said to be in conjunction, as were the planets Mars and Venus in Chaucer's *Complaint of Mars*. It was believed that the position of the planets at one's birth influenced one's character for life. The Wife of Bath explained her character by saying :

> I am al Venerien
> In feelinge, and myn harte is Marcien ;
> Venus me yaf my lust, my likerousness,
> And Mars yaf me my sturdy hardynesse.

So, for example, the moon might afflict with lunacy. Mars made men martial. One born under Mercury was mercurial. One born under Venus was fond of the soft delights of love. Jupiter made men jovial, and Saturn saturnine.

VIII

But probably these intellectual matters vexed the brain of the plain man in those days as little as their modern developments into the sciences of political theory, sociology, ethics, theology and astronomy trouble your family lawyer or your family grocer to-day. They were a part of the common sense of the age. They were taken for granted. Most men were actively engaged in war, trade or a profession ; and, for most men, life was work with little holiday, activity which left little time for thinking, just as it is to-day.

To us the age seems to be picturesque because " distance lends enchantment to the view." To them it seemed to be the natural state of man. And it may be a pleasant irony to think that in centuries to come some pedant will solemnly reconstruct the age we live in—and find it wanting in the splendid ideals of religion, economics and culture. There is no finality in life, and our age has only advanced a step or two beyond the fourteenth century. Our great advance has been in science and its application to industry ; but have we kept pace with this progress in religion and law, art and culture ? I wonder !

THE CANTERBURY TALES

THE writer of the ensuing tales has been rightly described as the father of English poetry. "Father" he is. Two centuries before Shakespeare, and contemporary with Petrarch and Boccaccio in Italy, he stood head and shoulders above the poets of his age. His successful fashioning of the rhythm of the decasyllabic line endured with only one modification —the abolition of "initial truncation"—until the casting aside of poetic tradition in the very age in which we live.

I

Geoffrey Chaucer, a son of John Chaucer, who was a wine merchant of Thames Street, London, began his career as a page in the household of Lionel, Duke of Clarence, in 1357. Two years later he served his liege lord in the campaign of 1359-60 against France. He was taken prisoner by the French and ransomed for £16 by Edward III. It is usually assumed that Chaucer was then aged about twenty and that he was born in 1340, but it is quite possible that he was still only sixteen or seventeen and that he was born c. 1343. The exact date of Chaucer's birth is unknown.

According to an Elizabethan tradition, after his return from France he studied at the Inner Temple, and is said to have been fined two shillings for beating a Franciscan friar in Fleet Street. He became a member of the household of Edward III, when, is uncertain ; but his rank as a valet and later as a squire is authenticated at any rate from 1367. He married Philippa, the daughter of a herald named Sir Payne

Roet. She was a lady-in-waiting firstly to Philippa of Hainault, the wife of Edward III, and later to Constance of Castile, the second wife of John of Gaunt. Chaucer was sent as a secretary on several important diplomatic missions between 1369 and 1378, visiting France and Flanders to discuss peace and the marriage of Prince Richard, and visiting Italy in 1373 (Genoa and Florence) and again in 1378 (Milan). For these services he received various rewards, an annuity of 20 marks a year (1367), a pitcher of wine daily (1374), the Controllership of the Customs of Wool and Hides (1374), the guardianship of two minors (1375), and from Richard II the Controllership of the Petty Customs of the Port of London (1382). In 1385 he was a Justice of the Peace for the county of Kent, and he represented Kent in the short parliament of October 1386. During this period he translated the *Romance of the Rose*, and Boethius's *Consolation of Philosophy*, he wrote the *Parlement of Fowles* (1377 or 1382), *Troilus and Criseyde*, the *House of Fame*, the *Legend of Good Women*, and some of the tales which were afterwards incorporated in the *Canterbury Tales*.

In December 1386 Chaucer suffered a reverse of fortune. His patron, John of Gaunt, was absent in Portugal, and during the government of Thomas, Duke of Gloucester, Chaucer was dismissed from both his offices as controller of customs. In the midst of his troubles his wife died in the summer of 1387. But in 1389 Richard II personally assumed the reins of government, and shortly afterwards, in July, Chaucer was appointed Commissioner of Works, a post which he held until 1391, when, after being robbed twice either by enemies or thieves, he retired. But he was not without an appointment. In 1390 he was made Forester of North Petherton by Sir Peter Courtenay (as Krauss suggested); steward of the forests of Somerset including Exmoor, a minor post, but one which, together with a pension of £20 a year granted by Richard II in 1394, and a further pension of 40 marks from Henry IV in 1399, relieved his old age from penury. In 1399 he leased a house in the garden of the Lady Chapel of Westminster Abbey, and there he died on 25th October 1400.

II

The *Canterbury Tales* were written in the later period of Chaucer's life between 1386 and 1400. The fiction of the pilgrimage was invented to account for the tales, some of which, such as the *Man of Law's Tale* and the *Clerk's Tale*, were written before the scheme of the Canterbury pilgrimage was thought of. One of the many excellences of the *Canterbury Tales* is their variety. Medieval collections of tales upon one theme were not uncommon : Chaucer's *Legend of Good Women* is a case in point. But there was in English no collection before the *Canterbury Tales* which offered such variety.

The pilgrims are not only varied individuals : some of them are contrasted types. They are not only described in the Prologue : they are also sketched in dialogue in the links between the tales, and are revealed too by the sorts of tale they tell. They have different occupations and different tastes. Their tales are not all upon one theme. They range over the possible variety of the novel at that time. Chaucer wrote romance in the tales of the Knight and Squire, and mocked at romance in his own tale of Sir Thopas. There are the sentimental tales of the Clerk (Griselda) and the Man of Law (Constance), and the stories of love and magic told by the Wife of Bath (The Wedding of Sir Gawaine) and the Franklin (Arveragus and Dorigen). There are the classical tales told by the Doctor of Physic (Appius and Virginia) and the Manciple (Phœbus and the Magpie). There is the fable of the Nun's Priest (Chanticleer and Russell), and the lives of the saints told by the Prioress and by the Second Nun

(St Cecilia). The monk relates his " tragedies," the parson preaches a sermon on penitence, and there are the racy and licentious fabliaux of the Miller, Reeve, Friar and Summoner, which though coarse and indecent at times, are, like the curate's egg, exceedingly good in parts.

Most of these tales are old tales made new : tales once heard or perhaps once read. But their merit recognized, Chaucer told them in his own way, which is personal and inimitable, and he usually made them entirely his own. Only rarely, as in the Clerk of Oxenford's *Tale of Griselda*, and in the Second Nun's *Life of St Cecilia*, does he cling at all closely to his original version.

III

There are eighty-four MSS. of the *Canterbury Tales* still in existence. These are widely scattered in various libraries —the British Museum for instance has 23—and in private collections. Photographic copies of these manuscripts have been made for Professor Manly and Miss Edith Rickert of the University of Chicago, who have promised from a comparison of these texts to produce a new edition of Chaucer's works. Eight of these manuscripts were printed, probably not without some errors, by the Chaucer Society, namely, the *Six-Text Edition*, which contains parallel texts of these manuscripts : Ellesmere (E.), Hengwrt 154 (Hn.), Cambridge University Library, Gg. 4 27 (Cm.), Corpus Christi College, Oxford (Cp.), Petworth (Pt.), and Lansdowne 851 (Ln.) in 1868-84 ; and also the Harleian MS., 7334 (Hl.) in 1885, and the MS. Cambridge University Library, Dd. 4 24, completed by Egerton, 2726 (Dd.), in 1901-2. The Ellesmere manuscript, now in the Huntington Library, in Pasadena, Hollywood, California, has also been reproduced in facsimile by the Manchester University Press.

It is upon these eight printed manuscripts that ultimately this edition is based, the Ellesmere MS. being taken as the transmitted text and corrected by variant readings of the other seven MSS. As this edition is intended for schools, *i* and *j*, *u* and *w* have been normalized, and Skeat's example in writing *y* for the long *i* has been followed. "To" and "too" have been differentiated, as have "naught" and "noght"; "thanne" is spelled *than*, "the" *thee*, and "thre" *three*. Some redundant final vowels *-e*, including the final *-e* in "hise," "youre," "hire," "oure," etc., which would only puzzle the young student, have been removed. This would be wrong if our aim had been to present the text as Chaucer wrote it. But that was not our aim. This is not a diplomatic text. It is quite frankly not Chaucerian in the sense that Chaucer might have written it as it stands; but as a text for beginners it is more regular than a critical text, and its spelling is not un-Chaucerian, although it is normalized.

IV

The Prologue to the *Canterbury Tales* describes a company of pilgrims who are about to set out for Canterbury in order to visit the tomb of Thomas à Beckett, the "hooly blisful martir" of line 7. Religious pilgrimages were in Chaucer's age popular amongst all ranks of society. They indicated a reverence for the saints and a belief in their powers of intervention with the Almighty. With many worldly people, even in Chaucer's age, a pilgrimage was an excuse for a holiday; and it is instructive to find that Chaucer gives no reason for the pilgrimage, except that it is spring:

> Than longen folk to goon on pilgrimages
> And palmers for to seken straunge strondes.

The Prologue is prized above all for its introduction to certain characters of the fourteenth century. Chaucer gives a most graphic description of his pilgrims, a description which is remarkable for its realistic and satirical observations of appearance and manners. In this power, not only of satire, but of satire coupled with realism, Chaucer stands alone in the English literature of his age. Indeed not until Elizabethan drama do we meet again with such vividly conceived characters. And yet it is obvious, when one reads the Prologue carefully, that not all the characters are conceived in the same way. Some figures, like the Knight, the Clerk and the Parson are idealized, and seen as perfect types of their class. Others, such as the Miller, Reeve, Wife of Bath, and the Host, are so natural and so realistic that Pollard and Manly have suggested that they are drawn from life. In *Some New Light on Chaucer* Manly has forcibly argued that in some instances Chaucer had a definite individual in mind, though of course he did not always make his imaginative conception agree with the reality in every detail. The idealized figures are important because they are not only types of what such men ought to be, but also they are excellences which throw into contrast the imperfections of the realistic figures.

The poem is not a purely realistic picture : it is idealized too in part. Above all, it is most English in spirit. In it, as in no other poem of the time, we can recognize our ancestors and their friends, all described with Chaucer's winged and penetrating humour, which, when occasion demands, can become satirical, though never unjust.

v

The *Prioress's Tale* is of a miracle performed by the Virgin Mary. It tells how a little chorister was murdered by Jews for his childish devotion to Our Lady, and how she put a

grain upon his tongue when he was slain, so that he sang
until he was found. It is a touching, sentimental story, and
it is told like the life of a saint; but Chaucer avoids naming
the martyr or the place where he lived. Chaucer had heard
tales of this kind, but evidently he preferred to think of them
as fiction rather than as fact. It is a story similar to that of
Hugh of Lincoln, a story that arose about 1255 before the
anti-Jewish outbreaks of Edward I's reign. The fact that
Chaucer told this tale at all indicates a sentimental and
credulous side to his nature; though he makes it the tale of
the Prioress, from whose lips it is apt.

Such tales, all ending with the miraculous finding of the
dead boy, either by a beam of light or by an object placed
on his tongue by Our Lady, were not uncommon in the
Middle Ages when hatred of the Jews was acute, when Jews
were the only financiers, protected by kings because they
lent money. But by Chaucer's age such tales were tales of
the olden time. There had been no Jews in England since
1290, when, yielding to the anti-Jewish feeling of his people,
Edward I had expelled them. That the story is an old one
is seen in the fact that it is found in the *Anglo-Saxon Chronicle*
for the reign of King Stephen under the date 1137. Here the
place is Norwich, and the martyr St William. The Chaucer
Society prints two versions in its *Originals and Analogues of
Some of the Canterbury Tales* (1888), pp. 251, 277. The first
is in Old French by Gautier de Coincy (1177-1236), and the
scene is " en la contree d'Angleterre." The second is from
The Miracles of Our Lady (Vernon MS., *c.* 1375), in the
Bodleian Library, Oxford. Here the scene is Paris. The
ballad of " The Jew's Daughter " in Percy's *Reliques of
Ancient English Poetry*, I, i, 3, sets the scene in " Mirry-land
toune " on the river " Pa," which Percy identifies as Milan
and the Po. The ballad of " Hugh of Lincoln " is quaintly
degraded to " Little Harry Hughes and the Duke's Daughter,"

in Child's *English and Scottish Popular Ballads*, 155, p. 371, which should certainly not be left unread.

It is scarcely necessary to say that Chaucer's tale does not copy any of these analogues. It is original in its setting and in its details, and, above all, in its poetic beauty. He retold an old story, but he enriched it perhaps more than can be imagined without reference to other versions of the story.

VI

The *Nun's Priest's Tale* is one of the most entertaining fables in the English language. Not only does it make a cock and hen talk like human beings, but with a genial cynicism for the inconclusiveness of learning it makes them talk at times like medieval scholars. The tale begins slowly with description appropriate to the setting. Chanticleer, the natural astronomer, and Partlet, his wife, are introduced, and their conversation concerning the humours, herbal lore and dreams, with learned examples, is so quaint and yet so humorously pedantic that it is never too long : and its conclusion, the victory of the male over the female of the species, and his complete self-assurance and his defiance of visions and dreams is utterly delightful.

Then the fox enters like a murderer, and Chaucer embarks on a discussion—quite futile, as he knew before he entered on it—of fate versus free-will. The tale describes with mingled wit and learning the capture of the cock by the fox by means of his trick to make the cock shut his eyes, which bit of pure flattery includes the moral tale of the cock and the parson's son, from Nigel's *Speculum Stultorum* or *Dan Burnel the Ass*. Then with a cry of despair to Destiny, Venus, and Geoffrey de Vinsauf, an incongruous trinity, the rout begins, noisy, swift and comic. The trick of the cock to make the fox open his mouth leads Chaucer to his moral,

16 C

which is directed against flattery, and to the end of his tale.

It is idle, I think, to search for an earlier " original " of Chaucer's *Nun's Priest's Tale*. The probability is that he recollected a story which he had heard told in French, ultimately a story from *Le Roman de Renard*. He retold this story in his own way, which, besides being personal and unique, happened to be in the fashion of two centuries later than the original story. It includes a good deal of description and characterization, and much personal learning, which is used as quaint and vivid decoration. Cicero's stories of dreams, the first of which is splendidly told, the story of St Kenelm, Andromache's dream, the philosophy of predestination, Physiologus on mermaids, the story from *Dan Burnel the Ass*, the lament for Friday, and the allusions to Pyrrhus, Nero and Hasdrubal's wife, are all in their context a satire on pedantry. The decoration forms four-fifths of the poem. Nevertheless, if earlier versions of the fable of the Cock and the Fox are required, one can give now, thanks to the labours of Miss Petersen, Mr Kenneth Sisam, and of earlier scholars, some kind of pedigree.

The fable of the Cock and the Fox makes its appearance in literature, not in Æsop, nor Phædrus, nor Romulus, but in a medieval fable told in Latin by Adhemar of Limoges as the Fox and the Partridge (*c.* 1025). It was told again as the versified fable of *Gallus et Vulpes* by an anonymous writer of the twelfth century, and recorded again in Old French by Marie de France, who wrote *c.* 1175 a collection of fables which included the Cock and the Fox, *Dou Coc et dou Werpil*. In all these early versions the fable has the two morals which Chaucer gives it. The fox flatters the cock and induces him to crow. The cock closes his eyes to crow, and the fox seizes him. The neighbours run shouting after the fox. Then the cock induces the fox to shout defiance, which he does, and the cock escapes. The moral of the fox is that it is folly to talk when one should keep silence. The moral of the cock is that eyes ought not to be shut when they should be open. But these are merely the earliest surviving forms of the story, and none of them is Chaucer's original source.

This fable finally became an episode in the Romance of Reynard, so called from Reynard the fox, its chief character. This romance grew up as a series of tales about animals—the fox, wolf, cat, bear, etc.—both in France (*Le Roman de Renard*), and in Germany (*Reinhart Fuchs*), during the twelfth century. The episode "Si comme Renart prist Chantecler le Coc" is substantially Chaucer's tale; but instead of a widow "somdel stape in age," the owner of Chantecler is a farmer named Constant Desnoes. The fox is called Renart, not Russell, and the hen is named Pinte, not Pertelote. The story is told in some 450 lines, written in octosyllabic couplets, but without any of Chaucer's learned decoration. It would appear that Chaucer's original remains unidentified. Very probably he had heard, told in prose or recited in French verse, a version of the story. It was a folk-story. It was also a fable. He recognized its merits, and used it (*cf.* ll. 554-60) to offer a warning against flattery.

> Lo, swich it is for to be recchelees
> And necligent, and truste on flaterye.

The fable of Marie de France and the episode of Reynard and Chanticleer from the *Roman de Renard* are to be found in *Originals and Analogues of Some of the Canterbury Tales* (Chaucer Society), p. 111. Mr Sisam, in his introduction to the *Nun's Priest's Tale*, Oxford, 1927, gives a good account of Adhemar, *Gallus et Vulpes*, Marie de France, and *Le Roman de Renard*.

VII

The *Pardoner's Tale*, with its powerful prologue, is a further characterization of the Pardoner, who makes his first appearance in the Prologue to the *Canterbury Tales*, ll. 669-714. In the Prologue to the *Pardoner's Tale* he lays bare the tricks of his trade, and shows himself not only a powerful preacher against the sins of gluttony and gambling, but a skilful rogue, who preys upon the credulous side of human nature. He frankly admits his greed for money, and illustrates his way of collecting it by the showing of false relics and the sale of indulgences. The *Pardoner's Tale* is an anecdote which he uses to exemplify his text: Radix malorum est cupiditas. Isolated from the perhaps too frank disclosures of the Pardoner, it is a magnificent story, beautiful in its early Flemish figure-drawing, and swift and unexpected in its action. The strange appearance of the old man, the careless pride of the three revellers, their greed, their lack of conscience, and their awful end, make it a fine tale of mystery and horror, a tale which can belong to any age.

The tale appears to be first told in a Persian poem of the twelfth century by Farid-ed-Din Attar (1216-1330). In this poem the person corresponding to the old man is Jesus. This may seem strange in a poem by a Mohammedan, but the followers of Mohammed accept Our Lord as a prophet, though not as a divinity. Jesus creates the gold by prayer, and after the death of the three rioters He turns it back again to dust. There are also Arabic versions of the same story; and probably from the Arabs, by means of the Crusaders, the tale came into Europe. In *Le Ciento Novelle Antike* (Il Novellino), a collection of stories which dates from the dawn of Italian prose, in the thirteenth century, a story is told which appears to be an intermediate version between that of Farid-ed-Din Attar and that of Chaucer in the

Pardoner's Tale.   Christ and His disciples when walking one day see a treasure of gold, and they watch what happens. Two men find it.   One goes to bring a mule to carry it home, and with the mule he brings back poisoned bread.   The other stabs him, and eats the bread.   A later version in the *Libro di Novelle,* printed at Florence in 1572, is strikingly like Chaucer's.   A hermit who has found a treasure meets three robbers and shows them his treasure, which he says is death ; and the story continues as in the *Pardoner's Tale.*

Wherever Chaucer heard the story—and it is possible that he heard it in Italy either in 1373 or in 1378—he made it his own by narrating and decorating it in his own individual way.   For instance, he made the scene Flanders, the country of the Flemish weavers who were ill-treated and killed in the Peasant Rising of 1381 (cf. *Nun's Priest's Tale,* ll. 624-6), a country moreover which, rightly or wrongly, was noted for its drunkenness.   Chaucer did not invent the *Pardoner's Tale,* but he did invent the Pardoner, with his long sermon against gluttony, drunkenness, gambling, and swearing, a sermon which, by the way, is illustrated by two *exempla* taken from John of Salisbury's *Polycraticus,* i. 5.

The analogues of the *Pardoner's Tale* are published by the Chaucer Society in *Originals and Analogues of Some of the Canterbury Tales* (1888), pp. 415 and 129.

THE LANGUAGE AND METRE OF CHAUCER

I. PRONUNCIATION

1. Chaucer, by birth a Londoner, spoke and wrote the dialect of official London, the English of the Court in the latter part of the fourteenth century. He was born in the city, and it is possible that his use of so-called " Kentish forms " (which belong equally to Essex) was a survival from this dialect. The basis of Chaucer's English is the East Midland dialect, as spoken in London, which later developed into Modern English. The pronunciation and scansion of Chaucer's English is different from ours. Some of his rimes are incorrect, and many of the lines do not scan, if they are read in the pronunciation of to-day.

2. Chaucer spelled his English more or less phonetically. His spelling was rather clumsy, but the first point to grasp is that the vowels had their original values, or nearly so ; the second is that the consonant group *gh*, which occurred medially and finally, had the sound of *ch* in Scots : *loch, nicht* ; the third is that final *-e* was pronounced like *-er*, the so-called obscure vowel [ə], except when it was elided before a vowel or a silent *h*. If we grasp this, we shall have gone a long way towards mastering Chaucer's pronunciation.

3. Let us now tabulate the chief differences of pronunciation.

Consonants.

Medial and final *-gh* was pronounced like Scots *ch* [χ] : *bright, doughter.* Initial *k*, *g*, and *w* before consonants were pronounced : *knowe, gnawe, wryte.* *r* was probably trilled as in Scots : *licour, fether.*

Medial and final *-gge* was usually equivalent to Modern English *-dge* [dʒ] as in *logge* (lodge), *hegge* (hedge); but, as the modern pronunciation indicates, it was *-gg* in *logge* (log) and *hogge* (hog).

Initial *ch* was pronounced as in Modern English [tʃ], even in French words: *chivalrye, chambre*.

Initial *h* is frequently silent, not only in French words like *honour*, and in Latin words like *habominable*, but also, rarely, in English words like *heve*. It is silent in *he, his, him, hir* when they are unstressed. Silent *h* is recognized by the fact that final *-e* is elided before it. Before sounded *h, an* was written: *an hare, an halle*.

4. *Vowels.*

The short vowels were pronounced as in *pat, pet, pit, pot* and *put*. It is necessary to remember to give each vowel its regular pronunciation before *r*: *ward* (*not* waud), *herte* (*not* hurt), *hir* (*not* hur), *purs* (*not* pers). Short *u* is written *o* before consonants written with down-strokes, such as *v* (which was written like *u*), *m* and *n*, as in *love, com, woning*. This perhaps is one reason why long *u* was written *ou*, as in *mouth* and *flour*.

There were eight long vowels, but only six symbols for them: *a, ee, y, oo, ou,* and *u*.

Modern *a* [ei]	was pronounced	*ā*:		*name, place.*
Modern *ea* [ii]	,,	*ɛ̄* (open *e*):		*breeth, deel.*
Modern *ee, ie* [ii]	,,	*ē* (close *e*):		*swete, seed.*
Modern *i* [ai]	,,	*ī*:		*wyf, pye.*
Modern *o, oa* [ou]	,,	*ɔ̄* (open *o*):		*stoon, throte.*
Modern *oo* [uu]	,,	*ō* (close *o*):		*good, doon.*
Modern *ou* [au]	,,	*ū*:		*hous, plenteous.*
Modern *u* [ju]	,,	*y* (French *u*), or *ju*:		*fortune, vertu.*

The exact pronunciation of French *u* is uncertain. It may have had a French pronunciation, but perhaps not.

5. There were also five diphthongs, for which there were six symbols : *ay, ey, au, ew, ow,* and *oy* ; *y* and *i, w* and *u* were interchangeable : they could write either *point* or *poynt, soul* or *sowl.*

Modern *ai, ei* [ei] was pronounced *ai* : *day, veyne.*
Modern *au* [ɔ]   ,,   *au* : *cause, saugh.*
Modern *ew, ue* [ju]   ,,   *ju* : *hewe, fewe.*
Modern *ou, ow* [ou]   ,,   *ɔu* : *knowe, owen.*
Modern *oi, oy* [ɔi]   ,,   *oi* : *joy, point.*

6. The final vowel *-e* was an unstressed vowel, and was pronounced like the *-a* in *china.* The endings *-es, -eth,* and *-ed* were probably pronounced *-iz, -ith,* and *id.* The endings *-ioun* and *-ial* had two syllables : *-i-oun,* and *-i-al.* Final *-ee* from French *-é* was a stressed vowel, as in *degree, contree, citee,* and was not elided before a vowel.

7. The final vowel *-e,* which occurred only in unstressed syllables, had two origins. It was originally the Middle English survival of an earlier inflexional ending. As such it was an integral part of the word and was, naturally, pronounced. But it was used in writing also, from Chaucer's time onwards, to indicate a preceding long vowel, as in Modern English " case," " theme," " wine," etc., and hence it became inserted in words of which it did not originally form a part, and where it was not pronounced. In this edition many of these " scribal " final *-e* have been deleted.

Inflexional *-e* is a grammatical inflexion. It occurs in these instances :

(1) The nominative singular of certain nouns and adjectives: *sone, dame, service ; grene, trewe.*

(2) The accusative, genitive and dative singular of O.E. strong feminine nouns, and extended to the nominative singular : *dede, speche.*

(3) The plural of monosyllabic adjectives : *olde bokes, ferne halwes.*

(4) The singular ending of monosyllabic adjectives after *the, this, that, his, hir ; the yonge sonne, his halfe cours.*

(5) In adjectives before personal names : *O yonge Hugh of Lyncoln.*

(6) As an ending of adverbs : *faire, smerte.*

(7) As the ending of many forms of the verb :

Present tense, 1st sing. : *I ryde, wryte, seye, telle.*

Present tense, plural : *we ryde(n), wryte(n), shape(n), telle(n).*

Weak past tense, 1st, 3rd sing. : *seyde, tolde.*

Past tense, plural : *we ride(n), write(n), seyde(n), tolde(n).*

Subjunctive, present : *helpe* (sing.), *helpe(n)* (plur.).

Infinitive : *ryde(n), wryte(n), seye(n), telle(n).*

Strong past participle : *y-ronne, y-write, y-come.*

Some of these verbal forms may end in *-en*, but frequently the *-n* is silent and the *-e* is pronounced. This inflexional final *-e* was usually silent after a short root-vowel : *com(e), son(e)* (son).

II. Metre

8. The correct scansion of Chaucer's verse depends upon recognition of the stress of words. He wrote his lines in an alternation of unstressed and stressed syllables :

. _ . _ . _ . _ . _.
And smale fowles maken melodye.

The stressed syllables may usually be recognized by the rhythm of the verse (see § 10).

A difficulty is offered by words of French origin, which usually have the stress on the last syllable, or on the last but one, if *-e* follows : *vertu, licour, coráge, devýse.* But words of two syllables may take the English mode of stress on the first syllable, if the rhythm demands it : *manéer* or *máner.*

Polysyllabic nouns have stress on the last syllable, and on the syllable which is two (or four) from the end : *mélodýe, impossíble, imáginácioún.*

Present participles in *-aunt* have the stress on the root-syllable of the verb : *accórdaunt* ; but derivative nouns have the stress on the penultimate syllable : *chévissáunce.*

9. Chaucer's commonest metres, exemplified in this book of selections, are :

(1) The Decasyllabic couplet (or Heroic couplet) as in the Prologue to the *Canterbury Tales*, the *Nun's Priest's Tale*, and the *Pardoner's Tale.*

(2) The Seven-line Stanza of decasyllabic lines riming *ababbcc* as in the *Prioress's Tale.*

10. *The Decasyllabic Couplet* : The normal line has five rising or iambic feet :

> Now by my fader soule that is deed.

The normal line is varied by the addition of a weak syllable at the end of the line :

> That streight was comen fro the court of Rome.

> Wel loved he garleek, oynons, and eek lekes.

Also, more rarely, by the suppression of the first unstressed syllable (" initial truncation ") :

> In a gowne of falding to the knee.

Or, more rarely still, by both combined :

> Whan that Aprille with his shoures soote.

Further variation is obtained by inversion of stress in the first foot :

> Strong was the wyn, and wel to drinke us leste.

Also by the use of additional unstressed syllables—one of the most striking examples of which is a line from the *Nun's Priest's Tale* (201), which has also inversion of stress in the second foot :

> Pekke hem up right as they growe, and ete hem in.

There is also a natural cæsura or half-pause in the line. Commonly it occurs after the fourth or fifth syllable, but its position varies constantly, and the variation adds much to the ease and grace of Chaucer's verse.

> That streight was comen ‖ fro the court of Rome.

> Whan that Aprille ‖ with his shoures soote.

> Strong was the wyn ‖ and wel to drinke us leste.

Before the cæsural pause there is no elision of -*e* before a vowel or silent *h*, and sometimes even an extra syllable is inserted (feminine cæsura) :

> Than had(de) your tale ‖ al be toold in veyn.

> But soore weep she ‖ if oon of hem were deed.

> That in hir coppe ‖ ther was no ferthing sene.

11. *The Seven-line Stanza* : The seven decasyllabic lines, which rime *ababbcc*, have the same rhythms as the lines of the decasyllabic couplet. Normally each stanza is complete in itself —that is, it is terminated by a full pause after the seventh line. Normally, too, there is a half pause (or *volta*), determinable by the sense, somewhere within the stanza. Usually it is found at the end of a line. Occasionally it is in the middle of a line. Thus, in the first stanza of the *Prioress's Tale* it comes after the fifth line, in the third (ll. 50-56) it comes after the third line, and in the fifth (ll. 64-70) it comes after the fourth line.

III. Accidence

12. *Nouns.*

The normal endings of nouns are as follows:

	Singular.	Plural.
Nom. Acc.	—	*-es*
Gen.	*-es*	*-es*
Dat.	*-e*	*-es*

Some nouns, however, end in *-e* in the nominative and accusative singular: *ende, dore, speche.*

The plural ending *-es* is a syllable as a rule: *corages, pilgrimages*; but in words of two or more syllables it may be reduced to *-s*: *palmers, housbonds, parisshens.*

A few nouns form plurals in *-en* or *-n*: *eyen, brethren, toon* (toes), and *kyn* or *keen* (cows). A few nouns with long root-vowels in Old English are uninflected in the plural: *hors, yeer*; also French nouns in *-s*: *caas* or *cas.*

Survivals of the uninflected genitive are the gen. sings.: *fader, doughter, mooder.*

Survivals of an old weak genitive in *-an* are: *lady* in *his lady grace*, *chirche* in *at chirche dore*, where the possessive word is either uninflected or ends in *-e.*

The dative singular—which occurs after *by, at, with, to, for*, etc.—is inflected with *-e*, but the ending was often silent: *with a yerde, for feere.*

13. *Adjectives.*

Adjectives, when uninflected, end usually in a consonant: *smal, good*; but a few uninflected adjectives end in *-e*: *swete, newe, dere, grene.* Adjectives of two or more syllables, and adjectives used predicatively, are usually uninflected.

The plural of adjectives ends in *-e*: *smale fowles, olde bokes, ferne halwes.*

The singular of adjectives ends in *-e* when it is preceded by a demonstrative or possessive adjective, or if it is used vocatively : *the olde book, his olde book, your rede colera, goode God, yonge Hugh of Lyncoln.* This is called the " weak " declension. The weak and plural form of *high* is *hye*.

So that in Chaucer's English there are two forms of the adjective, strong (or indefinite) and weak (or definite), which we may set out as follows :

	Strong.	Weak.
Singular :	*a smal fowl*	*the smale fowl.*
Plural :	*smale fowles*	*the smale fowles.*

Survival of the old genitive plural in *-ra* is seen in *aller, alder* (of all) ; *our aller cok, alderbeste.*

The comparative form of the adjective is ordinarily inflected with *-er,* and the superlatives with *-este.* Where *t* is the medial consonant it is doubled, and the preceding vowel becomes shortened.

Positive.	Comparative.	Superlative.
greet	*gretter*	*gretteste*
whyt	*whitter*	*whitteste*

Irregular are :

old	*elder*	*eldeste*
heigh, hy	*hyer*	*hyeste*
long	*lenger*	*lengeste*
strong	*strenger*	*strengeste*
yvel	*werse*	*werste*
muche(l)	*moore*	*moost*
lyte(l)	*lasse, lesse*	*leest*
fer	*ferre, ferrer*	*ferreste.*

14. *Adverbs.*

Many adverbs have the same form as the weak adjective : *hye* (highly), *loude* (loudly). Some have a different vowel, e.g. *swete* (adj.), *soote* or *swote* (adv., also used as an adjective).

Others are formed by adding -*ly* to the adjective : *swetely, trewely, gladly.*

The following are irregular comparative and superlative forms :

Positive.	Comparative.	Superlative.
ny	*neer*	*next*
wel	*bet, bettre*	*best.*

15. *Pronouns.*

Personal : *Thou* and *thee* are familiar, *ye* and *you* are either plurals or (if singular) polite forms of address. *Thou* is sometimes attached to a verb in the interrogative as -*tow* : *wiltow* (wilt thou), *woltow* (wilt thou).

The only personal pronominal forms which differ markedly from Modern English are the forms of the 3rd person plural : *they, hir* (their), and *hem* (them). *They* was borrowed from Old Norse ; *hir* and *hem* were survivals from Old English. *Hir*, which means *her* as well as *their*, is ambiguous, and its meaning can only be distinguished from the context. *His* is the possessive of *it* or *hit* as well as of *he*, and may mean either *his* or *its*.

Demonstrative : *thilke* (the same) ; *this, these* (pl.) ; *that, tho* (pl.) ; *swich* (such), *swiche* (pl.).

Relative : Usually *that*. Note that *that* . . . *he* = who, *that* . . . *his* = whose, *that* . . . *him* = whom. But *which, whiche* (pl.), is also used (like *that*) both of persons and things, also *which that*, and *the which that*.

Who is not used as a relative pronoun ; though the oblique cases *whos, whom* may be so used in the possessive and dative cases respectively.

Interrogative : *who, whos, whom* ; *which* (what kind ?), *whiche* (pl.) ; *what* (why ?).

Indefinite : *man* or *men* (one), e.g. *if men smoot it* ; *whoso* (if anyone) ; *he, she* (one), e.g. *if he gaf* (if one gave), *as she that* (as one who).

16. *Strong Verbs.*

Strong verbs form their past tenses and past participles by gradation of vowels.

Present Tense.		Past Tense.	
Sing.	*Plur.*	*Sing.*	*Plur.*
1. *speke*	*speke(n)*	*spak*	*speken*
2. *spekest*	*speke(n)*	*spak(e)*	*speken*
3. *speketh*	*speke(n)*	*spak*	*speken*

Subjunctive Present : sing. *speke* ; plur. *speke(n)*.
Imperative Present : sing. *spek* ; plur. *speketh* or *speke*.
Present Participle : *speking(e)*, or *spekyng(e)*.
Past Participle : *yspoke(n)*, or *spoke(n)*.
Infinitive : *speke(n)*.

The gerundial infinitive, which denotes purpose, ends in -*e(n)*, and is preceded by *for to* : *for to seke(n)*, *for to stonden*.

The ending -*eth*, the ending of the 3rd sing. present, frequently contracts to -*th*. Thus *bereth*, *cometh*, *maketh* may be monosyllabic. The ending -*th* coalesces with a preceding dental consonant, and appears as -*t* : *bit* for *biddeth*, *sit* for *sitteth*.

17. Before Chaucer's time, strong verbs had two different vowels in the Past Tense singular and plural, as are shown in *spak*, *speken*, above. But Chaucer's English, though it frequently preserves these two forms as in : *was*, *were(n)* ; *rood*, *riden* ; *cam*, *coomen* ; *fleigh*, *flowen* ; *saugh*, *syen*, also frequently confuses them, as in *they beer* or *baren*, *they ronne* or *ran*. The forms of the past tense therefore are often irregular, and often differ from the corresponding modern English forms. Chaucer has : *bigan*, *bigonne* (began) ; *bad*, *bede* (bade) ; *drank*, *dronke* (drank) ; *fil*, *fel* (fell, befell) ; *sat*, *sete* (sat) ; and *seigh*, *say*, *saugh*, *syen* (saw).

The past participle sometimes has the old prefix *y-*

(O.E. *ge-*): *ybore, ybounde, ycome, yfalle, yholde, ysprad, ywrite.* It ends in *-e*, or rarely in *-en*, when 'strong.'

18. *Weak Verbs.*

Weak verbs form their past tenses by adding *-ed(e)*, or *-de*, or *-te*; and their past participles by adding *-ed, -d* or *t* to the root.

Present Tense.		Past Tense.	
Sing.	Plur.	Sing.	Plur.
1. make	make(n)	made	maden
2. makest	make(n)	madest	maden
3. maketh	make(n)	maked or made	makeden or maden.

Subjunctive Present : sing. *make* ; plur. *make(n)*.
Imperative Present : sing. *make* ; plur. *maketh*.
Present Participle : *making(e)*, or *makyng(e)*.
Past Participle : *ymaked, maked,* or *maad.*
Infinitive : *make(n)*.

19. In some of the weak verbs the vowel is shortened in the past tense and past participle owing to doubling of the medial consonant :

fede	*fedde*	*fed*
lede	*ladde*	*lad*
mete	*mette*	*met*
have	*hadde*	*had*

In others the vowel differs in the past tense and past participle :

bye	*boughte*	*bought*
bringe	*broughte*	*brought*
reche (reach)	*raughte*	*raught*
recche (reck)	*roughte*	*rought*
seche (seek)	*soughte*	*sought*
selle	*solde*	*sold*

seye	*seyde, sayde*	*seyd, sayd*
teche	*taughte*	*taught*
telle	*tolde*	*told*
thinke (seem)	*thoughte*	*thought*
thenke (think)	*thoughte*	*thought*
werche	*wroughte*	*wrought*

20. *Strong-Weak Verbs.*

A peculiarity of these auxiliary verbs of mood is that the present tense is an old strong past tense ; and the past tense is weak, and ends in *-de* or *-te*.

Pres. Sing.	Pres. Plur.	Past Tense.
can	*conne(n)*	*koude*
dar		*dorste*
may	*mowe(n)*	*mighte*
moot	*moote(n)*	*moste*
shal	*shul(len)*	*sholde*
wil, wol	*wole(n)*	*wolde*
woot	*witen*	*wiste.*

21. A few peculiarities of syntax may be recorded.

That is used redundantly after adverbial conjunctions : *if that, though that, whan that* (when). Similarly *as* is redundant after relative adverbs : *wher as* (where), *ther as* (there, where). *As* is also without meaning before imperatives : *as lat* (let), *as taak* (take).

Impersonal verbs dispense with the implied subject *it* : *as him liste* (as it pleased him), *bifil that*, it happened that ; *no wonder is*, it is no wonder.

Maner is frequently used in apposition : *a maner daye*, a kind of dairywoman ; *everich maner doctrine*, every kind of teaching.

As may stand as a conjunction for modern *as if* : *as they were leyd in presse, as it were a meede, as he had been enoynt.*

16 D

It may also indicate a comparison like the Modern English *as*.

> His nekke whyt was as the flour-de-lys,
> Therto he strong was as a champioun.

Or it may indicate a comparison like the Modern English *like*: *as a forpyned goost. As* also often introduces an adverbial phrase: *as by his facultie* (with his position), *as of so litel space* (in so short a time), *as after my konnynge* (to the best of my power).

22. Variant forms. A relic of grammatical gender is found in the two forms *seint* and *seinte*, originally used in French of the masculine and feminine names of saints. Chaucer used *seint* and *seinte* without consistent references to gender : e.g. *seint Maure, seinte Marie* are correct, but we also find *seinte Loy* (possibly *seint Eloy*) and *seinte Poul*. It seems that in English, where the grammatical gender of adjectives was not observed, both forms were in use, and Chaucer used the form which best suited his rhythm.

23. The word *Hooste* (host) also occurs as *Hoost*, with loss of the final *-e*, as in *fors* (force).

THE PROLOGUE TO
THE CANTERBURY TALES

Here bigynneth the Book of the Tales of Caunterbury

WHÁN that Áprille with his shoures soote
The droughte of March hath perced to the roote,
And bathed every veyne in swich licóur
Of which vertú engendred is the flour ;
Whan Zephirus eek with his swetė breeth   A 5
Inspired hath in every holt and heeth
The tendrė croppes, and the yongė sonne
Hath in the Ram his halfė cours yronne,

1. **Whan that :** when. ' That ' is redundant after the conjunctive adverbs : *whan, as, if,* and *how.*—*Aprille :* April,
L. *Aprīlis,* O.F. *Avrill.*   The final *-e* is scribal.

3. **in swich licóur Of which vertú :** in that liquid by whose
power.   The ' liquor ' is, of course, water or sap.

7. **croppes :** shoots.—*the yonge sonne :* the sun is said to be
young, either because, according to the custom of the English
Church, the year began on Lady Day, March 25 ; or else
because the astronomical year began when the sun crossed the
celestial equator and entered the first point of Aries on March 12.

8. **the Ram :** the sign of the zodiac called Aries.   In Chaucer's
age the sun passed through the sign of Aries from March 12 until
April 11.   The sun, therefore, might be considered to run two
half-courses in the Ram, one in March and another in April.
Here it is the second half-course in April which is referred to.
Chaucer means that the Prologue opens in mid-April; *cf.* B 5,
where of the Hoste it is said :

> He wiste it was the eightetethe day
> Of April.

8. E. etc., *half,* Hl. *halfe.*

1

And smalĕ fowles maken melodye,
That slepen al the nyght with open eye,—   10
So priketh hem Natúre in hir coráges ;
Than longen folk to goon on pilgrimages,
And palmers for to seken straungĕ strondes,
To fernĕ halwes, kowthe in sondry londes ;
And specially, from every shires ende   15
Of Engĕlond, to Caunterbury they wende,
The hooly blisful martir for to seeke,
That hem hath holpen whan that they were seke.
   Bifil that in that seson on a day,
In Southwerk at the Tabard as I lay,   A 20

9. E. Hn. *foweles.*

12. The custom of making pilgrimages to the shrines of saints
as a penance to expiate sin, or to pray for a cure from disease
or injury, was one of the peculiarities of life in the Middle Ages.
In Chaucer's age, to some extent, pilgrimages had lost their dis-
tinctively religious character. Irreligious or irreverent people
gratified their love of travel and vanity, and amused themselves
incidentally with story and song. The Lollards objected to
pilgrimages. The Reformation ended them in England.

13. E. *palmeres.*

14. Favourite places of pilgrimage, amongst many, were Rome ;
Santiago de Compostella (in Galicia, Spain), where St James is
buried ; and Cologne, famous for St Christopher, and the bones of
the 11,000 virgins.

16. E. *Caunturbury.*

17. **The hooly blisful martir :** Thomas à Becket, Archbishop of
Canterbury, murdered December 29, 1170, by friends of Henry II.
Canonized as St Thomas of Canterbury in 1173, his remains in
the cathedral church were enclosed in 1220 by a shrine of gold
and precious stones.

18. E. *seeke.*

19. E. *Bifil,* Hn. *Bifel.*

20. **Southwerk at the Tabard :** Southwark, as its name implies,
was originally the southern defence of old London Bridge. In
Chaucer's day the High Street contained on the eastern side a
large inn called the Tabard. There is at present a smaller public-

Redy to wenden on my pilgrimage
To Caunterbury with ful devout corage,
At nyght was come into that hostelrye
Wel nyne and twenty in a compaignye
Of sondry folk, by áventure y-falle   25
In felaweshipe, and pilgrims were they alle,
That toward Caunterbury wolden ryde.
The chambres and the stables weren wyde,
And wel we weren esed attè beste.
And shortly, whan the sonnè was to reste,   30
So hadde I spoken with hem everychon,
That I was of hir felaweshipe anon,
And madè foreward erly for to ryse,
To take our wey ther as I you devyse.

        But nathelees, whil I have tyme and space,   35
Er that I ferther in this talè pace,
Me thinketh it acordaunt to resoun
To tellè you al the condicioun
Of ech of hem, so as it semed me,

house of the same name on a portion of the same site. A 'tabard'
is now, of course, a herald's coat, bearing the coat of arms of the
sovereign. In Chaucer's day the tabard, a sort of labourer's
smock, might be worn by a craftsman or a ploughman in working
dress. Not merely public-houses, but all houses and shops bore
signs before the streets were numbered.—*as I lay :* as I stayed or
spent the night.

    22. corage : intent, heart.

    23. E. *were*, others *was*.

    26. E. *pilgrimes*.

    30. was to reste : was gone to rest, had set.

    33. E. *forward*.

    34. ther as I you devyse : where I tell you, to the place which
I mention to you, *i.e.* Canterbury. 'As' is redundant after the
relative adverbs *ther* and *wher*.

    37. Me thinketh : It seems to me. An impersonal construction.
Note the two verbs : *thenken* (sometimes *thinken*), to think, and

And whiche they weren, and of what degree,   A 40
And eek in what array that they were inne ;
And at a knyght, than, wol I first biginne.

A KNYGHT ther was, and that a worthy man,

The   That fro the tymė that he first bigan
Knight   To ryden out, he loved chivalrye,   45

thinken (used impersonally), to seem.   The past tense of both is
thoghte or *thoughte*.

40. whiche : what sort of men.—Hl. *weren*, others *were*.

43. A Knyght ther was : A knight was not necessarily a
member of the aristocracy, but he was the holder of a certain
amount of land, called a knight's fee, for which he owed military
service either to a superior lord or to the king.   Knighthood
was also conferred by commanders on the battlefield to captains
who had distinguished themselves by military service.   The
order of knighthood was in Chaucer's age a military order.   There
were few civil knights, of whom the Lord Mayors of London,
beginning with Sir William Walworth, who killed Wat Tyler on
Blackheath in 1381, were the chief.

Chaucer's portrait of the knight is the picture of a crusader,
skilled in the use of arms, and faithful to his knightly oath, never
by word or deed to stain his character as a Christian.   It is an
idealized portrait.   The ideal of chivalry, the military virtues of
valour, loyalty and charity are emphasized at the expense of
other qualities.   We may assume that the knight had a wife and
friends, that he paid his debts honourably, and that somewhere
he had an estate where the villeins were well treated ; but the
domestic side of his nature is concealed in order to emphasize
his military worth.   This idealization is in keeping with the
romances of the Middle Ages ; yet Chaucer had taken part in
the campaign of 1359-60 against France, and had been taken
prisoner.   It is thus clear that, whatever he thought about war,
Chaucer regards the military virtues of knighthood most highly,
and honour, courtesy and bravery press right out of the picture
dirt and wounds and death.   The glory of war is emphasized.
Its cruelty is apparently taken for granted.   In this respect the
mentality of the Middle Ages differs from ours.

The Anglo-Saxon word *cniht*, from which *knyght* is derived,
originally meant a youth or retainer ; but in English its meaning

Trouthe and honóur, fredom and curteisye.
Ful worthy was he in his lordes werre,
And therto hadde he riden, no man ferre,
As wel in cristendom as in hethenesse,
And ever honóured for his worthinesse.   50
  At Alisaundre he was whan it was wonne;
Ful oftè tyme he hadde the bord bigonne
Aboven allè nacions in Pruce.

changed, and it came to mean one raised to the rank and status
of a mounted soldier who held his land from a feudal superior on
condition that he followed his lord in time of war for forty days
a year at his own cost.

  This knight's campaigns are all against infidels, and fall into
three groups: (1) with King Peter of Cyprus against the Turks
(Alisaundre, Lyeys, Satalye, Palatye); (2) with the Teutonic
knights against the pagan inhabitants of Lettow and Ruce;
(3) with King Alfonso XI of Castile against the Moors (Algezir,
Belmarye, Tramissene).

  44-45. That . . . he: who.

  47. worthy: brave and capable. Also in l. 64 and l. 68.—*his
lordes werre*: not, I think, his liege lord's war, or his feudal
superior's war, *i.e.* the Hundred Years' War with France. But
rather, *his Lord's war*, or as we should say, our Lord's war—the
Crusades, the wars of Christians against infidels.

  51. Alisaundre: Alexandria in Egypt. Captured by Pierre de
Lusignan, king of Cyprus, and an army of crusading knights in
1365. King Peter had visited the courts of Western Europe in
order to raise enthusiasm for his campaign against the infidel.
He was in England in November 1363, and several English
knights joined his army.

  52. he hadde the bord bigonne: he had taken the most honoured
place at table; he had been placed at dinner in the seat of
honour.

  53. in Pruce: in Prussia, *i.e.* in East Prussia amongst the
Teutonic knights. The order of Teutonic knights was founded
to serve a hospital in Jerusalem for Crusaders, and it became
a military order in 1198, bound by oath to wage war on the
heathen. Their distinguishing badge was a black cross on a

In Lettow hadde he reysed, and in Ruce,—
No cristen man so ofte of his degree.   55
In Gernade at the seege, eek hadde he be,
Of Algezir, and riden in Belmarye.
At Lyeys was he, and at Satalye
Whan they were wonne, and in the Gretė See
At many a noble armee hadde he be.   A 60

white robe. In the thirteenth century they migrated from the
Holy Land to Prussia, with their headquarters at the castle of
Marienburg, whence, after conquering and forcing conversion on
the Prussians, they fought the Lithuanians and Russians. The
order declined in importance after 1386 when the Lithuanians
accepted Christianity, and their duke became by marriage King
of Poland.

54. **Lettow**: Lithuania, which at that time stretched between
Poland and Russia from the Baltic to the Black Sea.—*Ruce:*
Russia.

56. He had also been in Granada at the siege of Algeciras.
Algeciras, next door to Gibraltar, had been in possession of the
Moors for seven centuries when, in 1344, it was recaptured for
Spain and Christendom by Alfonso XI, King of Castile, after a
long siege of nearly two years. Algeciras was a southern fortress
of the Moorish kingdom of Granada, the last remaining Mohammedan kingdom in Spain. Its siege was a famous international
affair. The Papacy aided Alfonso XI with money, and
knights came to fight the infidel from France, Germany, and
England.

57. **Belmarye**: part of Morocco; probably the name of a
tribe, the Beni-Marin, used for the district which they occupied.

58. **Lyeys**: Ayas or Lajazzo, a port on the southern coast of
Asia Minor near Aleppo. It was attacked by Pierre de Lusignan,
king of Cyprus, in 1367. He captured the city, but the Turks
remained masters of the citadel.—*Satalye:* Attalia, on the
southern coast of Asia Minor, north-west of Cyprus. It was
captured by Pierre de Lusignan, king of Cyprus in 1361. The
S is a relic of the Greek preposition εἰς (into).

59. **the Grete See**: the Mediterranean Sea.

60. **armee**: armada, expedition, such as those of King Peter

At mortal batailles hadde he been fiftene,
And foughten for our feith at Tramissene
In listes thryes, and ay slayn his foo.
This ilkè worthy knyght had been also
Somtymè with the lord of Palatye   65
Agayn another hethen in Turkye ;
And everemoore he hadde a sovereyn prys.
And though that he was worthy, he was wys,
And of his port as meek as is a mayde.
He never yet no vileynye ne sayde   70
In al his lyf, unto no maner wight.
He was a verray, parfit, gentil knyght.
 But for to tellen you of his array,
His hors were goodè, but he was nat gay ;
Of fustian he werede a gipoun   75
Ál bismotered with his habergeoun,
For he was late ycome from his viáge,
And wentè for to doon his pilgrimage.

---

of Cyprus against Satalye, Alisaundre and Lyeys.—Hl. Cm.
ariue, E. Hn. *armee*, Cp. Ln. *arme*.

62. Tramissene : Tlemsen, a city and province between
Morocco and Algeria, on the northern coast of Africa. We must
not be surprised to find tournaments in the Morocco of Chaucer's
age. At that time the Moors were more civilized than the
Spaniards.

65. the lord of Palatye : the Turkish ruler of Palatia, the
modern Balat, in Asia Minor.

68. Although he was brave, he was prudent as well.—Hl. etc.
was worthy, E. Hn. Cm. *were worthy*.

70. vileynye : foul language, or abuse due to loss of
temper.

74. gay : finely dressed.—E. Pt. *weren* ; Hl. Ln. *was*, others
were ; Hl. Hn. *he ne was*, others *he was*.

78. The knight's pilgrimage was perhaps the fulfilment of a
vow that, if he should return safely from his journey, he would
go on a pilgrimage to Canterbury.

With hym ther was his sone, a yong SQUIÉR,

The Squire. A lovyere, and a lusty bacheler,　　　　　　A 80
With lokkes crulle, as they were leyd in presse.
Of twenty yeer of age he was, I gesse.
Of his statúre he was of evene lengthe,
And wonderly deliver, and of greet strengthe ;
And he had been somtyme in chivachye,　　　　85

79. a yong Squier : An esquire (O.F. *esquier, escuier,* a shield-
bearer) was originally the shield-bearer of a knight.　The eldest
sons of knights and the eldest sons of the younger sons of peers
were esquires by birth.　Normally they served first as pages in
the household of some other knightly or aristocratic family,
attending when young the lady, and when older the lord.　When
old enough to follow his knight or lord to the wars, he acted as a
superior servant, arming him for battle, and attending him in
the fight.　In the castle or manor house the squire carved the
meat and waited on guests of high rank, and on his lord and lady.
During this period of probation he was learning the use of arms
and the code of honour, and preparing to become a knight.
Chaucer himself had been a page in the service of the household
of the Duke of Clarence, and served probably as a squire in the
campaign against France of 1359.

80. bacheler : probationer for knighthood, as a bachelor of
arts was a probationer for the master's degree.

82. Hl. Hn. *he was of age.*

84. Hl. Cp. etc. *greet of,* E. Hn. Cm. *of greet.*

85. in chivachye, In Flandres, in Artoys and Picardye : on a
raid in Flanders, and in Artois and Picardy.　Flanders, with
its chief cities Bruges and Ghent, was at that time an apanage
of Burgundy and a part of France.　Artois, with its capital city
Arras, was a northern county of Burgundy, corresponding
almost to the modern department of Pas-de-Calais.　Picardy
(capital Amiens) was the province which lay along the river
Somme from Champagne to the English Channel.　Flanders,
Artois and Picardy were the three most northerly provinces of
regal France.　They were always vulnerable by the English,
who held Calais and its surroundings.

The ' chivachy ' may have been an expedition of the Hundred
Years' War, or it may have been one which took place in the

In Flandres, in Artoys and Picardye,
And born him weel, as of so litel space,
In hope to stonden in his lady grace.
Embrouded was he, as it were a meede
Al ful of fresshè floures, whyte and reede ;   90
Singynge he was, or floytinge, al the day.
He was as fressh as is the month of May.
Short was his gowne, with sleves longe and wyde ;
Wel koude he sitte on hors and fairè ryde ;
He koudè songes make and wel endyte,   95
Juste and eek daunce, and weel purtreye and write.
So hoote he lovede that by nyghtertale
He sleep namoore than dooth a nyghtingale.
Curteis he was, lowly and servisable,
And carf biforn his fader at the table.   **A** 100

    A YEMAN hadde he and servántz namo

The Yeoman. At that tyme, for him listè rydè soo ;
And he was clad in cote and hood of grene.

summer of 1383, when the Bishop of Norwich led an English force to plunder the inhabitants because, instead of being loyal to Urban VI, the Pope of Rome, they supported the rival French Pope, Clement VII, with his seat at Avignon.

87. E. etc. *of*, Hl. Hn. *in*.

88. his lady grace : his lady's favour. ' Lady ' was in Old English a feminine noun, *hlæfdige*, with its genitive case ending in *-an*, which in Middle English became *-e*. This *-e* was not pronounced in Chaucer's English, but the word had not yet acquired the possessive ending *-es*. A trace of this still remains in English : *cf.* Lady Day with Lord's Day.

89. Embrouded was he : His short gown was embroidered.

98. Hl. Cp. *sleep*, E. etc. *slepte*.

100. carf biforn his fader : It was one of the duties of esquires to carve at table, and although this squire does not appear to have been in the service of his father, he would naturally carve the meat.

101. A Yeman : A yeoman was a small landowner ; but the word also meant a servant, as in *The Canon's Yeoman*, and

A sheef of pecok-arwes, bryghte and kene,
Under his belt he bar ful thriftily ;   105
Wel koude he dresse his takel yemanly :
His arwes drouped noght with fetheres lowe,
And in his hand he baar a myghty bowe.
A not-heed hadde he with a broun viságe.
Of woodècraft wel koude he al th' uságe.   110
Upon his arm he baar a gay bracér,
And by his syde a swerd and a bokler,
And on that oother syde a gay daggére,
Harneised wel, and sharp as point of spere ;
A Cristofre on his brest of silver sheene ;   115

The Yeomen of the Guard. This yeoman was presumably a
forester from the country estate of the knight, who had come
with the squire to meet the knight on his return from abroad
and to accompany him on his pilgrimage. He appears to have
been a small farmer, and a ranger of the knight's forest. That
he was a forester is indicated by his " cote and hood of grene,"
by his skill in archery, and by his horn and green baldric. He
carried a sword and buckler, not as instruments of war, but for
engaging in the sport of fighting with sword and buckler. The
miller also carries them. Perhaps the 'he' of l. 101 refers to the
knight.

103. cote and hood of grene : he is dressed, like Robin Hood,
as a forester.

107. with fetheres lowe : with weak feathers, or with feathers
trimmed too closely. ' Low ' feathers were (1) weak feathers
which cause the arrow to make a short, drooping flight ; or
(2) feathers on the arrow which had been trimmed too closely.
The yeoman was a good bowman who knew which feathers to
choose for his arrows, and knew not to trim them too closely.

108. a myghty bowe : a long-bow, not a cross-bow.

112. E. *a bokeler.*

114. Harneised wel : well decorated on the handle and sheath.

115. Cristofre : An image of St Christopher. St Christopher
was born in Syria and grew up a wild and ignorant man. His
ambition was to serve the greatest king in the world. In the
service of a great king he heard a minstrel sing a song in which

An horn he baar, the bawdrik was of grene.

A forster was he, soothly, as I gesse.

Ther was also a Nonne, a PRIORESSE,

The
Prioress.
That of hir smylyng was ful simple and coy ;
Hir gretteste ooth was but by seintè Loy, 120

the Devil was mentioned, and, seeing his master make the sign
of the cross, he believed the Devil to be a greater king, and set
out to serve him. In the desert he met the Devil, but as they
went along the road Christopher noticed that the Devil trembled
when they came to a cross. Thereupon St Christopher learned
the story of Christ from the Devil, and resolved henceforth to
serve Jesus Christ.

As a penance a hermit sent him to carry passengers across a
broad river. One night our Lord appeared to him as a little
child who desired to cross the river. As Christopher carried
Him, He grew heavier and heavier, until it was all he could do
to reach the farther bank. He upbraided the child, whereupon
He said : " Christopher, marvel not, for with me thou hast borne
the world and its creator."

The image of St Christopher was worn as a sign of devotion
to the saint, who, it was believed, would protect in times of
danger.—E. *Cristophere.*

118. a Prioresse : a nun, the head of a smaller religious house,
as an abbess was the head of a larger nunnery. In Chaucer's age
nunneries were not entirely devoted to prayers : they entertained guests, and sometimes educated the daughters of the rich.
Hence the prioress's table-manners. Chaucer draws a very
flattering portrait of the lady. She was modest and quiet,
earnest in her religious devotions. She was kind and happy,
even sentimental about mice, and yet she was dignified. It is
the touch of worldliness in her habits which adds humour to the
portrait.

119. simple and coy : modest and quiet.

120. by seinte Loy : St Loy or Eloi (L. *Eligius*), A.D. 588-658,
was the missionary who brought Christianity to Flanders. He
was originally a goldsmith, and master of the mint to Dagobert,
king of the Franks (628-638). He became Bishop of Noyon.—
All, *seint, seynt.*

Maitland, in *The Dark Ages,* showed that St Loy refused to

> And she was cleped Madame Eglentyne.
> Ful wel she soong the servicè divyne
> Entuned in hir nose ful semèly ;
> And Frenssh she spak ful faire and fetisly
> After the scole of Stratford-attè-Bowe,   125
> For Frenssh of Parys was to hir unknowe.

take an oath when pressed to do so by King Dagobert, and some commentators have held that the prioress minimized swearing by swearing by one who refused to swear. But Chaucer says that "by seinte Loy" was her greatest oath. In all probability there were minor ones, for Chaucer's was an age which took some pride in oaths, and he belonged to a swearing community.

Swearing by St Eloi, in the mouth of the prioress, implies familiarity with Flanders. Chaucer's wife, Philippa Roet, came from Hainault, and was in the service of Queen Philippa, wife of Edward III. Queen Philippa's sister, Elizabeth of Hainaut, as Professor Manly has shown, was a nun in St Leonard's, Stratford le Bow. The ladies of Hainaut may have introduced St Loy to English ears, and set a fashion.

121. Eglentyne : Eglantine is an old name for the sweet-briar, a kind of wild rose. This seems an impossible name for a nun. Perhaps Chaucer chose it in order to make the prioress appear definitely a fictitious character.

124. Frenssh she spak . . . After the scole of Stratford-atte-Bowe : *i.e.* She spoke the Anglo-Norman dialect of French, which as a girl she had learned at the convent school of Stratford le Bow. Possibly the prioress and the nine nuns of the convent at Stratford kept a school for the daughters of citizens of London. On the other hand, Manly, in *Some New Light on Chaucer*, states that the fashion of speaking French at Stratford must have been set by an aristocratic nun, Elizabeth of Hainaut, and hence the French of Stratford was not Anglo-Norman, but the Walloon dialect of French spoken in Hainaut (the county in which Mons and Valenciennes are situated).

Stratford is now Stratford le Bow, or simply Bow, in East London. The high road from Aldgate to Stratford, in Essex, crosses the river Lea at Bow Bridge. The nunnery was only two and a half miles from Aldgate, where Chaucer lived for twelve years, from 1374 to 1386.

At metė, wel ytaught was she withalle,
She leet no morsel from hir lippes falle,
Ne wette hir fingres in hir sauce depe.
Wel koude she carie a morsel, and wel kepe   130
Thát no drope ne fille upon hir brest ;
In curteisye was set ful muchel hir lest.
Hir overlippė wyped she so clene,
That in hir coppe ther was no ferthing sene
Of grecė, whan she dronken hadde hir draughte.   135
Ful semėly after hir mete she raughte,
And sikerly she was of greet desport,
And ful plesáunt and amiable of port,
And peyned hir to countrefetė cheere
Of court, and been estatlich of manére,   A 140
And to ben holden digne of reverence.

But, for to speken of hir conscience,
She was so charitable and so pitous
She woldė wepe, if that she saugh a mous
Kaught in a trappe, if it were deed or bledde.   145
Of smalė houndes had she that she fedde
With rosted flessh, or milk and wastel-breed ;
But soorė weep she, if óon of hem were deed,

127-135. These lines, as Tyrwhitt, the first annotator of
Chaucer's *Canterbury Tales*, pointed out, bear a striking resem-
blance to certain lines in *Le Roman de la Rose*, spoken by the
Duenna to illustrate and incidentally to inculcate a young lady's
table-manners.

131. E. *brist*.

132. E. *list*.

134. no ferthing sene : no morsel visible.

140. E. *and to been*.

142. conscience : tenderness, considerateness.

144. Hl. Hn. Cp. *sawe*.

146. Of smale houndes : some small dogs.   ' Of ' is partitive.—
E. etc. *hadde*.

148. weep : wept.   There are two reasons why this archaic

Or if men smoot it with a yerdė smerte ;
And al was conscience and tendrė herte.   150
   Ful semėly hir wimpel pinched was,
Hir nosė tretis, hir eyen greye as glas,
Hir mouth ful smal, and therto softe and reed ;
But sikerly she hadde a fair forheed,
It was almoost a spannė brood, I trowe,   155
For, hardily, she was nat undergrowe.
   Ful fetis was hir cloke, as I was war ;
Of smal coral aboute hir arm she bar
A peire of bedes, gauded al with grene,

past tense must have been written by Chaucer. One is that
'sleep,' a similar form, occurs in l. 98. The other is that 'wepte,'
which in Chaucer's English would have two syllables, would not
fit the scansion.—E. etc. *wepte*, E. *if any*.—*were deed :* died.

149. if men smoot it: if anyone hit it. If 'men' were the
plural of 'man,' the verb would be in the plural, which is 'smiten.'
The singular verb shows that 'men' is the 'weakened' form of
'man,' the indefinite pronoun.

152. E. *tretys*, Hl. Cp. *streight*.

155. Grey eyes and a broad forehead were considered beautiful
in Chaucer's age. The tomb of Queen Philippa, wife of
Edward III, in Westminster Abbey, bears her effigy, which
represents her as having a broad, high forehead.

159. A peire of bedes: a set of beads, a rosary. The word
'bead' originally meant a prayer.—*gauded al with grene :* the
paternosters of green stone. A rosary was arranged in sets of
ten small beads for the *Ave Marias*, followed by one larger bead
for the *Paternoster*. The number of sets is now fifteen, but the
rosary shown in Chaucer's left hand in Hoccleve's portrait seems
only to have ten. The large beads were known as 'gauds' (L.
gaudia, joys). Chaucer is using the regular description of a
rosary or paternoster " a pair of beads of *x* gaudied with *y*," as
old wills indicate.

'Gauded' can also mean dyed (green) with weld, from O.F.
gaude (weld), but that is not its meaning here. It was not the
coral beads which were green, but the larger beads, the paternosters.

And theron heng a brooch of gold ful sheene,   A 160
On which ther was first write a crowned A,
And after *Amor vincit omnia.*

The   Another NONNÉ with hir haddé she
Nun.   That was hir chapéleyne and PREESTES three.

A MONK ther was, a fair for the maistrye,   165

The   An outridere, that lovede venerye;
Monk.   A manly man, to been an abbot able.

161. a crowned A : signifying L. *Amor* (love), *i.e.* divine love crowned.—Hl. *iwriten.*

162. Amor vincit omnia : Love conquers all things. The sentiment is a common one. A classical example is found in Virgil, *Eclogue* X, 69 : " omnia vincit Amor."

163. Another Nonne : This is the person who tells the Life of St Cecilia in the *Tales.*

164. hir chapeleyne : her attendant and secretary, not a priest.—*and preestes three :* As Skeat pointed out, this passage presents some difficulty. Only one priest is mentioned elsewhere, the Nun's Priest, who tells the tale of Chauntecleer and Pertelote. It is curious that neither the second Nun nor the priests are described. The couplet may be an interpolation, or Chaucer may have left the description incomplete : "That was hire chapeleyne, and . . ." He may have left the record of the nun unfinished, breaking off at the word ' chapeleyne,' and some other hand may have added "and preestes three" to complete the rime, as Manly suggested.

165. A monk : a member of a contemplative religious order, devoted by vow to poverty and chastity. On this monk devolved the management of a ' cell' or subordinate monastery, so that possibly he was a prior. The management of the cell—which meant not merely oversight of its inmates—monks, lay-brothers, guests—but of its estates, which meant houses, farms and forests—would almost inevitably lead to contact with the outer world; and it is not surprising that this monk had something of the habits of a worldling. He was fond of hunting and of good food : he was not ascetic. He had no spiritual zeal, but he was not a bad man, and Chaucer admires him.

166. An outridere : one licensed by the abbot to act as land-

16 B

Ful many a deyntee hors hadde he in stable,
And, whan he rood, men myghte his brydel heere
Gínglen in a whistlinge wynd als cleere,   170
And eek as loude, as dooth the chapel belle
Ther as this lord was kepere of the celle.
The reule of seint Maure or of seint Beneit,
Bycause that it was old and somdel streit,
This ilkè monk leet oldè thinges pace,   175
And heeld after the newè world the space.
He yaf nat of that text a pulled hen,
That seith that hunters beth nat hooly men,
Ne that a monk, whan he is recchèlees,

agent for the farms and estates of the monastery, the monastic
equivalent of a steward.

172. celle: not a cell in the modern meaning of the word, but
a smaller monastic house subordinate to an abbey. It would
probably be in a different part of the country from the parent
house. It might even be the cell of a monastery in France or
Navarre.

173. seint Maure or of seint Beneit: St Beneit or, as he is now
called, St Benedict, founded the Benedictine order of monks at
Monte Cassino, in Italy, between Naples and Rome, in A.D. 529.
There he wrote the Benedictine Rule, the rule to which a Benedictine monk owed obedience, which enforced residence in a
monastery, moral endeavour, and obedience to the rule. The
monk was sworn to chastity, poverty, obedience and religious
devotion.

St Maure, or Maurus, was the apostle of the Benedictine order
in France. Being one of St Benedict's first disciples, he is
associated by Chaucer with the rule.

177. that text: the 'text' is a part of St Jerome's commentary
on Psalm xc. "Esau was a hunter because he was a sinner.
And in the whole of the Scriptures we do not find a single holy
man who is a hunter. Fishers as holy men we do find."

179. Nor (that other text which says) that a monk, when he
is negligent, is like a fish out of water. The text is a medieval
Latin proverb: 'Sicut piscis sine aqua caret vita, ita sine
monasterio monachus.' A monk out of his monastery is as dead

Is lykned til a fissh that is waterlees ;   A 180
(This is to seyn, a monk out of his cloistre).
But thilkė text heeld he nat worth an oystre ;
And I seyde his opinioun was good.

What sholde he studie, and make hymselven wood,
Upon a book in cloistre alwey to poure,   185
Or swinken with his handes and labóure
As Austyn bit ?   How shal the world be served ?
Lat Austyn have his swink to him reserved.
Therfore he was a prikasour aright ;
Grehoundes he hadde, as swift as fowel in flight. 190
Of prikyng and of huntyng for the hare
Was al his lust, for no cost wolde he spare.

I seigh his sleves ypurfiled at the hond
With grys, and that the fyneste of a lond ;
And, for to festne his hood under his chin,   195

as a fish out of water.—E. Hn. *recchelees*, Hl. *cloysterles*, Cp. Pt. Ln. *recheles*, Cm. *rekeles*.

181. That is to say, 'recchelees' implies a monk out of his cloister.

184. What: Why.

187. Austyn: St Augustine, the greatest early Christian father of the Western Church. He was an African, born in Numidia (the modern Algeria) in A.D. 354. Educated at Carthage, he went to Italy as a teacher of rhetoric, and was converted to Christianity by St Ambrose, Bishop of Milan, in 387. He became a priest in Numidia, wrote the *Confessions* (397), *The City of God* (426), and died at Hippo in 430. One of his works, *The Duty of Monks* (De Opere Monachorum), was an authority upon monastic conduct. He never wrote a 'rule,' like St Benedict, but one was derived from his writings ; and many monastic orders, *e.g* the Austin Canons, the Austin Friars, etc., owed allegiance to it.

Not to be confused with St Augustine of Canterbury, the apostle of the English.

188. E. *his owene swynk*.

191. prikyng: perhaps here 'tracking.'

193. Hl. Hn. Cm. *purfiled*.

He hadde, of gold ywroght, a curious pin ;
A loveknotte in the gretter ende ther was.
His heed was balled, that shoon as any glas,
And eek his face, as he had been enoynt.
He was a lord ful fat and in good poynt ;   A 200
His eyen stepe and rollinge in his heed,
That stemed as a forneys of a leed ;
His bootes souple, his hors in greet estaat.
Now certeinly he was a fair prelaat.

He was nat pale, as a forpyned goost :   205
A fat swan loved he best of any roost.
His palfrey was as broun as is a berye.

A FRERE ther was, a wantown and a merye,

The   A limitour, a ful solémpnè man,
Friar.   In alle the ordres foure is noon that kan 210

196. The gold pin, like the fur-trimmed sleeves, was a luxury ;
and not in accordance with the monk's vow of poverty.—E. etc.
a ful curious.

199. E. *as it hadde.*

201. stepe : bright.

202. Which gleamed like the furnace of a leaden cauldron.

205. Cm. Cp. *nas nat.*

208. A frere ther was : A friar was a member of a mendicant
(or begging) religious order, founded later than the Benedictine
order of monks and nuns with its offshoots, and protected by
the authority of the Pope. English bishops had no jurisdiction
over them. Monks and nuns were secluded from the world, and
had grown rich in the course of centuries. Friars came into
existence in the thirteenth century as an attempt to improve
upon the contemplative life by a life of service to men. The
friars therefore professed poverty. They were forbidden to hold
property and estates, and depended on voluntary contributions.
Where monasticism was aristocratic, leisured and comfortable,
the friars were poor, ascetic and self-denying. They supported
themselves by begging. But the cares of poverty proved to be
as harassing as the cares of property. Their activity and
influence were great, but according to Chaucer (and he is here

So muche of daliaunce and fair langáge ;
He haddė maad ful many a mariáge
Of yongė wommen at his owenė cost :
Unto his ordre he was a noble post.
Ful wel biloved and famulier was he   215

supported by Langland and Wycliffe) they had lost their earlier
idealism, and were content for money to take advantage of the
baser side of human nature.

210. the ordres foure : There were many orders of friars, but
the four chief orders in England here alluded to were :

(1) The Franciscans, or Grey Friars, founded by St Francis of
Assisi in Italy in 1208. A branch of them came to England in
1224. They had about 55 houses in England in the towns.

(2) The Dominicans, or Black Friars, founded by St Dominic
at Toulouse in 1215 as a preaching order, especially to combat
heresy. A branch of them came to England in 1221. They had
about 50 convents in England.

(3) The Carmelites, or White Friars, originally founded as an
association of hermits on Mount Carmel, in the Holy Land
during the Crusades. Their 'rule' dates from 1209. Driven
out by the Saracens, they settled in various countries of Christendom. Their first general meeting or 'chapter' in England
was held in 1245. Two years later they became a mendicant
order. They had 38 houses in England.

(4) The Austin Friars, an order of uncertain origin, organized
by Pope Innocent IV in the middle of the thirteenth century.
In 1256 they accepted a 'general' as president at the hands of
Pope Alexander IV. They followed the rule of St Augustine.
They had 33 convents in England.

It will be noted that Chaucer takes an aristocratic point of
view, and regards the friar as of a lower class than the monk.

211. E. *muchel.*

212. Secret weddings, like the wedding of Romeo and Juliet,
were performed by the friars. Perhaps this passage means that
the friar, in order to win popularity, married couples without
charging a fee : or it may mean that, without charging a fee as
a marriage broker, he found husbands for unattractive young
women. Respectable people would be married by the 'curat.'

215. E. *And wel.*

With frankeleyns overal in his contree,
Ánd with wórthy wommen of the toun ;
For he had power of confessioun,
As seyde hymself, moore than a curat,
For of his ordre he was licenciat.   A 220
Ful swetély herde he confessioun,
And pleasaunt was his absolucioun.
He was an esy man to yeve penaunce
Ther as he wiste to have a good pitaunce ;
For unto a poure ordre for to yive   225
Is signé that a man is wel yshrive ;
For, if he yaf, he dorsté make avaunt
He wisté that a man was répentaunt :
For many a man so hard is of his herte
He may nat wepe, althogh him soore smerte ;   230
Therfore, in stede of wepinge and preyeres,
Men moot yeve silver to the pouré freres.

His tipet was ay farsed ful of knyves
And pinnes, for to yeven faire wyves.
And certeinly he hadde a murye note ;   235
Wel koude he singe and pleyen on a rote :

217. Hl. Hn. *And eek.*

220. licenciat : The friar held a licence from his order which empowered him to hear confessions. Naturally it would be largely the disreputable who forsook their parish priest and went to the friar ; for the worst cases were reserved by the priest for the bishop, but the friar could give immediate absolution, even for weighty sins, owing to his papal licence. Chaucer implies that the friar's ' pleasant ' absolution encouraged sin by giving an easy penance.

224. E. *haue,* Hl. Cm. *han.*

227. if he yaf, he : if the man gave, the friar . . .

233. Evidently the friar gave knives and pins in order to encourage gifts of money. He did not sell them, but he was a beggar, and they were his ' bait.'

234. E. *yonge.*

Of yeddinges he baar outrely the pris ;
His nekkè whyt was as the flour-de-lys,
Therto he strong was as a champioun.
He knew the taverns wel in every toun,   A 240
And everich hostiler and tappestere
Bet than a lazar or a beggestere ;
For unto swich a worthy man as he
Acorded nat, as by his facultee,
To have with sikè lazars aqueyntaunce.   245
It is nat honeste, it may nat avaunce,
Fór to deelen with no swich poraille ;
But al with riche and sellers of vitaille.
And overal, ther as profit sholde arise,
Curteis he was and lowly of servise,   250
Ther nas no man nowher so vertuous.

    He was the bestè beggere in his hous ;
For though a widwe haddè noght a shoo,
So plesaunt was his *In principio*,
Yet wolde he have a ferthyng, er he wente.   255
His " purchas was wel bettre than his rente " ;
And rage he koude, as it were right a whelpe.

240. E. *in al the*.
244. It was not in keeping with his profession as a limitour.
After l. 252. Hengwrt MS. inserts:

> And yaf a certeyn ferme for the graunt
> Noon of his bretheren cam ther in his haunt.

254. In principio : The opening words of the first chapter of
the Gospel according to St John, read or said by friars in their
visits.
256. A proverbial saying : his gains amounted to more than
his regular income. Applied to the owners of property, it meant
that they earned by fair or foul means more than they received
in rent for their farms. Applied to the friar, it must not be
taken too literally. It simply means that he was a brilliant
beggar. He made money, not for himself, but for charity, for
he had no rent or income : he was vowed to poverty.

In lovèdayes ther koude he muchel helpe,
For there he was nat lyk a cloisterer
With a thrédbare cope, as is a poure scolér,   A 260
But he was lyk a maister, or a pope ;
Of double worsted was his semicope,
That rounded as a belle out of the presse.
Somewhat he lipsed for his wantownesse,
To make his Englissh sweete upon his tonge,   265
And in his harping, whan that he had songe,
His eyen twinkled in his heed aryght
As doon the sterres in the frosty nyght.
This worthy limitour was cleped Huberd.

A MARCHANT was ther with a forked berd,   270

The   In mottèley, and hye on horse he sat :
Merchant.   Upon his heed a Flaundrissh bevere hat,

269. Hl. *called.*

270. A marchant : A wholesale merchant who sent cargoes
of English exports to Middelburg, in Holland, and perhaps to
France ; sold them for foreign money, made another profit by
selling his foreign money for English money : and then bought
again English goods for export and repeated the process. He
was a shipper or exporter, who wished to impress people with
his wealth. He may, when occasion offered, have acted as
importer too, buying foreign goods such as wine or cloth with
the proceeds of his sales, and then selling the goods in England
for English money. Chaucer may have thought of him as
belonging to Ipswich, of which Orwell was the seaport. He is
dressed like a wealthy man in a tunic of motley, and he wore
a beaver hat.

271. motteley : blotched or spotted cloth (*cf.* F. *motte*, a clod).
Not the parti-coloured dress associated with the jesters of Tudor
times.

272. a Flaundrissh bevere hat : a hat made in Flanders, and
after the fashion of Flanders, from the fur of the beaver ; as
modern hats are made from the fur of the rabbit. The description implies an expensive kind of hat.

His bootes clasped faire and fetisly ;
His resons he spak ful solémpnely,
Sowninge alway th' encrees of his winning.   275
He wolde the see were kept, for any thing,
Bitwixè Middelburgh and Orèwelle.

276. **for any thing** : in spite of anything, against every enemy
craft.

277. Orwell is the name of the tidal river upon which Ipswich
stands, twelve miles from the sea. It appears to be used here
for the port and shipping of Ipswich, as the Mersey is now used
for Liverpool, and the Humber for Hull. Middelburgh is on the
island of Walcheren, near Flushing, at the mouth of the Scheldt.
I take this line to mean that the merchant wished the southern
part of the North Sea to be guarded against French privateers
in the interests of foreign trade. There was no English navy,
and the task of keeping the sea was farmed out to privateers.
The implication is that the merchant's trade was between
Ipswich and the river Scheldt, on which stand Antwerp and
Ghent.

The principal export from England was wool in Chaucer's
day, which was sent to Ypres, Ghent and Bruges, where it was
woven into cloth. The wool was stored and sold in one town,
called the ' staple,' which denoted both the market and the
commodity. The staple of wool was at first held in various
Flemish towns, especially Bruges. Edward III, after attempting
to hold the staple in England without success, fixed the staple at
Calais, then an English possession, in and after 1362. Flanders,
the country between the river Scheldt and the North Sea, was
a dependency of the Duke of Burgundy.

The staple of wool was removed from Calais to Middelburgh,
in Holland, from 1384 to 1388, and if Chaucer thought of his
merchant as a member of the staple, this passage implies that
the *Prologue* was written in the years 1384 to 1388. Against
this it is urged that not all merchants were members of the staple ;
and that this merchant may have been engaged not in the
export of raw materials such as wool, but in the export of manu-
factured goods, the organization for which was the Company
of Merchant Adventurers.

Wel koude he in eschaungė sheeldes selle.
This worthy man ful wel his wit bisette,
Ther wistė no wight that he was in dette,   **A** 280
So estatly was he of his governaunce,
With his bargaynes, and with his chevissaunce.
For sooth, he was a worthy man withalle,

278. sheeldes : French *écus*, or crowns. Flanders at that time was, like Artois, an apanage of Burgundy. If the merchant traded in wool at Calais, he would be compelled by law to exchange his ' sheeldes ' at the Calais mint, where the royal exchange had its fixed rates of exchange. The innuendo that the merchant knew well how to profit by selling French money, and presumably buying English money, rather points to attendance at one of the Flemish or French fairs, followed by dealings with money-changers, who were frequently the agents of Italian banks called ' Lombards.' The exchange of coinage was in England and Calais a royal prerogative, but it was farmed to bankers. The London Exchange was in the Tower of London.

280. Not necessarily a bankrupt. Until the discovery of fresh sources of supply of gold and silver in the sixteenth century, there was not enough coin for trade. That is one reason why prices were so low. A man of rank and estates might temporarily find himself short of ready money. Transactions such as those of the merchant were frequently settled not in cash but with exchange of bills. If the merchant sold £400 worth of wool and bought £450 of cloth for import from the same firm in Ghent, he might settle the transaction with a bill of exchange for £50 which the Lombard banker would discount. He would then have £450 worth of cloth to sell, nevertheless he would be in debt, temporarily.—Hl. Cm. *man.*

282. chevissaunce : completion of a bargain, money-lending, profit ; including interest on money and profit on the exchange of money. At that time Christians regarded interest on money as an unnatural and sinful form of profit. Hence finance was largely in the hands of Jews and of Italian merchants from Florence, Genoa and Venice, who were known as ' Lombards.' They were hated because they exacted interest on their loans.

But, sooth to seyn, I noot how men him calle.

A CLERK ther was of Oxenford also,   285

<small>The
Clerk.</small> That unto logyk haddė longe ygo.

As leenė was his hors as is a rake,

And he nas nat right fat, I undertake,

284. As Comptroller of Customs of Wool in London, Chaucer must have come in daily contact with merchants like the one whom he has sketched; perhaps that is why he takes care to make him a fictitious character.

285. A clerk: A clergyman and scholar, probably a fellow of one of the Oxford colleges. This clerk was a student and teacher. He had probably taken his degree, and was studying philosophy as a fellow of his college. Most students owned no books of their own, except note-books. He was therefore not an undergraduate, sharing a room with three or four more; but rather a fellow, with his own room, and his own collection of books, supplemented no doubt from the books of the college.

The course of study at a medieval university consisted of, firstly, Latin grammar and rhetoric, followed by logic. This was called the ' Trivium.' Later came the mathematical subjects of the age—arithmetic, geometry, astronomy (for the reckoning of time and the date of Easter), and music (for voices in the church services). This was known as the ' Quadrivium.' Finally, in the fourteenth century came the philosophy of Aristotle, consisting of physics (knowledge of the animal, vegetable and mineral worlds), metaphysics (knowledge of God and the nature of things), and ethics. The philosophical writings of Aristotle were translated into Latin, in which language they were read by scholars in all the countries of Western Europe.

Books were expensive, because printing was not yet invented. The books of Chaucer's age were all copied out by hand (manuscripts). They were bound, and looked very much like printed books, except that they were written and sometimes illustrated (illuminated) ; the pages were large, and they were sometimes elaborately bound.—*Oxenford :* Oxford.

286. logyk : the science of reasoning. Logic was the bridge between the use of language for argument, and metaphysics, the science of the cause and nature of things.

But looked holwe, and therto sobrely.
Ful thredbare was his overeste courtepy,   290
For he had geten him yet no benefice,
Ne was so worldly for to have office :
For him was levere have at his beddes heed
Twénty bookes clad in blak or reed,
Of Aristotle and his philosophye,   295
Than robes riche, or fithele, or gay sautrye.
  But al be that he was a philosóphre,

290. **overeste courtepy** : his short gown, literally his topmost short-cloak.

291. E. etc. *hadde.*

294. Twenty books was a large library in those days, though Chaucer himself owned sixty, concerned with fiction alone, if the Prologue to the *Legend of Good Women* (l. 273, Text A) is to be believed :

> "Yis ! God wot, sixty bokes olde and newe
> Hast thou thyself, alle fulle of stories grete,
> That bothe Romains and eek Grekes trete
> Of sundry wemen."

' Twenty bokes ' might be worth ten or twenty pounds—a page's ransom, or the price of a cottage. The scholastic philosophy which developed in the universities in the thirteenth century used Aristotle's logic, physics and metaphysics, as the basis of knowledge; reconciling his doctrines, where necessary, with Christian theology. Aristotle was regarded with profound reverence as an encyclopædic philosopher. Dante calls him (*Inferno*, iv. 131) *il maestro di color che sanno*, the master of those who know. Aristotle's works were not read in the original Greek, but in Latin translations, the most famous of which were the work of a Flemish Dominican, William of Moerbeke, made (c. 1265) in the lifetime of two great medieval philosophers, St Thomas Aquinas (*d.* 1274), and Albertus Magnus (*d.* 1280).

297. **a philosophre** : one who made all knowledge his province, like Roger Bacon of Oxford (*d. c.* 1295). But as knowledge included alchemy, and the search for the ' philosophers' stone ' that should have the property of transmuting other metals into gold (see *The Canon's Yeoman's Tale*), an accomplished philo-

Yet haddè he but litel gold in cofre ;
But al that he myghte of his freendes hente,
On bookes and on lerninge he it spente,   A 300
And bisily gan for the soules preye
Of hem that yaf him wherewith to scoleye.
Of studie took he moost cure and moost heed.
Noght o word spak he moorè than was need,
And that was seyd in forme and reverence,   305
And short and quik, and ful of hy sentence.
Sowninge in moral vertu was his speche,
And gladly wolde he lerne and gladly teche.
    A SERGEANT OF THE LAWE, war and wys,

The Man of Law.   That often haddè been at the Parvys   310
Ther was also, ful riche of excellence.

sopher should be able to make gold, and should therefore be rich.

299. It cost about £10 a year to keep an undergraduate at a university when Chaucer wrote his *Prologue*. If the clerk were a fellow, his college would pay him a stipend from its revenue, some £5 or so yearly. This young man appears, like many medieval scholars, to have been helped not only by his father, but by his relations and friends.

300. E. Hl. *his*, Hn. etc. *on*.

306. ful of hy sentence : full of deep meaning.—E. etc. *hy*, Hl. *gret*.

309. A sergeant of the lawe : A barrister of the highest rank belonging to a little group of perhaps a score. At a later period only those of sixteen years' standing as barristers could be appointed serjeant-at-law. They were appointed by a patent of the King on the recommendation of the Lord Chancellor, to whom they were recommended by the Justice of the Court of Common Pleas, in whose court they had exclusive audience. On appointment as serjeant they left the Inn of Court, to which they belonged, and joined Serjeants' Inn. Their official dress was elaborate—a violet-coloured robe with scarlet hood and a white (later a black) coif. The Court of Common Pleas, for the trial of ' civil ' cases, was abolished in 1875. Not long after-

Discreet he was, and of greet reverence ;
He semed swich, his wordes were so wise.
Justice he was ful often in assise,
By patente and by pleyn commissioun ;   315
For his science and for his heigh renoun,
Of fees and robes hadde he many oon ;
So greet a purchasour was nowher noon,

wards Serjeants' Inn was dissolved, and the order of serjeants came to an end.

From the serjeants were chosen the common law Judges of the King's Bench, the Common Pleas, and the Barons of the Exchequer. A serjeant was not a judge, but if there were a shortage of judges, owing to illness or pressure of business, he might temporarily be appointed judge by royal patent. A serjeant then was but one step from a judge, and the order of serjeants was important in the courts of the Common Law. The three courts were all held in Westminster Hall, so that serjeants were to be found in Westminster.

310. at the Parvys: at the porch, or at the enclosed area beside a church, here, probably, of Westminster Hall, where either he used to meet his clients in the afternoon, or would discuss cases with his friends. *In perviso* means at matriculation.

313. E. *weren*.

315. By letter of appointment from the king, and by a commission which gave him full power to act as judge in assizes (local sittings). The man of law was not a permanent judge, he was a barrister of the Courts of Common Law; but when legal business accumulated so that there were not enough judges to go on circuit, he was appointed a commissioner for certain assizes.

317. robes: robes were sometimes given by clients as fees to barristers. When appointed ' justice in assize,' he would receive robes from the king.

318. purchasour: buyer of landed property. He was so skilful and so cunning, that however the land was held, whether a feudal tenure and entailed, he could convey it to himself as if it were ' fee-simple.' A ' fee-simple ' is an estate which may be disposed of by will; as opposed to a ' fee tail,' which was an estate limited to a particular class of heirs, usually the eldest son.

Al was fee-simple to him in effect,
His purchasyng myghtė nat been infect.   **A** 320
Nowher so bisy a man as he, ther nas,
And yet he semed bisier than he was.

   In termes hadde he caas and doomes alle
That from the tyme of king William were falle.
Therto he koude endyte, and make a thyng,   325
Ther koudė no wight pinche at his writyng ;
And every statut koude he pleyn by rote.
He rood but hoomly in a medlee cote,
Girt with a ceint of silk, with barres smale ;
Of his array, telle I no lenger tale.   330

   A FRANKÉLEYN was in his compaignye ;
The   Whyt was his berd as is a dayesye,
Franklin. Of his complexioun he was sangwyn.

---

320. His conveyancing could not be invalidated (*i.e.* said to have no legal force).

323. He knew accurately all the cases and decisions which had happened since the days of William the Conqueror.

324. E. *yfalle*, others *falle*.

325. endyte : frame a charge, legally accuse.—*make a thyng* : draw up a deed.

326. E. Hn. *pynchen*, others *pinche*.

328. He rode in homely fashion, in a parti-coloured gown. The dress of a serjeant at law was a gown of two colours, which seem to have varied in different ages. In the picture in the Ellesmere MS. his gown is of scarlet faced with blue. Chaucer means that he wore a serjeant's dress, not a judge's.

331. A frankeleyn : A freeholder. A man not of noble blood, who owned his land in fee simple, free from feudal obligations. He is pictured here as a hearty old country gentleman, a squire, not a farmer ; but a commoner, not a noble. He lived well and kept open house, and he was a justice of the peace who had represented the shire in Parliament. He had also been sheriff and auditor of accounts for the shire. He is in company with the man of law, either because we are to suppose that they are neighbours, or because they have a common interest, namely,

Wel loved he by the morwe a sop in wyn ;
To liven in delyt was evere his wone,   335
For he was Epicurus owenè sone,
That heeld opinioun, that pleyn delyt

the law.   It is quite clear that Chaucer, who had himself been
a knight of the shire, admired the franklin's way of life.

332. E. *heed*, others *berd*.

333. complexioun : temperament, originally the combination
of the humours, or predominance of one of the humours.   There
were supposed to be four humours or fluids in the body—blood,
phlegm, bile, and black bile or melancholy.   If one of these
humours predominated in the constitution of a person, he was
sanguine, or phlegmatic, or bilious, or melancholy by 'complexion.'
But as the complexion determined not only the mood of a person
but his looks, the word complexion developed the meaning of
natural colour and appearance.   The original meaning of this
passage is that in temperament he was sanguine, *i.e.* courageous
and confident.

334. Beer and wine, or water, were the usual drinks in England
before tea and coffee were introduced.   A piece of cake dipped
in wine was the franklin's equivalent of an early morning cup
of tea.

336. Epicurus : A Greek philosopher of Samos, born 341 B.C.
He established a school of philosophy in Athens in 307 B.C.   The
doctrine by which he has been remembered is that pleasure is
the chief good and aim of life.   By 'pleasure' he did not mean
luxury or sensuality, but freedom of the body from pain, and
of the soul from fear.   Really he advocated temperance
and simplicity of life, and the practice of virtue.   He died in
270 B.C.

His opinions naturally lent themselves to distortion by holders
of more spiritual forms of belief.   In the ancient world the
contemporary philosophy of the Stoics, which held virtue to be
the chief good of life, and advocated mastery of the passions,
and indifference to pleasure and pain, was at daggers drawn with
Epicureanism.   Christianity had no point of contact with it.
Hence Chaucer's joke.

337. Who held the opinion that complete happiness was the
chief good of life.

Was verraily felicitee parfyt.
An housholdere, and that a greet, was he ;
Seint Julian he was in his contree.   A 340
His breed, his ale, was alweys after oon ;
A bettre envyned man was nowher noon :
Withouté baké mete was nevere his hous,
Of fissh and flessh, and that so plentevous,
It snewed in his hous of mete and drinke,   345
Of allé deyntees that men koudé thinke.
After the sondry sesons of the yeer,
So chaunged he his mete and his soper.
Ful many a fat partrich hadde he in muwe,
And many a breem, and many a luce in stuwe.   350
Wo was his cook, but if his saucé were
Poynaunt and sharp, and redy al his geere !
His table-dormant in his halle alway

338. E. etc. *verray*, Hl. *verraily*.

340. **Seint Julian :** St Julian, called the Hospitator, or the
Good Harbourer, was a knight who received a rich wife and lands
from the prince that he served. One day when his father and
mother came to see him, he was away from home. His wife
welcomed them and gave up to them her bedroom, taking the
second best for herself. Next day, whilst Julian's wife was at
church hearing Mass, her husband returned. He went into the
chamber to greet his wife, and seeing two people in his bed, he
drew his sword and killed them both. Then, still full of rage,
he flung himself out of the castle, and to his surprise met his
wife coming from church. In shame he asked her who lay in
their bed, and she told him that it was his father and mother.

In penance he built a hospital for travellers, and spent his life
hereafter in entertaining and helping strangers.

340. E. *was he*, others *he was*.

341. Hl. Cm. *alway*, E. Hn. Cp. *alweys*.

342. Hl. Pt. Cm. Dd. *nowher*, E. Hn. Cp. *neuere*.

350. Fish were kept in ' stews ' or fish-ponds against the fast-
days, when meat was not permitted by the custom of the Church.

353. **table-dormant :** The usual table of the age was composed

Stood redy covered al the longė day.

   At sessiouns, ther was he lord and sire ;   355
Ful oftė tyme he was knyght of the shire.
An anlaas, and a gipser al of silk,
Heeng at his girdel, whyt as mornė-milk.
A shirreve hadde he been, and a countour ;
Was nowher such a worthy vavasour.   A 360

   An HABERDASSHERE, and a CARPENTER,

The five   A WEBBE, a DYERE, and a TAPICER,
members of
a guild.   And they were clothed alle in o liveree
                        Of a solėmpne and greet fraternitee ;

of boards on trestles. It was set up in the hall for dinner, and
afterwards removed when the hall became a place of entertainment for the family and guests. The franklin was so rich and so
hospitable that he kept a table permanently covered with food
ready for the casual guest.

   355. The franklin presided over the sessions of the justices of
the peace or county magistrates. He had also often been
' knight of the shire ' or representative of the landed proprietors
in Parliament.

   359. countour : the exact meaning is unknown. It may
mean an accountant or auditor of the king's taxes. Or it may
mean a lawyer of lower rank, a solicitor or attorney (O.F. *conteor*,
which Godefroy defines as " avocat, procureur ").

   360. vavasour : a tenant of a vassal of the king, a feudal
subordinate landowner. The franklin was not a vavasour : he
was a freeholder, a vassal of the king. So that here, probably,
vavasour means simply country gentleman, or squire.

   361. A haberdasher was a dealer in small articles of dress, from
hats and ribbons down to needles, thread, and buttons. A
' webbe ' was a cloth-weaver. A ' tapicer ' was a weaver of
tapestry and carpets. These five guildsmen were evidently
members of a social and religious guild. Each would perhaps
also belong to the guild of his own particular trade ; but, as their
trades were diverse, the only guild which in Chaucer's age could
contain them all would be a social guild, the medieval equivalent
of the friendly society. Social guilds, dedicated to a patron
saint, were societies which assisted their members in sickness or

Ful fressh and newe hir geere apyked was, 365
Hir knyves werė chaped noght with bras,
But al with silver wrought ful clene and weel,
Hir girdles and hir pouches everydeel.
Wel semed ech of hem a fair burgeys
To sitten in a yeldhalle on a deys. 370
Éverich, for the wisdom that he kan,
Was shaply for to been an alderman,

poverty with a weekly allowance in return for an annual sub-
scription. They buried their dead members, and had Masses
sung for their souls. Sometimes they undertook other charitable
work, such as repairing a church or a road, supporting a school
or building a bridge. They met and feasted four times a
year.

That these men were all members of one guild is apparent from
the fact that they all wear one livery. The livery of a poor
guild consisted simply of a hood; but as this was a "solempne
and greet fraternitee" presumably the guildsmen wore both
gown and hood; though what its colour was, Chaucer does not
tell us. We may suppose that the five guildsmen were sent on
the pilgrimage by their fraternity.

Besides the social guilds, there were in Chaucer's age the trade
guilds, which regulated the conduct of each branch of trade.
These guilds were usually responsible for the Miracle Plays.
At an earlier period, some two centuries earlier, before handicraft
had separated itself from agriculture, a guild-merchant had
flourished in many towns. This, too, was a guild composed of
burgesses of many trades, but of merchants rather than of crafts-
men. In Chaucer's age the importance of merchant guilds had
waned before the rise of social and of trade guilds. All guilds,
whether merchant, trade, or social, were religious in constitution,
and had their patron saint, in whose honour they attended
Mass.

363. Hl. *Weren with vss eeke clothed in o lyveree*, others *And they
were clothed alle*, etc.

366. Hl. *ichapud*.

372. alderman: the president or 'warden' of a guild, not
necessarily a member of the town council.

For catel haddè they ynogh and rente ;
And eek hir wyves wolde it wel assente,
And elles certeyn werè they to blame.　　　375
It is ful fair to been ycleped ' Madame,'
And goon to vigilýes al bifore,
And have a mantel roialliche ybore.

　　A COOK they haddè with hem for the nones,　　379
　The　　To boille the chiknes with the mary-bones,
　Cook.　　And poudre-marchant tart, and galingale.
Wel koude he knowe a draughte of London ale :
He koude roste, and sethe, and boille, and frye,
Máken mortreux, and wel bake a pye.
But greet harm was it, as it thoughtè me,　　　385
That on his shine a mormal haddè he,
For blankmanger, that made he with the beste.

373. catel and rente: property and income. ' Catel' has
become cattle in Modern English, and its meaning has been
restricted since Elizabethan times to live stock, cf. ' chattel,'
which still retains the original meaning. Cattle (Norman and
Northern French) and Chattle (Central French) are both derived
from Latin capitāle (neut.), a thing of first importance, capital.

375. Hl. hadde they ben.

376. E. Hn. ycleped, Hl. clept, others cleped.

377. vigilyes : a meeting held on the evening before the festival
of the guild, which would be held on the day of the saint to whom
the guild was dedicated.

379. The Cook was a shopkeeper, as the Cóok's Prologue
(A 4325-4364) indicates :

　　　　For in thy shoppe is many a flye loos.

But he was not a member of the same social guild as his five
employees. He was just engaged ' for the nones ' to cook their
dinner, so that they at any rate should mess well, whatever the
inns were like on the way. He got drunk on the pilgrimage, as
we learn from the Prologue to the Manciples Tale, H 1-104.

383. E. Hl. boille, Cm. boyle, Hn. Cp. etc. broille.

386. mormal : a cancerous sore, caused by constant exposure
to the fire in cooking.

A SHIPMAN was ther, woninge fer by weste :

The
Shipman.
For aught I woot, he was of Dertèmouthe.

He rood upon a rouncy as he kouthe,　390

In a gowne of falding to the knee.

A daggere hanginge on a laas hadde he

Aboute his nekke, under his arm adoun.

The hootè sonne had maad his hewe al broun ;

And certeinly he was a good felawe.　395

Ful many a draughte of wyn had he ydrawe

Fro Burdeux-ward, whyl that the chapman sleep.

Of nycè conscience took he no keep.

If that he faught, and had the hyer hond,

By water he sente hem hoom to every lond.　A 400

But of his craft, to rekene wel his tydes,

388. A shipman : The captain of a small trading vessel of the times. The " Maudelayne " would be a small wooden vessel about the size of a small trawler. It would have a single mast and a square sail. The bow and stern would be built up in the form of castles, which would be used to shield archers when the " Maudelayne " was in action. There was constant war with the French, and every boat had to be prepared to fight.—*by weste :* in the west of England.

389. Dertemouthe : Dartmouth in Devonshire. Curiously enough there was a ship called the ' Magdaleyne' of Dartmouth, of which, at that time, a Peter Risshenden was master. Chaucer would meet such men at the Customs Wharf in the port of London. See *Essays on Chaucer*, Part V, ' Chaucer's Schipman and his Barge " The Maudelayne," ' by P. Q. Karkeek, Chaucer Society, 1884.

394. All : *somer.*　　　396. Cm. *idrawe*, others *drawe*.

397. fro Burdeux-ward : coming from Bordeaux. Bordeaux, on the river Garonne in France, was at that time an English possession. It is still famous for its red wines.

400. He threw them overboard.

401. But, for estimating the tides, the currents, and the perils to face, the depth of water in harbour, the phase of the moon, and for his use of the compass, there was not such another mariner

His stremes, and his daungers hym bisydes,
His herberwe, and his moone, his lodemenage,
Ther nas noon swich from Hullė to Cartage.
Hardy he was, and wys to undertake ;   405
With many a tempest hadde his berd been shake.
Hé knew alle the havenes, as they were,
From Gootlond to the Cape of Finistere,
And every cryke in Britaigne and in Spayne.
His barge ycleped was the Maudėlayne.   410

   With us ther was a DOCTOUR OF PHISIK ;

The
Doctor.   In al this world ne was ther noon him lyk,
          (To speke of phisik and of surgerye),

between Hull and Cartagena. 'Cartage' may be Carthage
(Tunis) in Africa, or it may be Cartagena in the south-east of
Spain.

407. Hl. *knew wel.*

408. Hl. *Scotland.*

408. From the island of Gothland to Cape Finisterre. Gothland is an island in the Baltic Sea, off the east coast of Sweden.
Its capital town, Wisby, was an important port. Cape Finisterre
is in the north-west of Spain, near Corunna.—Hl. *Scotland.*

409. Britaigne : the Duchy of Brittany in the north-west of
France.

411. a doctour of phisik : A doctor of medicine of the time.
The causes of disease are now thought of in such a different way
that it is hard to comprehend those far-off days when medicine
was still closely allied to magic.

It was thought that diseases arose because some cause upset
the balance of humours in the body. It was believed, following
Hippocrates, that there were four 'humours' or fluids in the
human body—namely, melancholy, phlegm, blood, and bile.
(There is, I think, no such fluid as melancholy or black bile. It
was assumed, in order to account for certain symptoms.) When
the patient was healthy, the complexion or mixture of the
humours was perfect. And this, we might note, was the original
meaning of the word complexion. But if one humour predominated, from some cause such as an error of diet or an
infection, then the excess of humour caused illness.

For he was grounded in astronomye.
He kepte his paciént a ful greet deel   415
In houres, by his magyk natureel.

It was believed in the primitive physics of the time that there
were four elements in the sublunary sphere—earth, water, air,
and fire; and medicine saw a subtle relationship between the
four elements and the four humours, because each possessed two
of the four qualities of matter, namely hot, cold, moist, and dry.
Thus:—

Earth was composed of the qualities of cold and dry, as was melancholy.
Water   ,,   ,,   ,,   cold and moist,   ,,   phlegm.
Air   ,,   ,,   ,,   hot and moist,   ,,   blood.
Fire   ,,   ,,   ,,   hot and dry,   ,,   bile.

The humours, therefore, were regarded as either hot, cold, moist
or dry. The hot humours were blood and bile. The cold
humours were melancholy and phlegm. The moist humours were
phlegm and blood. And the dry humours were melancholy and
bile. A proper mixture of the four humours, or a good 'complexion,' led to sound health and perfect temper; but excess of
one humour made a man either melancholy, or phlegmatic, or
sanguine, or choleric.

Medicine was also closely connected with astrology. It was
believed that each constellation of the zodiac ruled one particular
part of the human body, and could assist to produce or cure a
disease. A wise doctor knew which sign of the zodiac ruled the
particular part of the body that he had to treat. If the patient
were too sanguine, and needed bleeding, the doctor would bleed
him from the part of the body governed by the sign which
happened to be in the ascendant. Planets which might influence
the patient were:—the planet which was rising at his birth, and
the planet which was rising when he began to be ill. The doctor
attempted to determine the cause of the illness, and then to
restore the balance of the humours by bleeding or purging, or
by giving medicines; or astrologically by making images, l. 417.
—Hl. *Ther was also a.*

416. In houres: in hours of planetary influence, *e.g.* the first
hour of the disease, and the planet rising then, were important.
—*magyk natureel:* natural astrology, the science by which the
motions of the planets were predicted. It is now a part of

Wél koude he fortúnen th' áscendent
Of his images for his paciént.
He knew the cause of everich maladye,
Were it of hoot, or cold, or moyste, or drye,   A 420
And where they engendred, and of what humour ;
He was a verray, parfit praktisour.
The cause yknowe, and of his harm the root,
Anon he yaf the siké man his boot.
Ful redy hadde he his apothecáries,   425
To sende him drogges and his letuáries,
For ech of hem made oother for to winne ;
Hir frendshipe nas nat newé to biginne.
    Wél knew he th' olde Esculapius,
And Deïscorides, and eek Rufus ;   430

astronomy. Astrology was divided into two parts : (1) natural
astrology, as defined above, and (2) judicial astrology, which
finds a planetary cause for earthly events, and predicts fortune,
weather, and the future. Its pronouncements are as often
wrong as right.

417. He knew well how to say that the rising of the planets
corresponding to his talismans was favourable. He made
'images' which might exert a good influence over his patient,
i.e. talismans corresponding to the sun, moon or planets, at a
time when the influence of the planet upon the health of his
patient was supposed to be at its strongest, namely, at its
ascendant.

These 'images' were images of the astrological symbol of the
sun or moon or planets, and their influence was supposed to be
medicinal. They were not the images of a person which witches
and sorcerers made with intent to injure him by magic. The
ascendant is the rising above the eastern horizon of a planet or
of a sign of the zodiac. The planets, one might add, appear to
move within the limits of the zodiac.

421. **where they engendred** : where the maladies began.—E.
Cm. Hl. *where they*, Hn. *where it*, Ln. *whereof*, Dd. *wherof it*, Cp. Pt
where.

426. Hn. Cm. *sende his*.

430. E. *Risus*, Hl. Hn. Cp. Ln. *Rusus*, Pt. *Rufus*.

Olde Ypocras, Haly, and Galien ;
Serapion, Razis, and Avicen ;
Averrois, Damascien and Constantyn ;
Bernard, and Gatesden, and Gilbertyn.

429-34. He had studied all the best medical authorities.
Then follows a list of high-sounding names :—

Esculapius : Æsculapius, the name of the mythical founder of
   medicine.
Deiscorides : Dioscorides, a Greek physician of the second
   century A.D.
Rufus : a Greek physician of the second century A.D. He
   lived at Ephesus.
Ypocras : Hippocrates of Cos, *b.* 460 B.C., the greatest physician
   of antiquity. Many works were attributed to him. He
   introduced the doctrine of the four humours.
Haly : Alhazen, a Persian physician of the eleventh century,
   A.D., wrote a commentary on Galen.
Galien : Galen : a famous Greek physician of the second
   century A.D. He wrote many works which were, in the
   ninth century, translated into Arabic.
Serapion : an Arab physician of the eleventh century A.D.,
   who took the name of a famous Greek of Alexandria.
Razis : Rhazes of Cordova, an Arab physician of the tenth
   century.
Avicen : Avicenna, a Persian physician named Ibn Sina
   (980-1037). He wrote the *Canon Medicinae*, a famous
   text-book of medicine.
Averrois : Averroes, a Moorish philosopher and physician named
   Ibn Rashd (1126-1198). He wrote a medical book,
   Colliget, which was translated into Latin.
Damascien : said to be an Arabian physician of the ninth
   century.
Constantyn : Constantius Afer, a Benedictine monk of the
   twelfth century. One of the founders of the medical
   school at Salerno, Italy.
Bernard : Bernard Gordon, Professor of Medicine at Mont-
   pellier, in the south of France, during Chaucer's lifetime.
Gatesden : John Gatesden, of Merton College, Oxford, *d.* 1361.
   Physician to Edward II.

Of his dietè mesurable was he,   435
For it was of no superfluitee,
But of greet norissyng and digestíble.
His studie was but litel on the Bible.
In sangwyn and in pers he clad was al,
Lyned with taffata and with sendal.   A 440
And yet he was but esy of dispence ;
He keptè that he wan in pestilence,
For gold in phisik is a cordial ;
Therfore he lovede gold in special.

    A GOOD WYF was ther of bisydè BATHE,   445

The Wife   But she was somdel deef, and that was scathe.
of Bath.   Of clooth-makýng she haddè swich an haunt,

Gilbertyn : Gilbertus Anglicus, or Gilbert English, who wrote
    a *Compendium Medicinae* late in the thirteenth century.

The list tells us something of the history of medicine. Medicine
began as a study in the classical world (Hippocrates and Galen).
Then it passed to the Arabs in the seventh century A.D., after
they had conquered Persia, Palestine, Egypt, and the northern
African coast, and crossed the Strait of Gibraltar into Spain
(Avicenna, Averroes). From the Arabs the study of medicine
passed to Western Europe, and Chaucer mentions three famous
English doctors, Gilbertus Anglicus, John Gatesden, and Bernard
Gordon. The works of Hippocrates and Galen, and also of the
Arabian authorities, were translated into Latin, which was at
that time the learned language of Christendom.

439. He was robed in scarlet and bluish-grey, lined with
taffeta and silk. In other words, he was richly dressed.

442. wan in pestilence : gained in time of plague. After the
Black Death of 1349 there were outbreaks in 1369 and 1376.

444. For gold, used in medicine, strengthens the heart.
Modern medicine is based on experiment and practice. Ancient
medicine was fanciful. Gold, they thought, was a valuable
metal, and the metal of the sun. The heart was the most
valuable organ in the body, and influenced by the sun. Therefore gold must be good for the heart. One of the researches of
the times was to find ' aurum potabile,' drinkable gold.

She passed hem of Ypres and of Gaunt.
In al the parisshe, wyf ne was ther noon
That to th' offrýng bifore hir sholdè goon ;   45ᵃ
And if ther dide, certeyn, so wrooth was she,
That she was out of allè charitee.
Hir coverchiefs ful fynè were of ground,—
I dorstè swere they weyeden ten pound,—
That on a Sonday were upon hir heed.   455
Hir hosen weren of fyn scarlet-reed,

445. A good wyf of bisyde Bathe : The district around Bath
and Bristol was in the fourteenth century famous for its woollen
cloth ; and relics of the manufacture still remained in the broad-
cloth for which the district was still famous in the nineteenth
century. The Wife of Bath is a ' character.' From the prologue
to her charming fairy-tale we gather that she has in succession
ruled over five husbands. She was married first at the age of
twelve, and she married her fifth at forty. She was rich by
inheritance from her dead husbands.

446. She was deaf, because of a buffet given her by Jankin,
her fourth husband, when she tore the book from which he was
reading of the wickedness of women (D. 634-36, 666-86).

447. It is not clear whether she was engaged in cloth manufacture, or whether as the mistress of a household she supervised
the weaving of cloth for private use.

448. Ypres, Ghent and Bruges in Flanders were then famous
for their woollen cloth, and Edward III induced Flemish weavers
to settle in England.

450. The offertory was sung at Mass. The congregation
went up to the sanctuary in order of rank and placed their
offering within the railing, where they knelt before going back
to the nave. The Wife of Bath was the richest woman in her
parish. See note on l. 710.

453. The ' coverchief ' or kerchief was a linen covering for the
head. The Wife of Bath wore several, and built them up in
massive fashion over a framework of wire. No doubt their
weight would be added to by the pins which held the structure
together, but ' ten pounds ' is Chaucer's joke.—E. *weren.*

455. E. *weren.*

Ful streite yteyd, and shoes ful moyste and newe.
Boold was hir face, and fair, and reed of hewe.
   She was a worthy womman al hir lyve :
Housbonds at chirchė-dore she haddė fyve,   A 460
Withouten oother compaignye in youthe,
(But therof nedeth nat to speke as nouthe) :
And thryės had she been at Jerusalém,
She haddė passed many a straungė streem ;
At Rome she haddė been, and at Boloigne,   465
In Galice at Seint Jame, and at Coloigne,
She koudė muche of wandring by the weye :
Gat-tothed was she, soothly for to seye.
Upon an amblere esily she sat,

460. The first part of the marriage service was said outside
the church door, and then the priest returned to the altar to
celebrate Mass. No doubt the wedding took place outside the
door of the church, so that there should be nothing secret about it.
—Hl. Dd. *hadde she.*

463-66. Her pilgrimages were many and various. Indeed, in
her old age she was almost a professional pilgrim. At Jerusalem,
for which she had a special reverence, she would have visited the
Holy Sepulchre. At Rome there were the tombs of St Peter
and St Paul, and of the martyrs in the catacombs, besides the
living Pope and the ceremonies of the cathedral in the Vatican.
At Boulogne there was a famous statue of the Virgin Mary, but
Chaucer may mean Bologna in Italy, where St Dominic is buried.
' In Galice at Seint Jame ' refers to the shrine of St James at
Compostella (Santiago de Compostella), in Galicia in the north-
west corner of Spain. Pilgrims from England usually went by
sea. At Cologne was the tomb of the Three Wise Men of the
East, who brought to the infant Christ gold, frankincense and
myrrh.

463. **thryes:** A dissyllable, thry-es, as elsewhere in Chaucer's
works. Hence ' Jerusalem ' is either Jru-sa-leem or Jer-sa-leem,
with three syllables.

465. Dd. *had she be.*

467. E. Hn. *muchel,* Hl. Cp. Pt. *moche.*

Ywimpled wel, and on hir heed an hat   470
As brood as is a bokler or a targe ;
A foot-mantel aboute hir hipes large,
And on hir feet a paire of spores sharpe.
In felaweship wel koude she laughe and carpe.
Of remedies of love she knew perchaunce,   475
For she koude of that art the oldè daunce.

    A good man was ther of religioun,

The Parson.

And was a POURÈ PERSOUN OF A TOUN ;
But riche he was of hooly thought and werk.

470. Hl. *Wymplid ful wel.*

475. Of remedies of love : Either she knew Ovid's *Remedia Amoris*, which tells how to relieve the disappointments of un-requited love, or more probably she knew of charms and potions to cause and cure falling in love. 'Of' is partitive, as in l. 146.

476. Hl. Dd. *For of that art sche knew.*

478. A poure persoun of a toun : A parish priest, and evidently an idealized picture of what a priest ought to be. As this parson was the vicar of a town or village, and moreover of a large parish, the first question that occurs to one is : why was he poor ? In the palmy days of the monastic movement the patrons of manorial parish churches appropriated the whole or a part of the tithes to neighbouring monasteries. Sometimes a monastery was rector of the living, and took all the income, except a small stipend of £5 or so allowed to a resident vicar. Sometimes the tithes were shared between the parson and a monastery. So that in Chaucer's age parish priests were often very poor, and, like this man, of humble origin. Their par-ishioners were crude and uneducated, and priests were tempted by their poverty and loneliness to get employment as chantry priests. The church has been endowed in different ways at different times. In Chaucer's age a favourite way was to build and endow a 'chantry,' *i.e.* a chapel where Masses were said for the soul of the founder and his friends. Sometimes a chantry was a small church, like the one on Wakefield bridge : sometimes they were altars in existing churches. If a parish priest obtained such a post, either he left a vicar in charge of his parish and

He was also a lerned man, a clerk,   A 480
That Cristes gospel trewely woldė preche.
His parisshéns devoutly wolde he teche.
Benygne he was, and wonder diligent,
And in adversitee ful pacient ;
And swich he was ypreved oftė sythes.   485
Ful looth were hym to cursen for his tythes,
But rather wolde he yeven, out of doute,
Unto his pourė parisshéns aboute,
Of his offrýng, and eek of his substaunce :
He koude in litel thing have suffisáunce.   490
Wyd was his parisshe, and houses fer asonder,
But he ne laftė nat, for reyn ne thonder,
In siknesse nor in meschief, to visyte
The ferreste in his parisshe, muche and lyte,
Upon his feet, and in his hand a staf.   495
    This noble ensample to his sheepe he yaf,
That firste he wroughte, and afterward he taughte.
Out of the gospel he tho wordes caughte,
And this figure he added eek therto,
That if gold rustė, what shal iren do ?   A 500

made a profit out of his salary ; or he left his parish without a
priest whilst he was absent at his chantry.

The portrait is so highly idealized, and its contrast with the
pictures of the worldly monk and the grasping friar so obvious,
that it has been taken as an attack upon the religious orders.
Chaucer no doubt had his own views upon the state of the Church,
but he was not a militant reformer.

485. E. Cp. Pt. *preued*, Hl. *iproued*.

486. Parishioners who refused to pay their tithe were liable to
excommunication.   487. out of doute : indeed, surely.

489. Of his offryng and . . . substaunce : both from his (Easter)
offering and from his private property.

498. Cf. *St Matthew* v. 19. "Whosoever shall do and teach
them (*i.e.* the commandments), the same shall be called great
in the kingdom of heaven."

For if a preest be foul, on whom we truste,
No wonder is a lewed man to ruste ;
And shame it is, (if a preest takė keep),
A shiten shepherde and a clenė sheep.
Wel oughte a preest ensample for to yive,   505
By his clennesse, how that his sheep sholde live.
He settė nat his benefice to hyre,
And leet his sheep encombred in the myre,
And ran to London, unto Seintė Poules,
To seken hym a chaunterie for soules,   510
Or with a bretherhed to been withholde ;
But dwelte at hoom, and keptė wel his folde,
So that the wolf ne made it nat miscarie.
He was a shepherde, and noght a mercenarie.

500. Hl. Hn. Ln. Dd. *sholde*.

503. If a priest would take heed (he would see that) it is a shame for there to be a filthy shepherd and clean sheep, *i.e.* a foul priest and good parishioners. *Take* is pres. subjunctive implying a supposition.—Hl. *if that*, others *if a preest*.

507. He did not hand over his parish to a hired curate.

508. Hl. *lefte*.

509. Hl. Cp. *seynte*, others *seint*.

510. To look for a chantry for himself. A chantry was a chapel or altar endowed by a founder for a priest to say Masses for departed souls. The stipend was £5 or so, much the same as that usually obtained by a parish priest, but there were no parochial duties ; and of course if a priest could secure a chantry in addition to his living, he doubled his income.—E. Hn. *chauntrie*, Hl. Cp. Pt. Ln. *chaunterie*.

511. Or to be retained by a guild. Some of the richest guilds retained the services of a chaplain. Others temporarily employed a priest to say thirty Masses for the souls of members who had recently died.

512. E. *dwelleth* . . . *keepeth*, rest *dwelte* . . . *kepte*.

514. He was a pastor, not a mercenary. A mercenary is one who works merely for the pay, not from love of the work. A pastor is not merely a priest, but a shepherd of souls. The

And though he hooly were, and vertuous,   515
He was to sinful man noght despitous,
Ne of his speché daungerous ne digne,
But in his teching discreet and benygne.
To drawen folk to heven by fairnesse,
By good ensample,—this was his bisinesse.   A 520
But it were any person obstinat,
What-so he were, of heigh or low estat,
Hym wolde he snibben sharply for the nonis.
A bettre preest, I trowe that nowher noon is.
He waited after no pompe and reverénce,   525
Ne maked him a spyced consciénce ;
But Cristes loore, and his Apostles twelve,
He taughte, but first he folwed it hymselve.

allusion is to *St John* x. 12. " But he that is an hireling, and
not the shepherd, whose own the sheep are not, seeth the wolf
coming, and leaveth the sheep and fleeth." Hireling is in the
Latin version *mercenarius.*

516. E. and others : *He was nat to synful man despitous*, Hl.
to senful man nought.

517. Ne . . . daungerous ne digne : neither domineering nor
proud.

520. Hl. lacks *this*.

522. E. *lough.*

525. E. *waiteth*, others *waited*.

526. a spyced conscience : In Elizabethan times the phrase was
used meaning " a too scrupulous conscience."   Here the meaning
seems to be a conscience flavoured as with spices, a flattering
disposition, or an artificial or assumed considerateness ; for
compare the Wife of Bath speaking to Wilkin, her third husband.
D. 434.

> "Ye sholde been al pacient and meke,
> And han a sweete spiced conscience,
> Sith ye so preche of Jobes pacience."

In other words, the parson did not look for reverence and
respect, nor did he assume a considerateness which he did not
really feel. Chaucer evidently thought that the Prioress's
' conscience ' was a spiced conscience, a form of affectation.

With hym ther was a PLOWMAN, was his brother,

The
Plowman. That hadde ylad of dong ful many a fother,—

A trewe swinkere, and a good was he, 531

Livynge in pees and parfit charitee.

God loved he best, with al his hoolé herte,

At allé tymes, though him gamed or smerte,

And thanne his neighébor, right as himselve. 535

He woldé thresshe, and therto dyke and delve,

For Cristes sake, for every pouré wight,

Withouten hyre, if it lay in his myght.

His tythes payede he ful faire and wel,

Bothe of his propré swink and his catel. **A** 540

In a tabard he rood, upon a mere.

529. a Plowman : A labourer and small farmer, for he paid tithes. He was not therefore a mere serf, though he may have ranked still as a villein. His ' farm ' would not be the compact acreage which a similar man would rent to-day. He would have a small house in the village, and various unfenced plots of arable land on his lord's manor which he would hold yearly. He would have a pig or two, and perhaps a cow straying on the common pasture. He would plough his thirty or forty acres with a plough drawn by eight oxen, of which he would provide perhaps two. In addition to the work of his own farm, he would have to work for his landlord. He would take his team, for instance, to load dung for the lord of the manor; and there were certain days every week when his labour, by custom, would be given entirely to the domain. He was a ploughman, for instance. He would not only plough for the domain, he would harrow and reap and lead his landlord's corn home to the stack.

534. E. Pt. Ln. *he*, others *him*.

539. E. Hn. *payde*, Hl. Cm. *payede*, Cp. Pt. *payed*.

540. He paid a tenth part of his earnings and of the increase of his cattle.—Hl. *owne*, others *propre*.

541. a tabard : a smock. The tabard had once been fashionable among the gentry; for instance, heralds wore it, and wear it yet as an official dress richly emblazoned with arms. But the ploughman's tabard cannot have been this aristocratic

Ther was also a REVE and a MILLERE,

A SOMONOUR and a PARDONER also,

A MAUNCIPLE and myself, ther were namo.

The MILLERE was a stout carl for the nones,   545

The   Ful big he was of brawn, and eek of bones ;
Miller.   That proved wel, for overal ther he cam

At wrastling, he wolde have alwey the ram.

He was short-sholdred, brood, a thikkè knarre,

garment. It must have been a worker's overall or smock, for the social guilds of King's Lynn regularly forbade a member to attend meetings either barefooted or dressed in a tabard.

The ploughman kept a mare because he wanted foals, as well as work from it. No knightly person would have ridden a mare, but the ploughman was not proud.

542. Some of the characters fall into groups. There are the Knight, Squire and Yeomen ; the Prioress, Monk and Friar ; the Man of Law and the Franklin ; the Guildsmen and their Cook ; the Parson and his brother the Ploughman. This group is a group of rapscallions, and it is characteristic of Chaucer's humour that he includes himself in the party.

545. The miller kept either a water-mill or a wooden wind-mill raised on trestles, to which mill the tenants of the manor took their corn to be ground, and paid the miller a soken or toll according to the quantity. Millers were proverbially dishonest, and were reputed to steal corn, and to take toll more than once on the same lot of corn. There was proverbial enmity between the reeve (or manager of the manor) and the miller, arising out of this. Hence the tale which the miller tells against a reeve, and the reeve against a miller in the *Canterbury Tales.*

545. for the nones : for the occasion, literally "for the once," *cf.* ll. 379, 523. Here, however, the phrase seems to be mean-ingless, unless the sentence means : The miller who was with us on that occasion was a stout fellow.

547. That proved wel : which gave evidence of their quality.

548. A ram was offered as a prize at wrestling matches, *cf.* Chaucer's *Tale of Sir Thopas* (B. 1930).

Of wrastling was ther noon his peer,
Ther any ram shal stonde.

Ther was no dore that he nolde heve of harre,   550
Or breke it at a renning with his heed.
His berd, as any sowe or fox, was reed,
And therto brood, as though it were a spade.
Upon the cop right of his nose he hade
A werte, and theron stood a toft of heeres,   555
Reed as the brustles of a sowes eres ;
His nosèthirles blakè were and wyde.
A swerd and bokler bar he by his syde.
His mouth as wyd was as a greet forneys ;
He was a janglere and a goliardeys,   A 560

550. Cm. *nas*, others *was* ; E. Pt. Ln. *ne wolde*, others *nolde*.
556. E. *brustles*, Hn. *bristles*, Hl. Cp. *berstles*.
558. The miller carried a sword and buckler, like the Yeoman, not for war, but for the sport of fighting with sword and buckler. —Cp. *swerd and*, E. etc. *swerd and a*.
559. Hl. *as wyde was*, others *as greet was*.
560. goliardeys : the wandering scholars of the twelfth century called a drunken and riotous clerk a goliard ; and for this class of disreputable vagabonds a mythical Golias was invented as founder of the order. Numerous sermons, epistles and confessions, attributed to this mythical Golias, exist in manuscripts written in Latin verse, perhaps the most famous of which is a poem entitled *Confessio Goliae*, with its oft-quoted lines.

> Meum est propositum
> in taberna mori ;
> vinum sit oppositum
> morientis ori ;
> tunc cantabant laetius
> angelorum chori :
> ' Deus sit propitius
> huic potatori.'

' I am resolved to die in a tavern, so that wine may be near my dying mouth. Then shall sing more joyfully the choirs of angels : may God have mercy on this tippler.'
From Golias and goliard was derived the word goliardeys, O.F. *goliardois, gouliardois*, which was applied to minstrels and

And that was moost of sinne and harlotries.
Wel koude he stelen corn, and tollen thries ;
And yet he hadde a thombe of gold, pardee.
A whyt cote and a blew hood werede he.
A baggëpipe wel koude he blowe and sowne,   565
And therwithal he broughte us out of towne.

A gentil MAUNCIPLE was ther of a temple,

The Maunciple. Of which achátours myghtë take exemple
For to be wise in byinge of vitaille ;

tellers of fabliaux. Chaucer means that the miller was a coarse-grained teller of tales. See Waddell, *The Wandering Scholars*, viii.

563. There is an old proverb: " An honest miller has a thumb of gold " ; to which this may allude. He had a thumb of gold because he used his thumb to spread out a sample of corn, and his thumb made money for him ; but the proverb also means : an honest miller is as rare as a man with a thumb of gold, that is, honest millers don't exist.

I take this passage to mean : He often stole corn, and took toll more often than once ; but he was a good miller, and a good judge of corn.

565. Pilgrims were notorious for their songs and tales and the music of bagpipes. The miller seems to have been a strong man, a fencer, and a bagpiper in addition to his trade.

567. A gentil maunciple : a pleasant butler. A manciple was the steward's underling who acted as housekeeper for a lawyer's inn, or for a college. He was a man, of course, because such colleges were monastic in organisation, though not in vows. He bought the provisions for the college as one of his duties. Chaucer's manciple was a servant of one of the legal colleges— the Inner Temple and the Middle Temple—which had succeeded to the Knights Templars in the occupation of the Temple, or at any rate of a part of it. The Temple had been the English head-quarters of Knights Templars, a militant order which came into existence in the twelfth century to guard pilgrims to the Holy Sepulchre, and lasted but a short time until its suppression by Pope Clement V in 1312. The Temple Church still stands, and is the chapel of the Inner and Middle Temple. After the suppression of the Templars, their property was given to the

For, whether that he payde, or took by taille,   570
Algate he waited so in his acháat
That he was ay biforn and in good staat.
Now is nat that of God a ful fair grace,
That swich a lewed mannes wit shal pace
The wisdom of an heep of lerned men ?   575
Of maistres hadde he mo than thryės ten,
That were of lawe expert and curious,
Of which ther were a duzeyne in that hous,
Worthy to been stywards of rente and lond
Of any lord that is in Engėlond,   A 580
To make him liven by his proprė good
In honour dettelees, but if hė were wood,

Knights Hospitallers, who allowed two schools of lawyers to lease it.

The Temple was not the only legal college. There were several 'inns' which had grown up in the thirteenth century, when the legal profession became non-clerical. The law-courts were at Westminster Hall. The education obtained by a law-student at one of the inns was largely legal, but Latin, French and history were also taught. Many students studied there, not to become lawyers, but to learn the management of estates. According to an Elizabethan tradition, Chaucer himself had been a student of the Inner Temple.

570. Whether he paid cash or bought on credit. In the days before book-keeping by double-entry developed, first in Italy in the fifteenth century, purchasers who bought on credit received a tally, that is, a strip of wood notched to indicate the amount owing. The tally was split, and creditor and debtor each had an identical record of the transaction. On settling day each party produced his tallies, and on verifying that what the creditors claimed tallied with what the debtor was ready to pay, the debtor paid over the amount, and the tallies were destroyed.

571. waited : looked out, was careful.

581. E. *maken hym lyue*.

582. Cm. *but*, E. etc. *but if*.

Or live as scarsly as hym list desire ;
And able for to helpen al a shire
In any caas that myghtė falle or happe ;   585
And yet this Manciple sette hir aller cappe.

   The REVĖ was a sclendrė colerik man,

The Reeve.   His berd was shave as ny as ever he kan ;
                 His heer was by his eres round yshorn,

His top was dokked lyk a preest biforn ;   590
Ful longė were his legges and ful lene,
Ylyk a staf, ther was no calf ysene.
Wel koude he kepe a gerner and a binne ;
Ther was noon auditour koude on him winne.
Wel wiste he, by the droughte and by the reyn,   595
The yeldinge of his seed and of his greyn.
His lordes sheep, his neet, his dayėrye,

---

586. sette hir aller cappe : made fools of them all. The metaphor comes from the joke of tilting the hats of the sober and serious.

587. The reve : The reeve was the manager of a manor. He was not the bailiff or steward who managed the revenues of the whole estate, which might consist of many manors. This particular reeve was not a ploughman by trade, but he had been a carpenter. The whole picture is so precise that it seems likely to be drawn from life.

Professor Manly of Chicago has pointed out that Chaucer knew of Baldeswell in this way. During the minority of John Hastings, Earl of Pembroke, his estates were managed by Sir William Beauchamp from 1378 to 1386, and Chaucer was one of the mainpernors (or sureties) on his behalf. Baldeswell was a part of these estates in Norfolk. Probably Sir William Beauchamp had been in dispute with the reeve of this manor, who is now pictured as managing the manor for the young proprietor. In 1390 the Earl of Pembroke died, and Baldeswell became part of the estate of Lord Grey of Ruthyn.

589. Ln. *rounde*, E. etc. *ful round*, Hl. *neigh*.

590. He had a 'not-heed ' like the yeoman.

594. No auditor could get the better of him.—E. *of.*

His swyn, his hors, his stoor, and his pultrye
Was hoolly in this reves governyng,
And by his covenant yaf the rekenyng   A 600
Syn that his lord was twenty yeer of age ;
Ther koude no man bringe hym in arrerage.
Ther nas bailiff, ne herde, nor oother hyne,
That he ne knew his sleighte and his covyne ;
They were adrad of hym, as of the deeth.   605
    His woning was ful faire upon an heeth,
With grenė trees yshadwed was his place.
He koudė bettre than his lord purchace.
Ful riche he was astored prively,
His lord wel koude he plesen subtilly   610
To yeve and lene him of his owenė good
And have a thank, and yet a cote and hood.
In youth he haddė lerned a good mistér :
He was a wel good wrighte, a carpenter.
This Revė sat upon a ful good stot,   615
That was al pomely grey, and hightė Scot.
A long surcote of pers upon he hade,
And by his syde he baar a rusty blade.
Of Northfolk was this reve of which I telle,
Bisyde a toun men clepen Baldeswelle.   A 620

603. bailiff : agent for a landed proprietor, manager of the whole estate as opposed to one manor. Superior in rank to the reve.—*herde:* herdsman of sheep or swine. Inferior in rank to the reve.

604. his sleighte and his covyne : his cunning and his fraud. ' Covyne ' means an agreement to defraud.—E. Cm. lack *ne*.

605. the deeth : the plague. The allusion is to the Black Death, prevalent at that time.

607. Hl. Cm. *ischadewid*, Cp. Pt. *shadewed*, E. Hn. *shadwed*.

612. E. *gowne*, others *cote*, Hl. *a thank, a cote and eek an hood*.

613. E. Cm. Cp. *hadde lerned*, Hl. Hn. *lerned hadde*.

620. Baldeswelle : in the county of Norfolk. Now called Bawdswell.

Tukked he was, as is a frere, aboute,
And evere he rood the hyndreste of our route.

A SOMONOUR was ther with us in that place,

The   That hadde a fyr-reed cherubynnes face,
Summoner.   For sawcefleem he was, with eyen narwe.

As hoot he was, and lecherous, as a sparwe,   626
With scalled browes blake, and piled berd ;
Of his viságe children were aferd.

Ther nas quiksilver, litarge ne brimstoon,
Boras, ceruce, ne oille of tartre noon,   630

621. The reeve had hitched up his long gown within his girdle, so that he could ride more easily.

622. The miller led the way with his bagpipes, but the reeve rode last, for they hated each other.

623. A somonour : a constable of the ecclesiastical court of 'the bishop's eye,'—the archdeacon. Ecclesiastical courts dealt with offences against morals under the canon law, such as cases of witchcraft, defamation of character, neglect of the sacraments, usury, the buying or selling of ecclesiastical preferment (simony), and of offences against the marriage laws. See the beginning of the *Friar's Tale*, D. 1300-1320. The penalties were usually fines, but the extreme punishment was excommunication or 'cursing,' after which the prisoner was handed over to the civil law to be imprisoned, or in the case of heresy, to be burnt.

Summoners were notoriously dishonest in Chaucer's age, if the *Friar's Tale* is worthy of credence. They accepted bribes, and they brought false charges so as to be bribed to let the case drop. It is not a pleasant picture which Chaucer draws, but he makes his rogue a buffoon by making the summoner wear a garland, and carry a huge cake like a buckler.

624. a fyr-reed cherubynnes face : Cherubim, one of the orders of angels that were traditionally supposed to stand around the throne of God in heaven. They were represented with red faces. Cherub has a Hebrew plural in *-im*; but in Chaucer's English not only is the plural used for the singular, but it ends in *-n*, not in *-m*, probably because *-n* was a living ending, as in oxen, brethren, hosen, shoon, etc.

Ne oynément that woldé clense and byte,
That hym myghte helpen of the whelkes whyte,
Nor of the knobbes sittinge on his chekes.
Wel loved he garleek, oynons, and eek lekes,
And for to drinken strong wyn, reed as blood ;   635
Thanne wolde he speke, and crye as he were wood.
And whan that he wel dronken hadde the wyn,
Than wolde he speké no word but Latyn.
A fewé termes hadde he, two or three,
That he had lerned out of som decree,—   A 640
No wonder is, he herde it al the day ;
And eek ye knowen wel, how that a jay
Kan clepen ' Watte,' as wel as kan the pope.
But who-so koude in oother thing him grope,
Thanne hadde he spent al his philosophie :   645
Ay ' *questio quid juris* ' wolde he crye.
　　He was a gentil harlot and a kynde,
A bettre felaw sholdé men noght fynde.
He woldé suffre, for a quart of wyn,
A good felawe to have his concubyn   650
A twelfmonth, and excuse him atté fulle :
And prively a finch eek koude he pulle ;
And if he foond owher a good felawe,
He woldé techen him to have noon awe,

632. E. *the*, others *his*.
646. questio quid juris : the question is : which (part) of the law (applies).
647. harlot : rascal. The word was not applied to women until later than Chaucer's age.
650. A good felawe : a rogue ; here probably an unworthy priest.
652. E. Hl. Ln. *And*, others *Ful*.
654. He would tell him to have no fear, in such a case, of the archdeacon's excommunication, unless his soul resided in his purse, for his punishment would be a heavy bribe.

In swich caas, of the erchèdekenes curs,   655
But if a mannes soul were in his purs,
For in his purs he sholde ypunisshed be.
' Purs is the erchèdekenes helle,' seyde he.
But wel I woot he lyed right in dede,
Of cursing oughte ech gilty man to drede,   A 660
For curs wol slee, right as assoilling sayith ;
And also war him of a *Significávit*.
In daunger hadde he at his owenè gyse
The yongè girles of the diocise.
And knew hir conseil, and was al hir reed.   665
A gerland hadde he set upon his heed,
As greet as it were for an alè-stake ;
A bokler hadde he maad him of a cake.

With hym ther rood a gentil PARDONER   669
The
Pardoner. Of Rouncivale, his freend and his compeer,
That streight was comen fro the court of
Romè.
Ful loude he soong, ' *Com hider, lovè, tó me !* '

657. Hl. Cm. Cp. *ponyschid*.

660. Hl. Pt. *to*, Cp. Ln. *him*, lacking in E. Hn. Cm.

662. Significavit: When excommunication had been pronounced by the archdeacon, the bishop issued a writ called a ' significavit ' to the Crown, which signified that the sinner was recalcitrant, and he was therefore liable to imprisonment. A writ of this kind (*de excommunicato capiendo*) was commonly called a significavit, from its opening words : " *Significavit nobis venerabilis pater.*"

663. In his own way he had in his power the young men and women of the diocese ; and he knew their secrets and was altogether their adviser.

669. a gentil pardoner : a seller of pardons, or plenary indulgences. A papal pardon relieved the recipient from a certain period of penance. During the papal schism, when there were rival popes at Rome and at Avignon, from 1378 to 1417, the traffic in pardons was exceedingly lavish, and the rival popes contended against one another in prodigality.

A ' pardon' was a remission of the temporal punishment of sin, a remission of penance, not a remission of sins, which are forgiven only by God. The church in the person of its head, the pope, claimed the power of remitting penitential observance from the treasure of the inexhaustible goodness of Christ and the works of supererogation of His saints. The writs or ' bulls ' of indulgence were written on parchment with the papal seal attached. They were sold in return for an alms which was devoted to some religious work, such as building or repairing a church. A pardoner was a papal officer, and pardoners could only operate in a diocese with the permission of the bishop.

The system lent itself to abuse, and, judging by the criticisms made by Chaucer, Langland, Boccaccio, etc., even to fraud by ignorant and cunning pardoners. Pardoners, for instance, carried fraudulent relics, by the exhibition of which they received money. Indeed, they had a scandalous reputation as lovers of money, not all of which was reputed to be devoted to works of charity. The distinction between pardon from penance and pardon from sins was not always appreciated, and the fact that pardon could be bought for a longer period than a man could live made it seem that the pardoner's penitent was obtaining a release from punishment not in life but in eternity.

There are now no pardoners. Pardoners were suppressed entirely by the Church at the Council of Trent, in 1562.—E. *was*, others *rood, rode.*

670. Of Rouncivale : of the convent or hospital of Our Lady of Rouncival or Roncesvalles, which was where, in 1614, stood Northumberland House, Charing Cross, at the top of Northumberland Avenue almost where Charing Cross Station now stands. This convent was a cell or subordinate priory of Our Lady of Roncesvalles, in the Spanish Pyrenees, where Roland fought his last battle. The English cell was suppressed as an alien priory in 1414.

671. the court of Rome : There were two popes from 1378 to 1417. One at Rome, and a rival French pope at Avignon. The pope of Rome was recognised by England, Ireland, Germany, Bohemia and Hungary, and, of course, in Italy. Incidentally that is why Richard II married Anne of Bohemia, and not a French princess. The pope of Avignon was recognised by France, Scotland, Spain and Sicily. Both popes licensed pardoners.

672. Com hider, love, to me : Evidently a popular song of the time. Note the rime of *Rome* with *to me.*

This Somonour bar to hym a stif burdoun,
Was nevere trompe of half so greet a soun.

    This Pardoner hadde heer as yelow as wex,   675
But smothe it heeng, as dooth a strike of flex ;
By ounces henge his lokkes that he hadde
And therwith he his shuldres overspradde :
But thinne it lay, by colpons, oon and oon ;
But hood, for jolitee, he wered noon,   A 680
For it was trussed up in his walét.
Him thoughte he rood al of the newė jet ;
Dischevelee, save his cappe, he rood al bare.
Swiche glaringe eyen hadde he as an hare ;
A vernicle hadde he sowed upon his cappe,   685
His walet lay biforn him in his lappe,
Bretful of pardoun, comen from Rome al hoot.
A voys he hadde as smal as hath a goot ;
No berd hadde he, ne nevere sholdė have ;
As smothe it was, as it were late yshave :   690
I trowe he were a gelding or a mare.

673. **a stif burdoun :** a strong droning bass. The word
' bourdon,' which was of French or Low Latin origin, and
originally meant a drone, was confused with burthen or burden
(a load), which is of English origin.

680. Hl. *ne wered he,* E. etc. *wered he.*

685. **A vernicle :** a copy of the handkerchief of St Veronica,
which is in Rome. St Veronica, according to tradition, was one
of the women who saw Christ bear His cross on the way to
execution. She offered Him her white veil with which to wipe
the sweat from His brow. He accepted it, and used it to wipe
His face. When Veronica received again her veil she found
miraculously imprinted upon it an image of His face. The sacred
veil is kept in St Peter's at Rome. At various intervals it is
shown to the faithful ; and so the wearing of a miniature of the
Holy Face became a token of having been to Rome. Vernicle
(L. *Veronicula*) is a diminutive word formed from Veronica.

686. Hl. only *lay,* rest omit.

But of his craft, fro Berwik unto Ware
Ne was ther swich another pardoner.
For in his male he hadde a pilwe-beer,
Which that, he seydè, was our lady veyl ;　695
He seyde he hadde a gobet of the seyl
That Seintè Peter hadde, whan that he wente
Upon the see, til Jhesu Crist him hente.
He hadde a croys of latoun, ful of stones,
And in a glas he haddè pigges bones.　　A 700
But with thise relikes, whan that he fond
A pourè persoun dwellinge upon lond,
Upon a day he gat him moore moneye
Than that the persoun gat in monthes tweye ;
And thus, with feyned flaterye and japes,　705
He made the persoun and the peple his apes.
But, trewèly, to tellen attè laste,
He was in chirche a noble ecclesiaste.
Wel koude he rede a lessoun or a storie,
But alderbest he song an offertorie :　　710

690. Hl. Hn. *yshaue*, E. *shaue*.

691. Chaucer goes out of his way to be objectionable to pardoners. He means that the pardoner either had no sex or was a woman. In other words he was not virile, he was effeminate.

692. fro Berwik unto Ware : from Berwick-on-Tweed in the north, to Ware near Hertford, 20 miles north of London. In other words, along the whole length of the Great North Road from England to Scotland.

697. All *seynt*.

699. ful of stones : ornamented with semi-precious stones.

703. Upon a day : in one day.

706. made . . . his apes : made fools of them.

709. a lessoun or a storie : a lesson from the Bible or a story of a saint.

710. an offertorie : an anthem sung in the Mass after the Creed and before the consecration of the Host. Formerly it was sung by the officiating priest and his assistants, whilst the congregation

For wel he wistè, whan that song was songe,
He mostè preche, and wel affyle his tonge
To winnè silver, as he ful wel koude ;
Therfore he song so meriely and loude.

Now have I toold you soothly, in a clause,   715
Th' estaat, th' array, the nombre, and eek the cause
Why that assembled was this compaignye
In Southwerk, at this gentil hostelrye,
That highte the Tabard, fastè by the Belle.
But now is tymè to you for to telle   A 720
How that we baren us that ilkè nyght,
Whan we were in that hostelrie alyght ;
And after, wol I telle of our viáge,
And al the remenaunt of our pilgrimage.

But first, I pray you of your curteisye,   725
That ye n' arette it nat my vileynye,
Though that I pleynly speke in this mateere
To tellè you hir wordes and hir cheere,
Ne though I speke hir wordes proprely.
For this ye knowen also wel as I,   730
Whoso shal telle a tale after a man,
He moot reherce, as ny as evere he kan,
Everich a word, if it be in his charge,
Al speke he never so rudèliche or large ;
Or elles he moot telle his tale untrewe,   735
Or feynè thing, or fyndè wordes newe.

went up to the sanctuary in order of rank and gave their offering.
The offertory was consecrated to God. The pardoner received
his collection from the sale of pardons which would be after
Mass, or before it.

714. E. Hn. Cm. *the murierly*, Cp. Pt. Ln. *so meriely*, Hl. *jul meriely*.
715. E. Hl. *shortly*, Hn. Cm. Cp. *soothly*.
716. Hl. Hn. *Thestaat*, Cm. Cp. *The estat*, E. *The staat*.
726. vileynye : rudeness, ill-breeding. Also in l. 740.

He may nat spare, although he were his brother ;
He moot as wel seye o word as another.
Crist spak himself ful brode in hooly writ,
And wel ye woot no vileynye is it.   A 740
Eek Plato seith,—whoso kan hym rede,—
' The wordes moote be cosin to the dede.'
Also I prey you to foryeve it me,
Al have I nat set folk in hir degree
Heer in this tale, as that they sholdė stonde :   745
My wit is short, ye may wel understonde.

    Greet cheerė made our Hoost us everichon,
And to the soper sette he us anon,
And served us with vitaille at the beste :
Strong was the wyn, and wel to drinke us leste.   750
A semely man our HOOSTĖ was withalle

737. Hl. *though.*
739. As, for example, when He called the Pharisees ' a generation of vipers.'
741. Greek was not well known in Western Europe in Chaucer's
age, and Chaucer could not read Plato. The allusion is to
Boethius's *Consolation of Philosophy*, which Chaucer translated
as *Boece*, Book iii., Prose xii. (end) : "thou hast learned by the
sentence of Plato, that ' nedes the wordes moten be cosines to
the things of which they speken.' " The sentiment is also
uttered by Jean de Meung in *Le Roman de la Rose*. Plato
made the statement in *Timaeus*, 29 B.—" words are akin to the
things which they describe."
Chaucer means that if he has to describe a disagreeable
person, his portrait will be unpleasant, but he must tell the truth
about him.—Hl. *whoso that*, others lack *that*.
744. nat set folk in hir degree : not arranged the pilgrims
according to their station in life. In Chaucer's age the order of
precedence was insisted on.
751. our Hooste : The landlord of the Tabard Inn and the
interlocutor in the *Canterbury Tales*. He is a genial, worldly
soul. We learn from the Prologue to *The Cook's Tale* (A. 4358)
that his name was Henry Bailly. He smells a Lollard in the

Fór to been a marshal in an halle.
A largė man he was, with eyen stepe,
A fairer burgeys was ther noon in Chepe :
Boold of his speche, and wys, and well ytaught,   755
And of manhod him lakkedė right naught.
Eek therto he was right a mirie man,
And after soper pleyen he bigan,
And spak of mirthe amonges othere thinges,
Whan that we haddė maad our rekeninges ;   A 760
And seyde thus : ' Now, lordings, trewėly,
Ye, been to me right welcome, hertėly ;
For by my trouthe, if that I shal nat lye,
I saugh nat this yéer so mirie a compaignye
At ones in this herberwe as is now.   765
Fayn wolde I doon you mirthė, wiste I how.
And of a mirthe I am right now bithought,
To doon you ese, and it shal costė nought.

wind when he is reproved by the Parson for swearing (B. **1173**).
His wife appears to be called Godeleve or Goodelief (B. 3084).
He prefers a merry tale to a tragedy (B. 3976).

As Pollard and Manly have shown, there really was a Henry
Bailly or Bayliff, an innkeeper, living in Southwark in the last
thirty years of the fourteenth century. He was an important
person who had represented Southwark in parliament in 1376
and 1378. It seems therefore probable that the Host's portrait
is drawn from life.—E. *hoost.*

752. a marshal in an halle : a master of ceremonies.—Hl. *For
to han been.*

754. in Chepe : in the market-place of London. The name is
still preserved in ' Cheapside,' the broad street north of St Paul's
where corn and meat were marketed, and where, in the portion
leading to Lombard Street, the continuation where the bankers
congregated, general wares were sold. It was a compliment to
compare a burgess of Southwark with one of the great merchants
of London.—E. Hn. *was,* Hl. Cm. Cp. *is.*

756. E. *lakked,* Cm. Cp. *lakkede,* Hl. *lakkede he.*

764. Hl. *I ne saugh,* E. etc. *I saugh nat.*

' Ye goon to Caunterbury ; God you speede !
The blisful martir quytė you your meede ! 770
And, wel I woot, as ye goon by the weye,
Ye shapen you to talen and to pleye,
For trewėly, confort ne mirthe is noon
To rydė by the weye doumb as a stoon ;
And therfore wol I maken you disport, 775
As I seyde erst ; and doon you som confort.
And if you lyketh alle, by oon assent,
Fór to stonden at my juggėment,
And for to werken as I shal you seye,
To-morwė, whan ye ryden by the weye,— A 780
Now, by my fader soulė, that is deed,—
But ye be mirie, I wol yeve myn heed :
Hoold up your hond, withouten moorė speche.'

   Our conseil was nat longė for to seche,
Us thoughte it was noght worth to make it wys, 785
And graunted hym, withouten moore avys,
And bad him seye his verdit, as him leste.

   'Lordynges,' quod he, 'now herkneth for the beste ;
But taak it nought, I prey you, in desdeyn ;
This is the poynt, to speken short and pleyn, 790
That eche of you, to shortė with your weye

---

772. You are getting ready to tell tales and to jest. It was customary for pilgrims to enjoy themselves as they rode along with singing, tales, and the skirl of the bagpipes.

774. E. *as the,* Hl. Cp. Pt. *as a.*

778. Hl. *Now for.*

781. fader : father's. An instance of the uninflected genitive surviving from Old English. It originally occurred in nouns expressing relationship such as : fader, mooder, brother, suster, and doughter.

782. But : unless.—E. *But if*; E. Cm. Hn. *I wol yeue yow,* Hl. *smyteth of.*

791. to shorte with your weye : with which to shorten your way.—Hl. Cp. Dd. *youre,* others *oure.*

In this viage, shal tellė tales tweye,
(To Caunterbury-ward, I mene it so,
And hoomward he shal tellen othere two)
Of áventures that whilom han bifalle.   795
And which of you that bereth him best of alle,
That is to seyn, that telleth in this caas
Tales of best senténce and moost solaas,
Shal have a soper at oure aller cost,
Heer in this placė, sittinge by this post,   A 800
Whan that we come agayn fro Caunterbury.
And, for to makė you the moorė mury,
I wol myselven gladly with you ryde,
Right at myn owenė cost, and be your gyde ;
And whoso wole my juggėment withseye,   805
Shal paye al that we spenden by the weye.
And if ye vouchėsauf that it be so,
Tel me anon, withouten wordes mo,
And I wol erly shapė me therfore.'

    This thyng was graunted, and our othes swore   810
With ful glad herte, and preyden hym also
That he wold vouchėsauf for to do so,
And that he woldė been our governour,
And of our tales juge and réportour,
And sette a soper at a certeyn pris,   815

798. Tales of the best instruction and the greatest edification.
799. Hl. *your*.
800. post: It is not clear whether Chaucer means the sign-post of the Tabard or some internal wooden support.
803. E. *my self goodly*.
806. Hl. *for al we*.
811. preyden: we prayed, we asked. ' Swore ' in l. 810 is a past participle.
813. governour: leader.
814. reportour: commentator. He was to report on the merit and morality of the tales.

And we wold reuled been at his devys
In heigh and low ; and thus, by oon assent,
We been acorded to his juggėment.
And therupon the wyn was fet anon,
We dronken, and to restė wente echon,   A 820
Withouten any lenger taryinge.

    Amorwė, whan that day bigan to springe,
Up roos our Hoost, and was oure aller cok,
And gadrede us togidre alle in a flok ;
And forth we riden, a litel moore than paas,   825
Unto the wateryng of Seint Thomas.
And there our Hoost bigan his hors areste,
And seydė : ' Lordinges, herkneth, if you leste !
Ye woot your foreward, and I it you recorde ;
If even-song and morwe-song accorde,   830
Lat see now who shal telle the firstė tale.
As evere mote I drinkė wyn or ale,
Whoso be rebel to my juggėment,
Shal payė for al that by the way is spent !
Now draweth cut, er that we ferrer twinne ;   835
He which that hath the shorteste shal biginne.
Sire Knyght,' quod he, ' my maister and my lord,
Now draweth cut, for that is myn accord.

816. Hl. Pt. *wolde*, others *wol, wollen, wil*.
817. **In heigh and low** : in all things.
822. E. Hn. *that*, Hl. *that the*, Cp. Dd. etc. *the* ; E. *gan for to*,
Hl. Hn. Cp. *bigan to*, Pt. Ln. *gan to*.
826. **the wateryng of Seint Thomas** : A brook some two miles
out on the road from Southwark to Canterbury where the horses
would be watered.
829. E. Hn. omit *I*.
835. Hl. *forther*, Cp. Pt. Ln. *ferther*.
838. **draweth cut** : Imperative plural used in the polite form
of address, as in ll. 839 and 841. A number of straws or sticks
was held by the Host, and the pilgrims each selected one. The

Cometh neer,' quod he, ' my lady Prioresse,
And ye, sire Clerk, lat be your shamefastnesse,　A 840
Ne studieth noght ; ley hond to, every man ! '
　　Anon to drawen every wight bigan,
And, shortly, for to tellen as it was,
Were it by aventure, or sort, or cas,
The sothe is this, the cut fil to the knyght,　　　845
Of which ful blithe and glad was every wyght :
And telle he moste his tale, as was resoun,
By foreward and by composicioun,
As ye han herd ; what nedeth wordes mo ?
And whan this good-man saugh that it was so,　　850
As he that wys was and obedient
To kepe his foreward by his free assent,
He seydè, ' Syn I shal biginne the game,
What, welcome be the cut, a Goddes name !
Now lat us ryde, and herkneth what I seye.'　　855
　　And with that word we riden forth our weye ;
And he bigan with right a mirie cheere
His tale anon, and seyde in this manere.

Here endeth the prolog of this book.

one who drew the shortest told the first tale. The short straw
was called the ' cut.' Cf. *Pardoner's Tale*, 793-803.

　839. Cometh neer : come nearer.

　844. by aventure, or sort, or cas : by luck, or lot, or chance.

　845. E. *fil.*

　850. good-man : gentleman. The MSS. read ' this goode
man ' ; but the -*e* must be silent, or the line does not scan.
' Goode man ' and its plural ' goode men ' seem to have been
used at times as dissyllabic words, with a meaning only very
slightly differentiated from ' the goode man ' or ' men.'—All, *this
goode man saugh that it.*

　858. E. Hl. Dd. *in this manere*, Hn. Cp. *as ye may heere.*

THE PRIORESSES TALE

THE PROLOGUE OF THE PRIORESSES TALE

Domine, dominus noster

O LORD, our Lord, thy name how merveillous
Is in this largė world ysprad,—quod she ;—
For noght only thy laudė precious
Parfourned is by men of dignitee,
But by the mouth of children thy bountee   5
Parfourned is ; for on the brest soukinge
Somtymė shewen they thyn heryinge.

Wherfore in laude, as I best kan or may,   (B. 1650)
Of Thee, and of the whitė lilye-flour
Which that Thee bar, and is a mayde alway,   10
To telle a storie I wól do my labóur ;
Nat that I may encreesen hir honóur,
For she hirself is honour, and the root
Of bountee, next hir sone, and soules boot.

1-28. These four stanzas are a patchwork of religious thoughts.
Stanza i. owes a good deal to Psalm viii. ; Stanza iv. to Dante's
Paradiso xxxiii. 16.   5. thy bountee Parfourned is : Thy goodness
is declared.

6. on the brest soukinge : those who suck the breast, babes
and sucklings.

8. kan or may : can do or may do, have the power and ability
(to tell).

9. the white lilye-flour : the lily is the symbol of the Virgin
Mary—a symbol of purity ; cf. *Song of Solomon*, ii. 2. "As the
lily among thorns, so is my love among the daughters."

10. Which that Thee bar : who bore Thee, of whom Thou wert
born. 'That' is redundant after the pronoun 'which.'

14. soules boot : the soul's remedy, the helper of souls.

O mooder mayde ! O maydė mooder free !   15
O bush unbrent, brennynge in Moyses sighte !
That ravisedest doun fro the Deitee,
Thurgh thyn humblesse, the Goost that in th' alighte ;
Of whos vertu, whan He thyn hertė lighte,   (B. 1661)
Conceived was the Fadres sapience,   20
Helpe me to telle it in thy reverence !

Lady ! thy bountee, thy magnificence,
Thy vertu, and thy grete humilitee
Ther may no tonge expresse in no science ;
For somtyme, lady, er men praye to thee,   25
Thou goost biforn of thy benignitee,
And getest us the lyght, thurgh thy preyére,
To gyden us unto thy Sone so deere.

My konning is so wayk, O blisful queene,
For to declare thy gretė worthynesse,   30
That I ne may the weightė nat susteene,
But as a child of twelf month old, or lesse,
That kan unnethė any word expresse,

16. The allusion is to *Exodus* iii. 2-5, where Moses sees God
in a burning bush, yet the bush was not consumed by fire.   The
Blessed Virgin is like Moses's burning bush, which burned and
yet was not burnt, because she bore Our Lord and yet she was
still a virgin.

17-20. That, through thy humility, didst draw down from
God the Holy Spirit that descended upon thee : by whose power,
when he illuminated thy heart, the wisdom of the Father (*i.e.*
Christ) was conceived.

18. Hl. Cp. *the alight.*   22. magnificence: glory.

26. Thou goost biforn : thou preventest them, thou dost
anticipate their wishes.   ' Of ': by

27. E. *thurgh lyght of.*

33. E. Hn. *vnnethe*, Hl. Cp. Pt. *vnnethes.*

Right so fare I, and therfore I you preye,
Gydeth my song that I shal of you seye.   35

Explicit.

HEER BIGINNETH THE PRIORESSES TALE

Ther was in Asie, in a greet citee,
Amonges cristen folk, a jewerye,
Sustened by a lord of that contrée   (B. 1680)
For foule usure and lucre of vileynye,
Hateful to Crist and to his compaignye;   40
And thurgh the strete men myghtè ryde or wende,
For it was free, and open at eyther ende.

35. **Gydeth**: imperative plural used in polite and divine address.

36. **in Asie**: in Asia Minor. In other medieval tales of the same kind, the place of the miracle is ascribed to different places. That Chaucer had Lincoln, and the boy-martyr Hugh of Lincoln, in mind is apparent from l. 232. Philippa Chaucer, his wife, belonged to the religious guild of the friends of Lincoln Cathedral. She was admitted to membership on February 19, 1386.

39. **lucre of vileynye**: filthy lucre, evil gain. The Jews were notorious as money-lenders in the Middle Ages. Chaucer means that the overlord of the country, who in the time of the Crusades would be a Christian and a western European, probably French, permitted a Jewry in his city because the Jews were bankers. The Church in the Middle Ages regarded the lending of money on interest, and the charging of interest on a debt, as a sin. Hence partly its hatred of the Jews. Christendom had not yet developed finance, but Christian kings allowed Jewish bankers to practise, on condition that they paid for licences to trade, and (at times) lent money to the king. The Jews were expelled from England from 1290 until the reign of Charles II, and the 'Lombard' bankers took their place.—E. etc. *vileynye*, Hl. *felonye*.

42. **For it was free**: it was a thoroughfare. Medieval streets were usually narrow and frequently they were not thoroughfares. In that case sometimes they were barred against horsed traffic.

A litel scole of cristen folk ther stood
Doun at the ferther ende, in which ther were
Children an heep, ycomen of cristen blood,   45
That lerned in that scolé yeer by yere
Swich maner doctrine as men used there,
This is to seyn, to singen and to rede,
As smalé children doon in hir childhede.

Among thise children was a widwes sone,   50
A litel clergeon, seven yeer of age,
That day by day to scolé was his wone ;
And eek also, wher-as he saugh th' image
Of Cristes mooder, he hadde in usage

43. Chaucer is thinking in terms of the schools in the England
of his time. Schools were few, and to attend school was the
habit chiefly of boys who were destined for the priesthood, law
and medicine. The sons of merchants and tradesmen might be
educated too, but noblemen's sons had their education privately
from a tutor, and peasants' sons were uneducated, unless they
were destined for the service of the Church. Most people could
neither read nor write.

For those who wished to study at the universities or at the
inns of court there were Grammar Schools, connected with some
cathedral or chantry. They taught reading and writing, but
the basis of the education which they gave was Latin grammar,
together with some arithmetic. The school which Chaucer's
' litel clergeon ' attended was evidently a smaller and more
elementary school, probably a song-school, a school for the
choristers of a church. Here the object was to train choir-boys
in reading and singing, so that they could sing the services of
the church. As this little fellow was only seven or eight, he
still lived at home and attended school daily.

45. Children an heep : a number of boys.

47. Swich maner doctrine : such kind of teaching, namely,
reading and singing.

52. Whose custom was (to go) day by day to school. ' That
. . . his ' = whose.

53. Cp. Ln. Pt. *the ymage*, E. *thymage*.

As hym was taught, to knele adoun, and seye   55
His *Ave Marye* as he goth by the weye.

Thus hath this widwe hir litel child ytaught
Our blisful lady, Cristes mooder deere,   (B. 1700)
To worshipe ay, and he forgat it naught ;
For 'sely child wol alday soonè leere ' ;   60
But ay, whan I remembre on this mateere,
Seint Nicholas stant ever in my presence,
For he so yong to Crist dide reverence.

This litel child, his litel book lernynge,
As he sat in the scole at his prymer,   65
He *Alma redemptoris* herdè singe,

53. 'As' is redundant after the relative adverbs *ther* and *wher*.

56. Ave Marye : a Latin salutation to the Blessed Virgin : " Hail Mary, full of grace ; the Lord be with thee ; blessed art thou among women and blessed is the fruit of thy womb " : cf. *St Luke* i. 28 and i. 42. The child knelt down in the street and said his prayer whenever he passed an image of Christ's Mother. In those days Gothic buildings often had statues in niches, and there were sometimes images in shrines along the road.

57. E. *sone*, Hl. etc. *child*.

59. E. Pt. *forgate*.

60. A proverb : A good child will always learn quickly.— Hl. Hn. *alwey*.

62. St Nicholas too was pious from his infancy. Whilst he was still a child at his mother's breast he fasted on Wednesdays and Fridays ; and when other children frolicked and played, he went to church. St Nicholas, whose day is on December 6th, was the patron of schoolboys. Stant : standeth, is.

65. his prymer : his first reading-book, which would probably contain the alphabet, the Lord's Prayer, Ave Maria, the Apostles' Creed, the Ten Commandments, Graces before and after meat, and various prayers. It would be a manuscript book.

66. Alma redemptoris : Alma redemptoris mater : the open-ing words of a Latin anthem.

As children lerned hir antiphoner ;
And as he dorste, he drough him ner and ner,
And herkned ay the wordes and the note,
Til he the firstè vers koude al by rote.   70

Noght wiste he what this Latyn was to seye,
For he so yong and tendre was of age ;
But on a day his felawe gan he preye
T' expounden hym this song in his langage,
Or telle him why this song was in usage ;   75
This preyde he hym to cónstrue and declare
Ful often tyme upon hise knowes bare.

His felawe, which that elder was than he,   (B. 1720)
Answérde him thus : ' This song, I have herd seye,
Was maked of our blisful lady free,   80
Hir to salue, and eek hir for to preye
To been our help and socour whan we deye.
I kan namoore expounde in this mateere ;
I lernè song, I kan but smal grammeere.'

' And is this song maked in reverence   85
Of Cristes mooder ? ' seyde this innocent ;
' Now certes, I wol do my diligence

---

68. ner and ner : nearer and nearer. Cf. *Prologue*, l. 839 :
' Cometh neer,' come nearer.

70. koude al by rote : knew all by heart.

71. was to seye : meant.

77. E. Hl. *often*, others *ofte*.

84. "I am learning singing. I know only a little Latin." At
this school for choirboys, singing, and the ability to read words
and music, were the essentials. It was not essential that the
boys knew what the words meant. The school was not a
grammar school.

To konne it al, er Cristèmasse is went ;
Though that I for my prymer shal be shent,
And shal be beten thryès in an houre,   90
I wol it konne, our lady for t' honóure.'

His felawe taughte him hoomward prively,
Fro day to day, til he koude it by rote,
And than he song it wel and boldèly
Fro word to word, acordinge with the note ;   95
Twyès a day it passed thurgh his throte,
To scolèward and hoomward whan he wente ;
On Cristes mooder, set was his entente.   (B. 1740)

As I have seyd, thurghout the jewerye
This litel child, as he cam to and fro,   100
Ful murily than wolde he singe, and crye
O Alma redemptoris everemo.
The sweetnesse hath his hertè perced so
Of Cristes mooder, that to hir to preye
He kan nat stinte of singing by the weye.   105

Our firstè foo, the serpent Sathanas,
That hath in Jewes herte his waspes nest,
Up swal, and seide, ' O Hebrayk peple, allas !

89. Though I shall be punished because of my primer = for not
knowing my primer.

91. Hl. Cp. Pt. omit *for*.

101. E. Hn. *murily wolde*, Hl. etc. *murily than wolde*.

103. E. Hn. *swetnesse his herte*, Hl. etc. *swetnesse hath his herte*.

106-126. Usury was an offence against the law of the Church.
The Jews therefore were not only aliens, but sinners too, and
feeling against them was bitter. The attitude of Elizabethan
times can be seen in Marlowe's *Jew of Malta* and Shakespeare's
Merchant of Venice.

The serpent in the story of Adam and Eve was believed to be
Satan, the adversary of mankind ; and a Jew's heart is pictured
as being as full of malice as a wasp's nest, because Satan resides
in it. **108. Up swal :** swelled up, was enraged.

Is this to you a thing that is honést,
That swich a boy shal walken as him lest   110
In your despyt, and singe of swich sentence,
Which is agayn our lawes reverence ? '

Fro thennesforth, the Jewes han conspired
This innocent out of this world to chace ;
An homicidé therto han they hyred,   115
That in an aley hadde a privee place ;
And as the child gan forby for to pace,
This cursed Jew him hente and heeld him faste,
And kitte his throte, and in a pit him caste. (B. 1761)

I seye that in a wardrobe they him threwe   120
Where as thise Jewes purgen hir entraille.
O cursed folk, O Herodes al newe !
What may your yvel ententé you availle ?
' Mordre wol out,' certeyn, it wol nat faille,
And namely ther th' honóur of God shal sprede, 125
The blood outcryeth on your cursed dede.

' O martir, sowded to virginitee,
Now maystow singen, folwing ever in oon

111. "In contempt of you, and sing a song of such meaning."
The clerk in the Prologue to the *Canterbury Tales* also spoke
' short and quik, and ful of hy sentence " (l. 306). The word
' your ' is the genitive of ' you.'

112. "As is contrary to the honour in which we hold the law."
Chaucer said ' swich . . . which,' when we have to say such . . .
as. The law is of course the Pentateuch (*Torah*), the five
books (*Genesis, Exodus, Leviticus, Numbers, Deuteronomy*) of
the Old Testament.—Hl. Pt. Ln. *your(e)*, E. Hn. Cm. Cp. *oure*.

120. a wardrobe : a privy. Chaucer avoids the use of an
objectionable word, as we do when we call it a lavatory.

122. E. *O cursed folk of Herodes.*

125. Cp. Ln. Pt. omit *th*.

The whitė Lamb celestial,'—quod she ;—
' Of which the grete Evaungelist, Seint John   130
In Pathmos wroot, which seith that they that goon
Biforn this Lamb, and singe a song al newe,
That nevere fleshly wommen they ne knewe.'

This pourė widwe awaiteth al that nyght
After hir litel child, but he cam noght ;   135
For which, as soone as it was dayes lyght,
With facė pale of drede and bisy thought,
She hath at scole and elleswhere him sought, (B. 1780)
Til finally she gan so fer espye
That he last seyn was in the jewerye.   140

With moodres pitee in hir brest enclosed
She gooth, as she were half out of hir mynde,
To every placė where she hath supposed
By lyklihede hir litel child to fynde ;
And ever on Cristes mooder, meeke and kynde,   145
She crydė ; and attė lastė thus she wroughte,
Among the cursed Jewes she him soughte.

She frayneth and she preyeth pitously
To every Jew that dwelte in thilkė place,
To telle hir if hir child wente oght forby.   150
They seyde ' Nay ' ; but Jhesu of his grace
Yaf in hir thought withinne a litel space

130. Pathmos : Patmos. The allusion is to the last book in
the New Testament, *The Revelation of St John*, xiv. 3-4.
   133. fleshly : in the flesh, carnally. ' Fleshly' is here an
adverb, not an adjective. The second *that* in l. 131 is redundant.
   139. she gan so fer espye : she did see so far, she discovered.
   146. thus she wroughte : she did this.
   150. wente oght forby : had gone by at all.
   151. E. Hn. Cm. *Ihu*, Cp. Pt. Ln. *Ihc*.
   152. Hl. Cm. Cp. *withinne*, E. Hn. Pt. Ln. *inwith*.

That, in that place, after hir sone she cryde,
Where he was casten in a pit bisyde.

O gretė God, that parfournest thy laude   155
By mouth of innocents, lo, heer thy myght!
This gemme of chastitee, this emeraude,
And eek of martirdom the ruby bright,   (B. 1800)
Ther he, with throte ykorven, lay upright,
He *Alma redemptoris* gan to singe   160
So loude, that al the placė gan to ringe.

The cristene folk, that thurgh the stretė wente,
In coomen, for to wondre upon this thing ;
And hastily they for the provost sente.
He cam anon, withouten tarying,   165
And herieth Crist that is of heven king,
And eek his mooder, honour of mankynde,
And after that, the Jewes leet he bynde.

This child with pitous lamentacioun
Up taken was, singynge his song alway ;   170
And with honóur of greet processioun
They carien hym unto the nexte abbay.
His mooder swowninge by his beerė lay ;
Unnethė myghte the peple that was theere
This newė Rachel bringė fro his beere.   175

155. parfournest thy laude : dost declare thy praise.
159. lay upright : lay on his back. Cf. *Nun's Priest's Tale*,
l. 276.
163. E. Hn. Hl. **Cm.** *vpon*, Cp. Pt. *wondren on*, Ln. *wonderne
of*.
175. This newe Rachel : this second Rachel. The allusion is
to *St Matthew*, ii. 18 : " Rachel weeping for her children, and
would not be comforted, because they are not."

With torment, and with shameful deeth, echon
This provost dooth the Jewes for to sterve
That of this mordre wiste, and that anon ;   (B. 1820)
He noldė no swich cursednesse observe.
' Yvel shal he have, that yvel wol deserve.'   180
Therfor with wildė hors he dide hem drawe,
And after that, he heng hem by the lawe.

Upon his beere ay lyth this innocent
Biforn the chief auter, whil the massė laste,
And after that, th' abbot with his covent   185
Han sped hem for to burien hym ful faste ;
And whan they hooly water on him caste,
Yet spak this child, whan spreynd was hooly water,
And song—' *O Alma redemptoris mater !* '

This abbot, which that was an hooly man   190
As monkes been, or elles oghtė be,
This yongė child to conjure he bigan,
And seyde, ' O deerė child, I halsė thee,
In vertu of the hooly Trinitee,—
Tel me what is thy causė for to singe,   195
Sith that thy throte is kut, to my semynge ? '

177. E. *the*, others, *thise, these.*
180. A proverb: He that desires evil, shall have evil.—E. Cm. *shal he*, Pt. *he ṣhal*, others omit *he.*
181. hors: horses. ' Hors ' had the same form in the singular as in the plural, cf. *Prologue* l. 74, ' His hors were goode,'' where the plural verb shows that ' hors ' is plural.
183. Hl. Hn. *his*, E. etc. *this*
184. The fact that the child's body lay in the choir seems to indicate that he had been a clerk, a ' clergeon.'—Cp. Pt. Ln. omit *the* in *the massė.*
185. covent: the monks of his abbey. The word convent was not restricted to houses of nuns. It was applied to monastic establishments whether of monks or nuns, and later also to the houses of friars.—Hl. *thabbot.*

' My throte is kut unto my nekkė boon,'
Seydė this child, ' and, as by wey of kynde,   (B. 1840)
I sholde have dyed, ye, longė tyme agon ;
But Jhesu Crist, as ye in bookes fynde,   200
Wil that his glorie laste and be in mynde,
And, for the worship of his mooder deere,
Yet may I singe ' *O Alma* ' loude and cleere.

This welle of mercy, Cristes mooder sweete,
I lovede alwey, as after my konninge ;   205
And whan that I my lyf sholdė forlete,
To me she cam, and bad me for to singe
This antem verraily in my deyínge,
As ye han herd, and whan that I hadde songe,
Me thoughte, she leyde a greyn upon my tonge.   210

Wherfore I singe, and singe I moot certeyn
In honour of that blisful mayden free,
Til fro my tonge off-taken is the greyn ;
And afterward thus seydė she to me,
" My litel child, now wol I fecchė thee   215

198. **as by wey of kynde** : in the course of nature, in the natural
order of things. ' As ' merely introduces the clause and is
meaningless. The child means that his suspended animation is
a miracle.

201. **Wil that his glorie laste** : wishes that his glory may
endure. ' Laste ' is subjunctive mood.

205. **as after my konninge** : according to my skill, as far as I
was able. ' As ' merely introduces the clause and is meaningless.

208. E. *Anthephen*, Hn. *antheme*, others *anteme*, *antym*.

210. **a greyn** : a grain of corn.

212. **blisful mayden free** : blessed, generous maiden. Note the
construction, which was only originally possible because English
adjectives came before the noun, and French adjectives came
after it, *cf.* " white Lamb celestial," in l. 129. It has remained
as one of the resources of English poetry ever since.

Whan that the greyn is fro thy tonge ytake ;
Be nat agast, I wol thee nat forsake." '

This hooly monk, this abbot, hym mene I,   (B. 1860)
His tong out-caughte, and took awey the greyn
And he yaf up the goost ful softèly.   220
And whan this abbot hadde this wonder seyn,
His saltè teeres trikled doun as reyn ;
And gruf he fel, al plat upon the grounde,
And stille he lay as he had been ybounde.

The covent eek lay on the pavèment   225
Wepynge, and herien Cristes mooder deere,
And after that they rise, and forth been went,
And tooken awey this martir from his beere ;
And in a tombe of marbul stones cleere
Enclosen they his litel body sweete ;   230
Ther he is now, God leve us for to meete.

O yongè Hugh of Lyncoln, slayn also
With cursed Jewes, as it is notáble,

224. Hl. Cp. *ben*, Pt. Ln. *bene*, E. Hn. Cm. *leyn*.
227. rise, and forth been went : rose and are gone (went) forth.
'Rise' has a short vowel, ris-e, and is the past tense plural.—
Hl. *thay went*, others, *been, ben went*.
229. E. *temple*, others *tombe*.
231. God grant us to meet (him) where he now is, *i.e.* in heaven.
232. Hugh of Lyncoln : Saint Hugh of Lincoln, a child of eight
years old, who in the year 1255 was stolen by Jews and killed
by crucifixion after being mocked and scourged. His body was
thrown into a well where his mother found it. A Jew named
Copyn confessed the crime, and some forty Jews were dragged to
the gallows and hanged.
   The body of Saint Hugh was buried in Lincoln Cathedral, and
his tomb became a place of pilgrimage. The day dedicated to
him was June 29th.
   It is perhaps hardly necessary to say that owing to the hatred

For it nis but a litel while ago ;
Preye eek for us, we synful folk unstable,   235
That, of his mercy, God so merciable
On us his gretè mercy multiplye,
For reverence of his mooder Marye.   (B. 1880)
                    Amen.

Heere is ended the Prioresses Tale.

BIHOOLD THE MURYE WORDES OF THE HOOST TO CHAUCER

Whan seyd was al this miracle, every man
As sobre was, that wonder was to see,   240
Til that our Hoostè japen tho bigan,
And than at erst he looked upon me,
And seydè thus : ' What man artow ? ' quod he,
' Thou lookest as thou woldest fynde an hare,
For ever upon the ground I see thee stare.   245

Approchè neer, and looke up murily.
Now war you, sires, and lat this man have place ;
He in the waast is shape as wel as I.   (B. 1890)

of the Jews in the Middle Ages similar tales were widespread
and common, but they were not necessarily true. One of the
peculiarities of examination under torture is that an accused
person will confess to anything.

234. E. Hn. Cm. *is*, Hl. Cp. Pt. Ln. *nys.*

239. miracle : life of a saint.

240. As sobre was : so serious was.

241. Cm. Cp. *tho*, E. *to*, Hn. *he*, others omit.

242. me : Chaucer, who pictures himself as one of the pilgrims.
His looking upon the ground was perhaps not a permanent
feature, like his fatness, but his way of taking the Prioress's
touching story.

246. neer : nearer.

This were a popet in an arm t' enbrace
For any womman, smal and fair of face.   250
He semeth elvish by his contenaunce,
For unto no wight dooth he daliaunce.

Sey now somwhat, syn oother folk han sayd ;
Telle us a tale of mirthe, and that anon.'
' Hóost,' quod I, ' ne beth nat yvel apayd,   255
For oother talê certes kan I noon,
But of a rym I lerned longe agoon.'
' Ye, that is good,' quod he ; ' now shul we heere
Som deyntee thing, me thinketh, by his cheere.'

Explicit.

252. For he talks to nobody.

253. Tell us something, since other people have told tales.

255. ne beth nat yvel apayd : be not ill pleased, don't take it amiss.—E. Hn. Cm. *Hoost*, Cp. Ln. *Oste*

258. **Ye**: Yea. An affirmative which is weaker than ' yis.' 'Yea' often assents to what the last speaker has said. 'Yes' often affirms a question or a statement containing a negative.—E. *ye heere*, others *we heere*.

THE NUN'S PRIEST'S TALE

THE PROLOGUE OF THE NONNË PRESTES TALE

'Ho!' quod the Knyght, 'good sire, namoore of this!
That ye han seyd is right ynough ywis,
And muchel moore; for litel hevinesse
Is right ynough to muchë folk, I gesse.   (B. 3960)
I seye for me, it is a greet disese,   5
Where as men han been in greet welthe and ese,
To heeren of hir sodeyn fall, allas!
And the contrárie is joye and greet solas,
As whan a man hath been in poure estaat,
And clymbeth up, and wexeth fortunat,   10
And there abydeth in prosperitee;
Swich thing is gladsom, as it thinketh me,
And of swich thyng were goodly for to telle.'
    'Ye,' quod our Hoost, 'by Seintë Poules belle!

1. The Knight, the most courteous of the pilgrims, stops the monk at his seventeenth tragic tale, the story of Croesus, king of Lydia.

2. What you have told is quite enough indeed, and much more than enough; for a little sadness is quite enough for many people, I think.

3. E. *muchel*.

6. Where as: 'As' is redundant after the relative adverbs *wher* and *ther*.

12. it thinketh me: it seems to me. An impersonal construction. Note the two verbs: *thenken* (sometimes *thinken*), to think, and *thinken* (used impersonally), to seem. The past tense of both is *thoghte* or *thoughte*.

14. Seinte Poules: St Paul's. The bell of the cathedral

Ye seye right sooth. This Monk, he clappeth loude ;
He spak, how " Fortune covered with a cloude "   16
I noot nevere what,—and als of a " Tragédie "—
Right now ye herde,—and, pardee, no remédie
It is for to biwaillè, ne compleyne
That that is doon ; and als, it is a peyne   20
As ye han seyd, to heere of hevinesse.

    Sir Monk, namoore of this, so God you blesse !
Your tale anoyeth all this compaignye ;
Swich talking is nat worth a boterflye,   (B. 3980)
For therinne is ther no desport ne game.   25
Wherfore, sir Monk, daun Piers by your name,

church of the City of London. The curious spelling is due to
the fact that Poul is derived from the Old French name Pol,
cf. St Pol in France, north-west of Arras ; whereas Paul is
borrowed straight from the Latin Paulus, and must have come
into use directly from the Latin Bible, as in l. 671.—E. *hoost* ;
E. etc. *seint.*

15. Hl. *hath clappid.*

16. The Monk has just been telling his ' tragedies '—tragic stories
in verse *De casibus Virorum illustrium,* and was busy with the
story of Croesus, when the Knight interrupted with the prologue,
which is the criticism of the Monk's Tale by the Knight and the
Host. The allusion is to the last stanza of the Monk's Tale :

> Anhanged was Cresús the proudè king
> His royal tronè myghte him nat availle.
> Tragédie is noon other maner thing,
> Ne kan in singing cryè ne bewaille,
> But for that Fortune alwey wol assaile
> With unwar strook the regnes that been proude.
> For whan men trusteth hir, then wol she faille,
> And covere hir bryghtè facè with a cloude.

17. E. *also.*

25. Hn. Cp. *Youre tales doon vs no desport ne game.*

26. daun Piers by your name : Daun or Dan is derived from
L. *dominus* (lord). It was a title given to graduates of a medieval
university and to clerks in holy orders. Another title of respect
is ' Sir,' *cf.* Sir John in l. 44 and l. 54. ' Daun ' may be used

I pray you hertely, telle us somwhat elles,
For sikerly, nere clinking of your belles,
That on your brydel hange on every syde,
By hevene king, that for us allè dyde !   30
I sholde er this han fallen doun for sleep,
Althogh the slough had never been so deep ;
Than hadde your tale al be toold in veyn,
For certeinly, as that thise clerkes seyn,
" Where as a man may have noon audiénce,   35
Noght helpeth it to tellen his senténce."

playfully, as in " Daun Burnel the Asse," l. 542, and " daun Russel," l. 564.

Piers is the Old French form of Peter. It is found in Piers Plowman, and in the surname Pierce.

28. Hl. *gingling of the belles.*

30. By hevene king : by the King of Heaven. An instance of a feminine genitive in *-e* surviving from the *n-* declension in Old English, to which oxen (*masc.*) belonged. Other examples are : his lady(e) grace, and the Nonne Preest.

32. the slough : the mire of the road. Most roads were unpaved in Chaucer's age. In fact the macadamized road only dates from Macadam's endeavour to improve the surface of roads, *c.* 1810, and the tarred road-surface only dates from *c.* 1900.

33. I think this line should scan :

Than had(de) | your tal- | è al | be told | in veyn ;

Where the *-e* of ' tale ' is unelided before the vowel in ' al.' But others would scan :

Than had- | de your | tale al | be told | in veyn.

35-36. Where one cannot get a hearing, it is of no avail to speak. ' Sentence' here means opinion, matter. Chaucer attributes the saying to Solomon in his tale of Melibeus : " for Salomon seith, ' Ther as thou ne mayst have noon audience, enforce thee not to speke.' " Skeat refers to the apocryphal book of *Ecclesiasticus*, xxxii. 6 : " ubi auditus non est, non

And wel I woot the substance is in me,
If any thing shal wel reported be.
Sir, sey somwhat of hunting, I you preye.'

'Nay!' quod this Monk, 'I have no lust to pleye;
Now lat another telle, as I have toold.'   41

Than spak our Hoost with rudė speche and boold,
And seyde unto the Nonnės Preest anon,
'Com neer, thou preest, com hider, thou Sir John.
Telle us swich thing as may our hertes glade; (B. 4001)
Be blithė, though thou ryde upon a jade.   46
What though thyn hors be bothė foul and lene?
If he wol serve thee, rekkė nat a bene;
Look that thyn herte be murie everemo!'

'Yis, sir,' quod he, 'yis, Hoost, so moot I go,   50

effundas sermonem"; *cf.* English version, xx. 7: "A wise man
will hold his tongue till he see opportunity."

37. substance: the material of a good listener. 'Substance'
was a word used in the philosophy of the times where it was
applied to the inner and essential nature of a thing which 'stood
under' its outward qualities or 'accidents.'

44. Com neer: come nearer. 'Sir' in Sir John is a title not
only of knighthood, but of reverence for holy orders. The Host
however speaks, as l. 42 tells us, "with rude speche and boold."
He 'thous' Sir John, and uses the familiar imperative singular.
He thought himself richer and of higher social rank than the
Nun's Priest. There is no mention of the Nun's Priest, who is
in attendance on the Prioress, in the Prologue to the *Canterbury
Tales.* He is evidently included in the "and PREESTES three"
of l. 164. We gather from this passage that he rode upon a lean
and ungroomed old horse, and was treated jocularly and as an
inferior by the Host. But he tells a splendid tale, and he appears
to be a man of some learning.

49. E. Hn. *murie,* others *mery.*

50. so moot I go: so must I proceed, that is just what I must
do. 'So' very often introduces a phrase expressing a hope or
wish; but in this instance it appears to have a separate meaning:
in such a way. Others interpret: as I hope to walk.

But I be mirie, ywis, I wol be blamed.'
And right anon his tale he hath attamed,
And thus he seyde unto us everichon,
This sweetė preest, this goodly man, Sir John.

Explicit.

HEERE BIGYNNETH THE NONNE PREESTES TALE OF THE COK AND HEN, CHAUNTE-CLEER AND PERTELOTE

A pourė widwė, somdel stape in age,   55
Was whilom dwelling in a narwe cotáge
Beside a grovė, stondinge in a dale.
This widwe of which I tellė you my tale,
Syn thilkė day that she was last a wyf,
In paciénce ladde a ful simple lyf,   60
For litel was hir catel and hir rente.
By housbondrie of swich as God hir sente
She foond hirself, and eek hir doughtren two.
Three largė sowes hadde she and namo ;   (B. 4020)
Three kyn, and eek a sheep that hightė Malle.   65

55. **somdel stape in age** : lit. somewhat stepped in age, *i.e.*
somewhat advanced in years.—E. Hn. *stape*, others *stope*.

57. E. *greue*, Hn. etc. *groue*.

59. Since the day when she was last a wife, that is, since her
husband died. ' Thilke '=the ilke ; the same.

61. **hir catel and hir rente** : her property and her income. See
Note on Prologue to the *Canterbury Tales*, l. 373. The phrase
does *not* mean that she paid a small rent.

63. **She foond hirself** : she provided for herself. The verb
' find ' still has this as one of its meanings : *cf.* the firm does not
find supper if overtime is worked ; all found (of servants' wages,
meaning lodging, dress, etc., provided). Cf. *Pardoner's Tale*,
l. 246.

65. **kyn** : kine. The Ellesmere MS. reads ' keen,' which is a

Ful sooty was hir bour, and eek hir halle,
In which she eet ful many a sklendre meel ;
Of poynaunt sauce hir neded never a deel.
No deyntee morsel passed thurgh hir throte,
Hir diete was accordant to hir cote ;   70
Replecioun ne made hir nevere sik,
Attempree diete was al hir phisik,
And exercise, and hertes suffisáunce.
The goutė lette hir nothing for to daunce,
N' apóplexyė shentė nat hir heed.   75
No wyn ne drank she, neither whyt ne reed ;
Hir bord was served moost with whyt and blak,—
Milk and broun breed,—in which she foond no lak ;
Seynd bacon, and somtyme an ey or tweye,
For she was, as it were, a maner deye.   80
  A yeerd she hadde, enclosed al aboute
With stikkes, and a dryė dich withoute,

Kentish or south-eastern form. *highte Malle :* was called Molly,
short for Matilda.—E. *keen*, Hl. Hn. Cp. *kyn*.
  66. The widow's cottage would be a little thatched hut built
of timber, and the walls filled in with mud or clay. It would
probably have only one storey and two rooms, a " but and ben,"
a hall and bower as Chaucer calls them. The inner room would
be the bedroom and the outer room would be the living room of
the family. There were chimneys in Chaucer's times, but as a
primitive cottage like the widow's would be old-fashioned, it
would probably not have one, hence the sootiness of the interior.
She would burn wood, not coal.
  70. Her food was in keeping with her cottage, *i.e.* simple and
poor. 71. E. *Repleccioun*.
  74. The gout did not hinder her from dancing, *i.e.* she was not
troubled with gout.
  79. *Seynd bacon* : lit. singed bacon. One is tempted to think
that this means bacon hung and smoked in the rafters. But other
commentators say it means singed or broiled, where ' broiled '
means grilled or toasted. **Seynd** may mean fat, from O.F. **sain**,
lard.

In which she hadde a cok, heet Chauntècleer :
In al the land, of crowing nas his peer.   (B. 4040)
His voys was murier than the murie orgón   85
On messèdayes that in the chirchè gon ;
Wel sikerer was his crowing in his logge
Than is a clokke, or an abbey-orlogge.
By nature he knew eche ascencioun

83. heet Chauntecleer : (who) was called Chanticleer. This is
a traditional name given to the cock. Evidently it refers to his
power of crowing (chant-clear). ' Heet' like ' Highte' in l. 65
is a past tense of a verb *hoten*, to promise, or to be called. The
corresponding verb in Old English, *hātan*, had two past tenses,
hēt (active) called, and *hatte* (passive) was called. Confusion between
the two forms took place, and hence ' heet,' though it corresponds
to O.E. *hēt*, is passive in meaning ; and ' highte' appears to come
from an early O.E. form *heht*, Gothic *hathdit*.—E. Hn. *heet*, others
that hight.

85. orgon : The word organ was regularly used in the plural
because an organ consisted (and still consists) of several sets of
pipes. But this is not organs but ' orgon.' On the other hand
' gon' is plural, and as a verb it could hardly be applied to
singing, even to the stately march of an anthem. I am inclined
to translate the sentence : his voice was sweeter than the lovely
organ which plays in the church on festivals.

88. an abbey-orlogge : the great, public clock of an abbey.
Portable clocks with a mainspring date from the beginning of
the fourteenth century. The horologe or great clock, which had
weights for motive power (like a grandfather's clock), is an older
invention, and most of the great cathedrals and monasteries had
great clocks in the first half of the fourteenth century.—E. etc.
an, Hn. Cp. *any*.

89. He knew by nature (that is, it was innate knowledge and
not acquired from books) every degree of celestial longitude on
the celestial equator as seen in that village ; for when the equinoctial had moved round for fifteen degrees, he crowed so well
that it could not be bettered. This is one way of saying that
he crowed every hour.

The equinoctial line is the celestial equator—the imaginary

Of th' equinoxial in thilkė toun ;   90
For whan degrees fiftenė were ascended,
Than crew he, that it myghte nat been amended.
His coomb was redder than the fyn corál,
And batailled, as it were a castel-wall.
His bill was blak, and as the jeet it shoon ;   95
Lyk asure were his legges and his toon ;
His nayles whiter than the lilie flour,
And lyk the burnissht gold was his colóur.

    This gentil cok hadde in his governaunce
Sevene hennes for to doon al his plesaunce,   100
Whiche were his sustres and his paramours,
And wonder lyk to hym, as of colóurs ;
Of whiche the faireste hewed on hir throte
Was cleped fairė damoysele Pertėlote.   (B. 4060)

line which old astronomers traced on the celestial globe as a
parallel to the earthly equator. It is so called because when the
sun appears to cross it in spring and autumn, nights are equal
to days in length. 'Ascencioun,' literally, rising or ascent,
means that degree of the equinoctial which is rising above the
eastern horizon at any given moment. As the equinoctial is a
circle, it is divided into 360 degrees of celestial longitude, and
as it appears to revolve once every twenty-four hours, it must
move through fifteen degrees in every hour. The times at which
a given point on the equinoctial rises vary with one's longitude
on earth. Hence Chaucer adds "in thilke toun."—E. Pt. *he
crew*, Hl. *knew he*, others *he knew*.

   93. The description of the cock is fanciful, not realistic; like
a medieval picture of what a cock ought to be, rather than a
true picture of what he was.

   98. Hl. Cp. Pt. Ln. *burnischt*, E. etc. *burned*.

   102. as of colours: in colour. 'As' introduces the plural
and is meaningless.

   104. damoysele Pertelote: Partlet. A woman's name, O.Fr.
Pertelote, used as a name for a hen perhaps because of its likeness
to M.E. *pertrich*, partridge. 'Damoysele' must already have

Curteis she was, discreet, and debonaire,   105
And compaignáble, and bar hirself so faire
Syn thilkè day that she was seven nyght old,
That trewèly she hath the herte in hoold
Of Chauntècleer, loken in every lith ;
He lovede hir so, that wel was hym therwith.   110
But swiche a joye was it to here hem singe,
Whan that the brightè sonne bigan to springe,
In sweete accord, ' My lief is faren in londe ' ;
For thilkè tyme, as I have understonde,
Beestes and briddes koudè speke and singe.   115
    And so bifel that in the dawèninge
As Chauntècleer among his wyves alle
Sat on his perchè, that was in the halle,
And next him sat this fairè Pertelote,

been pronounced damsel, if ' faire ' was weak and dissyllabic
before the proper name, as I think it was.

108. That certainly she has the heart of Chanticleer in her
possession (who was) bound in every limb. ' Lith,' in Chaucer
as in O.E., is applied only to limbs and parts of the body. In
modern use its meaning is extended, and one can speak of the
lith of an orange, meaning a division or ' quarter.'

113. My lief is faren in londe : my beloved has gone away.
The first line of a song. Skeat found a verse of a song beginning
with these words in a MS. in Trinity College, Cambridge (R. 3,
19) and communicated it to the *Athenæum*, Oct. 24, 1896.

> My lefe is faren in lond
>   Allas ! why is she so?
> And I am so sore bound
>   I may nat com her to.
> She hath my hert in hold
>   Wherever she ryde or go
> With trew love a thousand-fold.

Chaucer must have been thinking of this song, for the words
" she hath the herte in hoold " of l. 108 are a repetition of l. 5.

116. Hl. *a*, E. Pt. *the*.

This Chauntécleer gan gronen in his throte,   120
As man that in his dreem is drecched soore.

  And whan that Pertélote thus herde him roore,
She was agast, and seyde, ' O hertè deere !
What eyleth you, to grone in this manére ?   (B. 4080)
Ye been a verray slepere ; fy ! for shame ! '   125

  And he answérde and seydè thus, ' Madame,
I pray you that ye take it nat agrief ;
By God, me mette I was in swich meschief
Right now, that yet myn herte is soore afright.
Now God,' quod he, ' my sweven recche aright,   130
And kepe my body out of foul prisóun !
Me mette how that I romed up and doun
Withinne our yeerd, wheras I saugh a beest
Was lyk an hound, and wolde han maad areest
Upon my body, and wolde han me deed.   135
His colour was bitwixè yelow and reed,
And tipped was his tayl and bothe his eres
With blak, unlyk the remenaunt of his heeres ;
His snowtè smal, with glowinge eyen tweye,—
Yet of his look, for feere, almoost I deye.   140
This caused me my groning doutèlees.'

  ' Avoy ! ' quod she, ' fy on you, hertèlees !
Allas ! ' quod she, ' for, by that God above !

123. E. *O herte*, Hn. Cm. etc. *herte*.
128. E. *me thoughte*.
130. **my sweven recche aright**: interpret my dream favourably, let my dream happen well.
133. **wheras**: where.   Where I saw a beast (that) was like
a dog.
134. **Was lyk**: that was like.   The relative pronoun is
omitted, as in l. 407.
135. E. etc. *and han had*, Hl. Cp. *and wolde han*.
139. Hl. Dd. *was smal*.
140. **Yet**: even now.

Now han ye lost myn herte and al my love. (B. 4100)
I kan nat love a coward, by my feith !   145
For certes, what-so any womman seith,
We alle desiren, if it myghtê be,
To han housbondes hardy, wise, and free,
And secree, and no nigard, ne no fool,
Ne hym that is agast of every tool,   150
Ne noon avauntour.   By that God above !
How dorste ye seyn, for shame, unto youre love
That anything myghte makê you aferd ?
Have ye no mannes herte, and han a berd ?

   ' Allas ! and konne ye been agast of swevenis ? 155
Nothing, God woot ! but vanitee, in swevene is.
Swevenes engendren of replecióuns,
And ofte of fume, and of compleccióuns,

148. hardy, wise, and free : bold, wise and generous, and discreet, neither a miser nor a spendthrift, nor one that is afraid of every weapon.

157-158. Dreams are produced by over-eating, and often by vapours and by excess of humours. ' Fume ' means the ' vapour ' which was supposed to rise from the stomach to the brain after excessive eating or drinking. ' Complecciouns ' are combinations of humours in which one humour predominates, and is therefore in excess.

In the medicine of Chaucer's age, which was derived ultimately from Hippocrates and Galen, diseases were supposed to arise because some cause upset the balance of humours in the body. There were supposed to be four humours or fluids in the body— melancholy, phlegm, blood, and bile. When the patient was healthy, the complexion of the humours was perfect ; but if one humour, it was thought, predominated, from some external cause such as eating or drinking unsuitable food, or eating or drinking to excess, then the excess of humour caused illness, one of the symptoms of which was found in dreams. One in whom bile predominated, for instance, was supposed to dream of yellow or red things ; one in whom the humour of melancholy predominated was supposed to dream of black. As Chanticleer

Whan humours been too habundant in a wight.
Certes, this dreem, which ye han met to-nyght,   160
Cometh of the gretė superfluitee
Óf your redė colera, pardee,
Which causeth fólk to dreden in hir dremes
Of arwes, and of fyr with redė lemes ;   (B. 4120)
Of redė beestes, that they wol hem byte,   165
Of conteks, and of whelpes, grete and lyte ;
Right as the humour of maléncolye
Causeth ful many a man in sleepe to crye,
For feere of blakė beres, or boles blake,
Or elles blakė develes wole hem take.   170

Of othere humours koude I telle also
That werken many a man in sleepe ful wo ;
But I wol passe as lightly as I kan.
Lo, Catoun, which that was so wys a man,

has dreamed of a beast whose " colour was bitwixe yelow and reed " but whose tail and ears were black, Partlet's diagnosis is that he is suffering from excess both of bile and melancholy, which must be purged away with suitable herbs. This is not a fanciful diagnosis, it was the ordinary medicine of the time. Its fun was not in its quaintness, but in the fact that it is attributed to a hen.

Our names for the temperaments go back to this medical doctrine of the humours. Excess of black bile was supposed to make a man melancholy; excess of phlegm, phlegmatic; excess of blood, sanguine; and excess of bile, choleric.

162. rede colera : bile. It is called ' red,' because it was supposed to make a man see yellow or red things.

163. E. Hn. Cm. *dreden*, others *dremen*.

165. E. *grete*, others *rede*.

169. E. Hn. Cm. Dd. *of blake beres*, Hl. Cp. *of beres or (and) of.*

174. Catoun : The allusion is to a school-book—the *Liber Catonis*, or Book of Cato—four books composed of 40, 31, 24 and 49 distichs or couplets, to which 57 maxims were prefixed. Cato's distichs was one of the oldest and most popular books of moral wisdom. It was written so long ago that it was ascribed

Seyde he nat thus, " Ne do no fors of dremes ? " 175
  ' Now, sire,' quod she, ' whan we flee fro the bemes,
For Goddes love, as taak som laxatyf !
Up peril of my soule, and of my lyf,
I conseille you the beste,—I wol nat lye,—
That bothe of colere and of maléncolye 180
Ye purgė you ; and for ye shul nat tarie,
Though in this toun is noon apothecárie,
I shal myself to herbes techen you (B. 4139)
That shul been for your hele, and for your prow ;
And in our yeerd tho herbes shall I fynde 185
The whiche han of hir propretee by kynde
To purgė you, binethe and eek above.

to Cato the Censor, but it probably belongs to the declining
years of imperial Rome, to the fourth century A.D. or even
earlier. It uttered its wisdom in the form of couplets in hexa-
meter verse, and because they were both wise and well expressed,
it was used as a Latin reader for well over a thousand years.
The miller says of the carpenter in his tale (A. 3227) :

> He knew not Catoun, for his wit was rude.

The saying alluded to : " Ne do no fors of dremes," comes
from one of Cato's distichs, bk. ii. 31 :

> Somnia ne cures, nam mens humana quod optat
> Dum vigilat, verum per somnum cernit id ipsum.

Pay no heed to dreams, for truly the human mind sees the
very thing in sleep, for which it hopes when awake.

176. E. *ye*, others *we* ; Hl. *thise*, others *the*.

177. as taak som laxatyf : ' As ' here introduces a sentence
containing an impérative, which is not so much a command as
a polite wish ; Just take (or pray take) some laxative. The
construction is peculiar to Chaucer.

181. for ye shul nat tarie : so that you shall not wait, since
you ought not to wait.

187. Both to purge you and to make you sick. Old herbals
specify of certain plants that they " work upwards and downwards."

Foryet nat this, for Goddes owenė love !
Ye been ful colerik of compleccioun :
Warė the sonne in his ascencioun   190
Ne fynde you nát repleet of humours hoote ;
And if it do, I dar wel leye a grote
That ye shul have a fever terciáne,
Ór an ague that may be your bane.
A day or two ye shul have digestyves   195
Of wormes, er ye take your laxatyves
Of lawriol, centáure and fumetere,
Or elles of ellėbor that groweth there,
Of katapucė, or of gaitrys béryis,
Of herbive, growing in our yeerd, ther méry is ;   200

189. **ful colerik of compleccioun :** very bilious in temperament.
190. **in his ascencioun :** in his rising, *i.e.* in the forenoon.
191. **humours hoote :** There was a fanciful belief that the qualities which entered into the four elements (earth, water, air, and fire), namely, hot, cold, moist, and dry entered also into the humours. Thus black bile was supposed to be composed of cold and dry, phlegm was cold and moist, blood was hot and moist, and colera or bile was hot and dry. Hence the hot humours were excess of blood or of bile.
195-200. The remedy consisted of (1) a digestive of worms, *i.e.* worms eaten to promote digestion, followed by (2) herbs taken as laxatives.
The herbs have been identified as follows, though the two last are uncertain :
   lawriol : spurge laurel, used to purge bile and phlegm.
   centaure : lesser centaury, used to purge bile and phlegm.
   fumetere : fumitory, used to purge melancholy.
   ellebor : black hellebore, used to purge melancholy.
   katapuce : caper-spurge, used to purge phlegm, melancholy and bile.
   gaitrys beryis : buckthorn berries, used to purge bile and phlegm.
   herbive : crowfoot or marsh trefoil, used to purge bile.
The point is that a medieval countrywoman who happened to

16 K

Pekke hem up, right as they grówe, and ete hem in ;
Be mirie, housbond, for your fader kin !
Dredeth no dreem ; I kan sey you namoore.' (B. 4159)
    ' Madame,' quod he, ' *graunt merci* of your loore,
But nathélees, as touching Daun Catoun,   205
That hath of wisdom swich a greet renoun,
Though that he bad no dremes for to drede,
By God! men may in oldè bookes rede
Of many a man, moore of auctoritee
Than evere Catoun was, so mòot I thee !   210
That al the révers seyn of his senténce,
And han wel founden by experience
That dremes been significaciouns
As wel of joye, as of tribulaciouns
That folk enduren in this lyf présent.   215
Ther nedeth make of this noon argument,
The verray preevè sheweth it, in dede.
    Oon of the gretteste auctours that men rede

be herb-wise could have prescribed exactly such herbs as these
for Chanticleer's complaint in her husband—though the worms
are purely ornithological.—*ther mery is* : where it is pleasant.

202. for your fader kin : for the sake of your father's kindred,
for your family's sake. An instance of the uninflected genitive
surviving from Old English. It originally occurred in nouns
expressing relationship such as : fader, mooder, brother, suster,
and doughter.

211. E. Pt. *this*, others *his*.

214. E. Hl. Cm. Cp. Ln. *as of*, others omit *of*.

217. The very test (of the matter, from literature) proves it
indeed.

218. Cicero, in *De Divinatione* i., ch. 27, first told the two
stories which follow. From him they were borrowed by Valerius
Maximus in his *Facta et Dicta Memorabilia*, i., ch. 8. From him
again they were borrowed as *exempla* or sermon-illustrations in
his book *Libri Sapientiae* by a Dominican friar named Robert
Holkot, who died in 1349.

It seems probable that " oon of the gretteste auctours that

Seith thus, that whilom two felawès wente
On pilgrimage, in a ful good entente,   220
And happed so they coomen in a toun,
Wher-as ther was swich congregacioun
Of peple, and eek so streit of herbergage,
That they ne founde as muche as o cotage   (B. 4180)
In which they bothe myghte ylogged be ;   225
Wherfore they mosten, of necessitee,
As for that nyght, departen compaignye ;
And ech of hem gooth to his hostelrye,
And took his logging as it woldè falle.
That oon of hem was logged in a stalle,   230
Fer in a yeerd, with oxen of the plough ;
That oother man was logged wel ynough,
As was his áventure or his fortúne,
That us govérneth alle as in commune.

   And so bifel that, longe er it were day,   235
This man mette in his bed, ther-as he lay,

men rede " is Valerius Maximus, who was more widely read
than Cicero in the Middle Ages; and it is not unlikely, as Miss
Petersen showed in her dissertation *On the Sources of the Nonne
Prestes Tale*, Boston, 1898, that Chaucer had read the stories
in the *Libri Sapientiae* of Holkot, who gives Valerius Maximus
as his source. Even if so, and the matter is one of conjecture,
the great author would still be Valerius, and not Holkot.—Hl.
auctorite, Cm. *autourys*, others *auctour*.

  225. E. *logged*.

  233. As was his luck, or his fortune, that is the ruler of us all
in common. Fortune, the Roman blind goddess of luck, good
or ill, was pictured by Boethius in his *Consolation of Philosophy*,
ii., 1-3, as being the fickle ruler of the earthly destinies of mankind. Chaucer translated the book as " Boece de consolacione
philosophie," and from him took over the conception. It was
not entirely a pagan conception, for Fortune was considered to
work under the direction of God, as did Nature in the sphere of
generation, so that Fortune is really the providence of God.

How that his felawe gan upon him calle,
And seyde, "Allas! for in an oxes stalle
This nyght I shal be mordred ther I lye!
Now help me, deerė brother, or I dye;   24c
In allė hastė com to me!" he sayde.

    This man out of his sleep for feere abrayde;
But whan that he was wakened of his sleep,
He turned hym, and took of this no keep;   (B. 4200)
Him thoughte his dreem nas but a vanitee.   245
Thus twyės in his sleping dremed he,
And attė thriddė tyme yet his feláwe
Cam, as him thoughte, and seide, "I am now slawe!
Bihoold my bloody woundes, depe and wyde;
Arys up erly in the morwė-tyde,   250
And at the west gate of the toun," quod he,
"A cartė ful of dong ther shaltow see,
In which my body is hid ful privėly;
Do thilkė carte arresten boldėly.
My gold caused my mordre, sooth to sayn."   255
And tolde him every point how he was slayn,
With a ful pitous facė, pale of hewe.
And trustė wel, his dreem he foond ful trewe;
For on the morwe, as soone as it was day,
To his feláwes inn he took the way,   260
And whan that he cam to this oxes stalle,
After his felawe he bigan to calle.

    The hostiler answérede him anon
And seydė, "Sire, your felawe is agon;   (B. 4220)

238. E. *oxes*, Hl. Cp. Ln. *oxe*.
240. E. Hl. Hn. *or*, Ln. *ar*.
244. E. *it*, others *this*.
254. Do thilke carte arresten: Have that cart stopped. The
construction is like the French: faites arrêter cette charette.
261. E. *oxes*, Hl. Cp. Ln. *oxe*.
263. E. Hn. *answerde*, Hl. Cp. *answered*.

As soone as day he wente out of the toun." 265
   This man gan fallen in suspecioun,
(Remembringe on his dremes, that he mette)
And forth he gooth, ne lenger wolde he lette,
Unto the west gate of the toun, and fond
A dong-carte, as it went to dongė lond, 270
That was arrayed in that samė wyse
As ye han herd the dedė man devyse ;
And with an hardy herte he gan to crye
Vengeance and justice of this felonye.
" My felawe mordred is this samė nyght, 275
And in this carte heer lyth gaping upright !
I crye out on the ministres," quod he,
" That sholden kepe and reulen this citee ;
Harrow ! allas ! heer lyth my felawe slayn ! "
   What sholde I moore unto this talė sayn ? 280
The peple outsterte, and caste the cart to grounde,
And in the middel of the dong they founde
The dedė man, that mordred was al newe.
   O blisful God, that art so just and trewe ! (B. 4240)
Lo, how that thou biwreyest mordre alway ! 285
Mordre wol out, that see we day by day ;
Mordre is so wlatsom, and abhominable
To God, that is so just and resonable,
That he ne wol nat suffre it heled be,
Though it abyde a yeer, or two, or three : 290

---

266. **gan fallen in suspecioun** : became suspicious.—E. etc.
in suspecioun, Hl. *in a s.*, Cp. Pt. Ln. *falle in grete s.*

270. E. *as it were*, Hl. Hn. Cm. *wente as it were*, Cp. Pt. Ln. *as he wente.*

276. **lyth gaping upright** : lies face-upwards and gaping, lies on his back with his mouth open.—E. Hn. Cm. *carte here he lith*, others *carte he lith.*

288. **resonable** : not ' reasonable ' in the human sense of being willing to listen to reason, but rather the source of all reason.

Mordre wol out, this is mý conclusióun.

　And right anon, minístres of that toun
Han hent the carter, and so soore him pyned,
And eek the hostiler so soore engýned,
That they biknewe hir wikkednesse anon,　　　295
And were anhanged by the nekkė-boon.

　Heer may men seen that dremes been to drede !
And certes, in the samė book I rede,
Right in the nextė chapitre after this,—
I gabbė nat, so have I joye or blis !　　　300
Two men that wolde han passed over see,
For certeyn cause, into a fer contrée,
If that the wynd ne haddė been contrárie,
That made hem in a citee for to tarie　　　(B. 4260)
That stood ful mirie upon an haven-syde.　　　305
But on a day, agayn the even-tyde,

---

291. E. Hn. Cm. *this*, others *this is*.

297. to drede : to be dreaded.　An example of use of the O.E. gerundial infinitive, *to drædanne,* which also frequently expresses purpose ;　*cf.* ' a house to let.'

299. In Cicero's *De Divinatione* this second story of Chaucer's precedes the first.　In Valerius Maximus's *Facta et Dicta Memorabilia* also the second story is the first, and moreover it is separated by several paragraphs.　In Holkot's *Libri Sapientiae* the stories are in the same order as Chaucer's, though not " in the nexte chapitre."　It was their order which led Miss Petersen to believe that Chaucer found the stories in Holkot.　This may be, but Holkot is not " oon of the gretteste auctours that men rede."　Chaucer may have reversed Cicero's and Valerius's order because he was writing from memory, which plays queer tricks.

301. that : the word is not grammatically necessary, and can be omitted.

305. haven : haven's.　' Haven ' was in Old English a feminine noun, *hæfen,* with its genitive case ending in *-e.*　This *-e* had disappeared in Chaucer's English, but the word had not yet acquired the possessive ending in *-es.*

The wynd gan chaunge, and blew right as hem leste,
Jolif and glad they wenten unto reste,
And casten hem ful erly for to saille.

But—herkneth!—to that o man fil a greet mervaílle;
That oon of hem, in sleping as he lay,   311
Him mette a wonder dreem, agayn the day ;
Him thoughte a man stood by his beddes syde
And hym comanded that he sholde abyde,
And seyde him thus : " If thou to-morwè wende,   315
Thou shalt be dreynt, my tale is at an ende."

He wook, and tolde his felawe what he mette,
And preyde him his viagè for to lette ;
As for that day, he preyede him to byde.

His felawe, that lay by his beddes syde,   320

308. E. *wente vn to hir reste.*

310. herkneth : The metre of the verse is perfect without this
address to the audience, which must belong, not to the original
composition, but to the poem as read aloud either by Chaucer
or by others. The hero of this story in Cicero is Simonides the
Greek lyrical poet, and the vision is the apparition of a man
whose body he had buried.

318. And begged him to delay his crossing. ' Lette ' here
means to hinder, O.E. *lettan*. The scansion of this line depends
upon whether one follows the Ellesmere MS. in omitting " for (to
lette)," or whether one inserts it, as do other and later MSS.
Most MSS. read *preyde*. The usual pronunciation of viage is
viáge : only once in Chaucer is it víage. Sisam would scan :

> And prey- | ede hym | his ví- | agè | to lette.

Skeat would scan :

> And preyde | him his | viág | -e for | to lette.

Pollard would scan presumably :

> And prey | -dè hym | his ví | -age for | to lette.

I prefer Skeat's scansion here.—E. Hl. Hn. omit, others insert *for*
(*to lette*).

Gan for to laughe, and scorned him ful faste ;
"No dreem," quod he, "may so myn herte agaste,
That I wol lettè for to do my thynges.
I settè nat a straw by thy dremynges, (B. 4280)
For swevenes been but vanitees and japes ; 325
Men dreme alday of owles or of apes,
Ánd of many a mazè therwithal ;
Men dreme of thing that nevere was, ne shal.
But sith I see that thou wolt heer abyde,
And thus forslewthen wilfully thy tyde, 330
God woot, it reweth me, and have good day ! "
　　And thus he took his leve, and wente his way.
But er that he hadde half his cours yseyled,
Noot I nat why, ne what mischaunce it eyled,
But casuelly the shippes botmè rente, 335
And ship and man under the water wente
In sighte of othere shippes it bisyde,
That with hem seyled at the samè tyde !
And therfore, fairè Pertèlote so deere,
By swiche ensamples oldè maistow leere, 340
That no man sholdè been too recchelees
Of dremes, for I seye thee, doutèlees,
That many a dreem ful soore is for to drede.
　　Lo ! in the lyf of Seint Kenelm I rede,— (B. 4300)

323. That I will delay doing my business.　327. Hl. only, *And eke*.
328. Men dream of something that never was, nor shall be ;
men dream of things which do not exist.
337. In Chaucer's day merchant ships sailed in a fleet for pro-
tection against privateers and pirates.—E. *it*, Hl. *ther*.
338. at the same tyde : at the same time.　Cp. Pt. *him*, Ln.
hem.
344. Saint Kenelm, at his death, was only seven years old.
When his father, King Kenulphus (O.E. *Cēnwulf*), died in A.D.
819 Kenelm succeeded to the throne of Mercia.　But his wicked
sister Cwenthryth envied him, and thought that if she could kill

That was Kenulphus sone, the noble king   345
Of Mercenrike,—how Kenelm mette a thing
A lite er he was mordred ; on a day,
His mordre in his avisioun he say.
His norice him expouned everydeel
His sweven, and bad him for to kepe him weel   350
For traison ; but he nas but seven yeer oold,
And therfore litel talė hath he toold
Of any dreem, so hooly was his herte.
By God, I haddė lever than my sherte
That ye hadde rad his legende, as have I.   355
　　Dame Pertėlote, I sey you trewėly,
Macrobeus, that writ th' avisioun

him she would obtain the crown. One day Kenelm dreamed a
dream. He dreamed that he saw a great tree standing beside
his bed, decorated with candles and lamps, and laden with
fruit and flowers. He dreamed that he climbed to the top of this
tree, but even as he did so, his dearest friend came and chopped
down the tree. Thereupon Kenelm was changed into a little
bird and flew up to heaven.

He told the dream to his nurse, but she saw in it only a prophecy
of his death.

Cwenthryth suborned Kenelm's guardian Ashberht, who slew
Kenelm in the wood of Clent, near Hales Owen, in Worcester-
shire, and she became queen. But murder will out. Cwenthryth
came to an evil end, and the martyred Kenelm became a saint.

346. Mercenrike : Mercia, the March of Wales.—E. etc. *Merten-
rike*, Ln. *Mercenrike*.

351. For traison : against treason.

352. litel tale hath he toold : he has taken little account, he has
paid little attention (to).

353. E. *is*, others *was*.

357. th' avisioun . . of the worthy Cipioun : The Vision of
Scipio, or *Somnium Scipionis*, was written by Cicero, and formed
the last part of his work On the State, or *De Republica*. It is an
account of a vision seen by Scipio Africanus Minor in 150 B.C.,
when staying in Africa with King Masinissa, during the campaign

In Affrike of the worthy Cipioun
Affermeth dremes, and seïth that they been
Warninge of thinges that men after seen.　　　360

　　And forthermoore, I pray you, looketh wel
In th' Oldè Testament of Daniel,
If he heeld dremes any vanitee.

　　Reed eek of Joseph, and ther shul ye see　(B. 4320)
Wher dremes be somtyme,—I sey nat alle—　365
Warninge of thinges that shul after falle.

　　Looke of Egipte the king, daun Pharaó,
His baker and his butiller also,

against Carthage. Scipio Africanus Major appeared to him in a
dream, and told him something of the life after death, the structure of the universe, of time, and the immortality of the soul.

The *De Republica* was lost, and the *Somnium Scipionis* only
was preserved because a commentary on it was written by
Macrobius, a Latin grammarian, who wrote at the beginning of
the fifth century A.D., where he discussed dreams, the immortality
of the soul, and the structure of the universe—subjects in which
the learned men of medieval times were profoundly interested.
It was probably the influence of Macrobius's commentary,
together with Boethius's *Consolation of Philosophy*, which made
so many medieval poets choose a dream as a vehicle for their
imagination, for example Dante's *Divine Comedy*, *The Romance
of the Rose*, by Guillaume de Lorris and Jean de Meun, and
Langland's *Vision of Piers Plowman*.

Macrobius's commentary on the *Somnium Scipionis* was well-
known to Chaucer, and he gives a summary of it in *The Parlement
of Foules*, ll. 29-84.

362. of Daniel: concerning Daniel. "Daniel had understand-
ing in all visions and dreams" (*Daniel* i. 17). He interpreted
the dreams of Nebuchadnezzar, and the handwriting on the wall
at Belshazzar's feast. He also saw visions, as the Book of Daniel
shows.

364. of Joseph: The dreams of Pharaoh's butler and baker,
and Joseph's interpretation of them are told in *Genesis* xl.

368. Cm. Ln. *boteler*, Pt. *botelere*.

Wher they ne feltė noon effect in dremes !
Whoso wol seken actes of sondry remes   370
May rede of dremes many a wonder thing.
    Lo, Cresus, which that was of Lydė king,
Mette he nat that he sat upon a tree,
Which signified he sholde anhanged be ?
    Lo heer, Andromacha, Ectóres wyf,   375
That day that Ector sholdė lese his lyf,
She dremed on the samė nyght biforn
How that the lyf of Ector sholde be lorn,
If thilkė day he wente into batáille ;
She warned hym, but it myghte nat availle ;   380

369. Wher : whether. A contracted form, as in l. 365.

370. seken actes : read the chronicles.

372. Cresus : Crœsus, the last King of Lydia, 560-546 B.C.
Famous for his wealth, he was defeated by Cyrus, King of Persia,
and overthrown. The account of his dream—" Upon a tree he
was "—is told by Chaucer in the last story in *The Monk's Tale*
(B. 3917-3956), which the knight interrupts with the opening
words of the prologue to *The Nun's Priest's Tale*, l. 1 of this
edition.

375. Andromache was the wife of Hector, the champion of
Troy, in Homer's *Iliad*. But this dream is taken not from
Homer, but from medieval tradition. It is found first in the
Latin prose ' history ' of Dares Phrygius, *De Excidio Troiae
Historia*, a fictitious history of the Trojan war which was
written some time in the dark ages by an unknown Latin and
attributed to Dares the Phrygian, a priest of Troy. Hence it
passed into the *Historia Troiana* (1287) of an Italian named
Guido delle Colonne, and from there into the M.E. alliterative
poem, *The Destruction of Troy*, and into Lydgate's *Troy Book*.

In the Middle Ages Homer was not the great name that he
now is. Few scholars knew Greek, and as the Latin nations
sympathised with the Trojans rather than with the Greeks, and
as Britain was supposed to have been colonised by Trojan
refugees, Homer was supposed to be biased, and Dares Phrygius
was supposed to be truthful.—E. etc, *Adromacha*.

He wentè for to fightè nathèles,
But he was slayn anon of Achilles.
But thilkè tale is al too longe to telle,—
And eek it is ny day,—I may nat dwelle ;   (B. 4340)
Shortly I seye, as for conclusioun,   385
That I shal han of this avisioun
Adversitee ; and I seye forthermoor
That I ne telle of laxatives no stoor,
For they been venimous, I woot it weel ;
I hem diffye ! I love hem never a deel !   390
    Now let us speke of mirthe, and stinte al this ;
Madamè Pertèlote, so have I blis !
Of o thing God hath sent me largè grace ;
For whan I see the beautee of your face
Ye been so scarlet-reed aboute youre eyen,   395
It maketh al my dredè for to dyen,
For, also siker as *In principio*,
Mulier est hominis confusio,—
Madame, the sentence of this Latin is,
" Womman is mannes joye and al his blis " ;   400

389. E. Hn. Cm. *venymes* (poisons), others *venymous* (poisonous).
395. The comb and wattle on poultry go bright red when they
are laying.
397. In principio : the opening words of the Gospel according
to St John, which were read or said by friars in their visits, *cf.*
Prologue to the *Canterbury Tales*, l. 254. Chaucer means that
the sentence which follows is gospel truth.
398. Tyrwhitt first pointed out that the original source of this
sentence was the *Speculum Historiale* of Vincent of Beauvais,
an outline of history written *c.* 1250. It is found in a conversation between the Emperor Hadrian and the philosopher Secundus
(xi. 71). Hadrian asks : Quid est mulier ? Secundus answers :
Hominis confusio, insaturabilis bestia, continua sollicitudo,
indesinens pugna, viri continentis naufragium, humanum man-
cipium. But by Chaucer's time ' hominis confusio ' had probably
become proverbiai.

For whan I fele a-nyght your softe syde
I am so ful of joye and of solás   (B. 4360)
That I diffyë bothe sweven and dreem ” ;
And with that word, he fleigh doun fro the beem,
(For it was day), and eke his hennes alle ;   405
And with a ‘ chuk ’ he gan hem for to calle,
For he hadde founde a corn, lay in the yerd.
Reál he was, he was namoore aferd.
He looketh as it were a grim leóun,
And on his toos he rometh up and doun ;   410
Him deigned nat to sette his foot to grounde.
He chukketh whan he hath a corn yfounde,
And to him rennen thanne his wyves alle ;
Thus, roial as a prince is in his halle,
Leve I this Chauntecleer in his pastúre,   415
And after, wol I telle his áventure.

Whan that the month in which the world bigan,
That highte March,—whan God first maked man,—
Wás compléet, and passed were also
Syn March was complet thritty dayes and two,   420

404. Hl. Cp. *fleigh*, Hn. Cm. *fley*, E. *fly*.

407. **lay in the yerd**: that lay in the yard. The relative
pronoun is omitted, as in l. 134.

408. **Real**: royal. An Old French and Spanish form of L.
regalis (regal).—E. etc. *Real*, Cm. Ln. *Royal*, cf. l. 414.

416. Hl. *his*, E. Cm. *an*.

418. According to Jewish and early Christian tradition the
earth was created at the time of the spring equinox.

419. Dd. *ipassed*, rest *passed*.

420. **Syn March was complet**: All MSS. read: “ Syn March
bigan.” Either Chaucer wrote ‘ syn March bigan ’ or the error
dates from the earliest copy of his poem. For the date indicated
is May 3rd, as the astronomical allusion which follows in ll. 424-5
makes clear. March was ended, and thirty-two more days had
passed, *i.e.* May 2nd had passed. The sun had run in the sign of
Taurus twenty-one degrees and ‘ somewhat more.’ As the sun

Bifel that Chauntècleer in al his pryde,   (B. 4381)
His seven wyves walkinge by his syde,
Caste up his eyen to the brightè sonne
That in the signe of Taurus hadde yronne
Twenty degrees and oon, and somwhat moore   425
And knew by kynde, and by noon oother loore,
That it was pryme, and crew with blisful stevene.
' The sonne,' he seyde, ' is clomben up on hevene
Fourty degrees and oon, and moore, ywis.
Madamè Pertèlote, my worldes blis,   430
Herkneth thise blisful briddes, how they singe !

appeared to enter the sign of the zodiac called Taurus on April 12th,
and moved through it at the rate of one degree a day (for there
are twelve signs or months to be run in the grand circle of 360°,
and each sign therefore covers roughly 30°), April 12th plus
21 days brings us to May 2nd, and the "somwhat more" is the
few hours after the opening of the next day.

May 3rd seems to have been considered an unlucky day by
Chaucer, as Pollard has pointed out. It was on May 3rd that
Pandarus persuaded Cressida (*Troilus and Criseyde*, ii. 56) and
it was on the night of May 3rd that Palamoun broke prison
(*Knight's Tale*, 1462).

I alter ' began' to ' was complet' for two reasons. The first is
that ' Syn March began,' etc., does not scan, and the presumption
is that there is a corruption somewhere in the line. The second is
that it does not make sense. If ' Syn March bigan ' is correct,
' Taurus ' should be Aries, and the date would be April 2nd. If
' Taurus' is correct, the phrase should be " Syn Aprille began,"
which is metrically harsh. There is no doubt, I think, about the
date May 3rd, " Syn March was complet" makes sense, scans, and
the corruption could be accounted for by the confusion of " was
complet" with "Was compleet" in the previous line.—All,
bigan, Hl. *tway monthes and dayes tuo*.

422. Hn. Cm. Cp. Dd. *him bisyde*, E. etc. *by his syde*.

427. pryme: nine o'clock in the morning.

429. On May 3rd the sun by 9 a.m. would have ascended just
over 41°.—Hl. *Twenty*.

And see the fresshè floures, how they springe !
Ful is myn herte of revel and solás ! '
  But sodeynly him fil a sorweful cas,
For ever the latter ende of joye is wo.   435
God woot that worldly joye is soone ago !
And if a rethor koudè faire endyte,
He in a cronicle saufly myghte it wryte,
As for a sovereyn notabilitee.
Now every wys man, lat him herknè me ;   (B. 4400)
This storie is also trewe, I undertake,   441
As is the book of Launcelot de Lake
That wommen holde in ful greet reverence.
Now wol I turne agayn to my senténce.

  A col-fox, ful of sly iniquitee,   445
That in the grove hadde wonned yeres three,
By heigh imaginacioun forncast,
The samè nyght thurghout the hegges brast
Into the yerd, ther Chauntècleer the faire
Was wont (and eek his wyves) to repaire ;   450
And in a bed of wortes stille he lay,
Til it was passed undren of the day,
Waitinge his tyme on Chauntècleer to falle ;
As gladly doon thise homicydes alle
That in await liggen to mordre men.   455

434. But suddenly a sad mischance befell him.
438. Hl. Cp. *cronique*, others *cronycle*.
442. the book of Launcelot de Lake : the romance of Lancelot
du Lac, an old French romance which told of the adventures of
Lancelot and of his love for Queen Guinevere.
444. E. *come*, Hl. etc. *torne*.
447. By deep imagination afore-thought, *i.e.* foretold by
Chanticleer's dream.
448. The same nyght : on the same night as Chanticleer had
dreamed his dream.—Hl. *hegge*. Brast : burst, suddenly appeared.   452. undren : the forenoon.

O falsė mordrour lurking in thy den !
O newė Scariot ! newė Genilon !
Falsė dissimulour, O Greek Sinon
That broughtest Troye al outrėly to sorwe !
O Chauntėcleer, acursed be that morwe,   (B. 4420)
That thou into that yerd flough fro the bemes !   461
Thou were ful wel ywarned by thy dremes
That thilkė day was perilous to thee.

But what that God forewoot, moot nedes be,—
After the opinion of certein clerkis.   465
Witnesse on hym that any parfit clerk is,
That in scole is greet altercacioun
In this mateere, and greet disputisoun,
And hath been of an hundred thousand men.
But I ne kan nat bulte it to the bren,   470

457. Three notable traitors are mentioned : Judas Iscariot ;
Ganelon, who betrayed Roland and his rearguard to the Moors
at Roncesvalles—an allusion to the *Chanson de Roland,* a great
early French epic poem ; and Sinon, who suggested the stratagem
of the wooden horse at Troy—an allusion to *Æneid* ii.

461. E. Hn. *flaugh,* Hl. *flough,* Cp. *fleyӡe,* Cm. *flaw.*

470. Chaucer was deeply interested in the dilemma of predestination and free will. If every occurrence is predestined, man
has no freewill. If man has perfect freewill, nothing affecting
human life is predestined. He cites authorities on the subject :—

Augustyn : St Augustine, the great father of the Church in
the west. He was an African (A.D. 354-430). In opposition to the
monk Pelagius, who asserted that man's will was free to choose
either good or evil, Augustine asserted the doctrine of predestination, that God foreordains all events, and that only by
the grace of God can man be ' elected ' to act according to His
will.

Boece : Boethius, the author of *De Consolatione Philosophiae,*
which Chaucer translated. Anicius Manlius Severinus Boethius
(A.D. 480-524) was a Roman senator, a Christian, who fell under
the displeasure of Theodoric, the Ostrogothic Emperor, and
was put to death. *The Consolation of Philosophy* was written

As kan the hooly doctour Augustyn,
Or Boece, or the Bisshop Bradwardyn,—
Whether that Goddes worthy forewityng
Streyneth me nedely for to doon a thing,—
(Nedely clepe I " simple necessitee ") ;   475
Or elles, if free choys be graunted me
To do that samè thyng, or do it noght,
Though God forewoot it, er that it was wroght ;

in prison.   In Book V he takes the view that there is evil in the
world, but it is subject to the providence of God.

Bradwardyn : Thomas Bradwardine (*c.* 1290-1349) lectured in
support of predestination at Oxford, and wrote a book entitled
De Causa Dei, in which he followed St Augustine in maintaining
the doctrines of God's foreknowledge and grace.   He became
Professor of Divinity at Oxford, Chancellor of the University,
and in the year of his death Archbishop of Canterbury.

473. Whether God's noble foreknowledge constrains me
necessarily to do an action—"necessarily" I call "simple
necessity" (or the inevitable) ;—or whether I possess free will
either to do or not to do that same action, although God foresaw
it before the action was performed ; or whether His foreknowledge only constrains me by "conditional necessity."

Chaucer states three possibilities: Predestination or determin-
ism, secondly, Free Will, and thirdly, a compromise between them
in which God's foreknowledge is limited, and man's will is only free
within certain limits.   He seems to incline to the third possibility,
which reconciles two opposite points of view.   The attempt to
reconcile the opposing points of view was made earlier by Boethius,
who, in the *Consolation of Philosophy* v. pr. 6 (the final chapter),
distinguished between "simple necessity," which implies the
absolute foreknowledge of God, and "conditional necessity,"
which implies God's foreknowledge of what will happen, but
allows free will to man—in other words God's providence guides,
rather than predestination determines.   God's foreknowledge of
events does not make them inevitable, for to God there is no
time, and all eternity is also the present.   It is a very thorny
subject.

474. E. *nedefully to doon.*

16 L

Or if his witing streyneth never a deel,
But by " necessitee condicioneel."   (B. 4440)
    I wil nat han to do of swich matéere,   481
My tale is of a cok, as ye may heere,
That took his conseil of his wyf with sorwe,
To walken in the yerd upon that morwe
That he hadde met the dreem that I you tolde.   485
Wommennes conseils been ful ofté colde ;
Wommannes conseil broghte us first to wo,
And made Adam fro Paradys to go,
Ther as he was ful mirie and wel at ese.
But, for I noot to whom it myght displese,   490
If I conséil of wommen woldé blame,
Passe over, for I seyde it in my game.
Rede auctours where they trete of swich mateere,
And what they seyn of wommen ye may heere.
Thise been the cokkes wordes, and nat myne ;   495
I kan noon harm of no womman divyne.
    Faire in the soond, to bathe hir mirily,
Lyth Pertélote, and alle hir sustres by,
Agayn the sonne, and Chauntécleer so free
Soong murier than the mermayde in the see ;   (B. 4460)
For Phisiologus seith sikerly,   501
How that they singen wel and mirily.

485. E. *of tolde*.
486. A proverb : Women's counsel is often cold counsel.
' Cold ' here means depressing, bad, as in " cold comfort."
488. E. *Adam out of*.
492. E. *seye*.
501. **Phisiologus :** The allusion is to the natural histories of
the Middle Ages.   They were called *Physiologus* after the earliest
book of the kind, which was written in Greek.   Such books were
very popular.   They described not only existing animals and
birds, but also imaginary and fabulous specimens such as the uni-
corn and the phœnix.   The description of the beast was followed
by its signification, the spiritual meaning which it typified.   Such

And so bifel that as he cast his eye
Among the wortes on a boterflye,
He was war of this fox that lay ful lowe.   505
Nothyng ne liste him thannė for to crowe,
But cryde anon, ' Cok cok ! ' and up he sterte,
As man that was affrayed in his herte ;—
For natureelly, a beest desireth flee
Fro his contrárie, if he may it see,   510
Though he never érst had seyn it with his eye.

This Chauntėcleer, whan he gan hym espye,
He wolde han fled, but that the fox anon
Seyde, ' Gentil sire, allas ! wher wol ye gon ?
Be ye affrayed of me that am your freend ?   515
Now certes, I were worsė than a feend,
If I to you wolde harm or vileynye.
I am nat come your conseil for t' espye,
But trewėly the cause of my comynge
Was oonly for to herkne how that ye singe;   (B. 4480)
For trewėly, ye have as mirie a stevene   521
As any aungel hath that is in hevene.
Therwith ye han in musik moore feelynge
Than hadde Boéce, or any that kan singe.

books are often called Bestiaries, and are found in all European
literatures.

Tyrwhitt says that Chaucer is alluding to a bestiary written
by a monk named Theobald in Latin hexameters and entitled
Phisiologus de naturis xii animalium, which contains a chapter
on sirens. Sirens live in the sea and sing with loud and beautiful
voice. They send to sleep the sailors who hear them by the
sweetness of their voices.

The bestiaries copied one another, and Chaucer may have
read of Sirens not only in a Latin Physiologus, but in French
and English books of the same kind.

522. E. omits *hath*.

524. Boece : Boethius also wrote a treatise on music in five
books, *De Musica*, which is still valuable for its information on

My lord your fader,—(God his soulè blesse !)   525
And eek your mooder, of hire gentillesse,
Han in myn hous ybeen, to my greet ese,
And certes, sire, ful fayn wolde I you plese.

But for men speke of singing, I wol seye—
So moote I broukè wel myne eyen tweye !—   530
Save you, I herdè nevere man so singe
As dide your fader in the morweninge.
Certes, it was of herte, al that he song ;
And for to make his voys the moorè strong,
He wolde so peyne him, that with bothe his eyen 535
He mostè winke, so loude he woldè cryen ;
And stonden on his tiptoon therwithal,
And strecchè forth his nekkè, long and smal.
And eek he was of swich discrecioun
That ther nas no man, in no regioun,   (B. 4500)
That hym in song or wisdom myghtè passe.   541

I have wel rad, in Daun Burnel the Asse
Among his vers, how that ther was a cok,

the music of the ancient world ; but whether he could sing,
history does not relate.

529. But since singing is mentioned, I will say this—as sure
as I hope to enjoy the use of my two eyes !—that, with the
exception of you, I never heard anybody sing as your father did
in the morning.—E. *wol yow seye.*

531. E. *herde I neuere man yet synge.*

542. **Daun Burnel the Asse :** the story of Burnel the Ass is told
in a long satirical poem of the twelfth century by a monk of
Canterbury named Nigel, who wrote in Latin elegiac verse
Speculum Stultorum—the mirror of fools. Burnel the Ass left
his master because he desired a longer tail, and with this end in
view visited the medical school of Salerno to procure the in-
gredients for his cure. On his way back, near Lyons, he was
set upon by dogs who bit off half his tail and upset his packet of
medicines, so he decided to go to the University of Paris to
become a scholar. On the way he met a travelling scholar
named Arnold who was also going to Paris to study. Arnold

For that a preestes sone yaf hym a knok
Upon his leg, whil he was yong and nyce,   545
He made him for to lese his benefice ;
But certeyn ther nis no comparisoun
Bitwix the wisdom and discrecioun
Óf your fader, and of his subtiltee.
Now singeth, sire, for seinté charitee !   550
Lat see, konne ye your fader countrefete.'

told him the story of the son of the parson and the chicken, in
order to advise Burnel not to provoke those who seemed low
and unimportant.

Gundulf, the son of a priest, found one day a hen and her
chickens in the barn, pecking corn, so he chased them out, and
in so doing he happened to hit one of the chickens with his stick,
which broke its leg. The chicken grew up to be a cock, and its
leg healed. Then came the great day when the bishop was going
to ordain Gundulf priest, so that he might succeed his father in
the living. Friends were invited to an evening party to celebrate
Gundulf's good fortune, and the wine circulated. It was
necessary to rise early so as to get to the city in time, and
Gundulf depended on the crowing of the cock. But the cock,
which years earlier had been the injured chicken, paid Gundulf
out by refusing to crow. So Gundulf slept too long, got up late,
arrived late in the city, and when he got to the cathedral the
ordination service was over, and the bishop had gone. Worse
still followed, for the father died. Gundulf was not ordained,
and had to become a poor beggar in the city.

Burnel studied at Paris but he was too stupid to learn anything, so he became a monk. But when he was proposing to
found a new order of monks, his old master, Bernard, appeared
and claimed him as a beast of burden.

The poem is published in Wright's *Anglo-Latin Satirical Poets
and Epigrammatists of the Twelfth Century* (Rolls Series, 1872),
vol. i., pp. 54-62.

544. E. *For that*, Dd. *That for*.

545. *whil he was yong and nyce*: whilst the priest's son was
young and foolish.

547. But certainly there is no comparison between the wisdom

This Chauntècleer his winges gan to bete,
As man that koude his trayson nat espye,
So was he ravisshed with his flaterye.

Allas ! ye lordes, many a fals flatóur   555
Is in your courts, and many a losengeour,
That plesen you wel moorè, by my feith,
Than he that soothfastnesse unto you seith.
Redeth Ecclesiaste of flaterye ;—
Beth war, ye lordes, of hir trecherye !   (B. 4520)
This Chauntècleer stood hye upon his toes   561
Strecchynge his nekke, and heeld his eyen cloos,
And gan to crowè loudè for the nones,
And daun Russell the fox stirte up at ones,
And by the gargat hentè Chauntècleer,   565
And on his bak toward the wode him beer ;
For yet ne was ther no man that him sewed.

O Destinee, that mayst nat been eschewed !
Allas, that Chauntècleer fleigh fro the bemes !
Allas, his wyf ne roughtè nat of dremes !   570
And on a Friday fil al this meschaunce.

O Venus, that art goddesse of plesáunce,
Syn that thy servant was this Chauntècleer
And in thy service dide al his powéer,

and discretion of your father and the subtlety of Gundulf's
cock.   The second ' of ' is ungrammatical.

556. E. *courtes*, Hl. *hous*.

559. Ecclesiaste : *Ecclesiasticus*, an apocryphal book containing the wisdom of Jesus the son of Sirach.   His advice is to be
found in ch. xii. 10-18 : " Never trust thine enemy," etc.

564. daun Russell : an old name for a fox.   It is a diminutive
of Fr. *roux* (russet).

571. on a Friday : Friday is traditionally an unlucky day.
Friday is in Latin the day of the planet Venus, *Dies Veneris*,
Fr. *Vendredi*.   The Germanic names, English Friday, Ger.
Freitag, ascribe the day to the Germanic Venus, Frige, the wife

Moore for delyt, than world to multiplye,   575
Why woltow suffre him on thy day to dye ?
   O Gaufred, deerè maister soverayn,
That, whan thy worthy king, Richárd, was slayn
With shot, compleynèdest his deeth so soore !
Why nadde I now thy sentence, and thy   (B. 4540)
   loore,   580
The Friday for to chyde, as diden ye ?—
For on a Friday, soothly, slayn was he.
Than wolde I shewe you how that I koude pleyne
For Chauntècleeres drede, and for his peyne.

   Certes, swich cry, ne lamentacioun   585
Was nevere of ladyes maad whan Ylioun
Was wonne ; and Pirrus with his streitè swerd

of Woden. Hence Chaucer's apostrophe to Venus.—E. Hn. Cm.
fil, others *fel*.

   576. Dd. *woltow*, E. *woltestow*, Hl. etc. *woldestow*.

   577. Gaufred : Geoffroi de Vinsauf, who wrote an art of
poetry, *Poetria Nova* (*c.* 1210), in a most rhetorical style. It
was a manual for poets, which devoted much attention to the
proper diction of Latin verse, and it contained examples of his
own. One of these, as Tyrwhitt first pointed out, was a specimen
in " the plaintive style " on the death of Richard Cœur de Lion,
who was wounded by an arrow on Friday, March 26, 1199,
whilst besieging a vassal in the castle of Chaluz, near Limoges
in Aquitaine. Geoffroi chides Friday in these words :

> "O Veneris lacrimosa dies ! O sidus amarum !
> Illa dies tua nox fuit, et Venus illa venenum."

O tearful Friday : O bitter planet. That day was thy night,
and that Venus thy bane.
   Chaucer is, of course, laughing at his bombast.

   580. E. *Why ne hadde I*.

   586. Ylioun : Ilium, the citadel of Troy.

   587. Pirrus : Pyrrhus, son of Achilles, who, according to
Virgil, *Æneid* ii. 469-558, slew Priam, king of Troy.—*with his
streite swerd :* with his drawn sword. Skeat pointed out that
' streite ' is a recollection, not of the passage about Pyrrhus and

Whan he hadde hent king Priam by the berd,
And slayn hym (as seith us *Eneÿdos*),
As maden alle the hennes in the clos   590
Whan they had seyn, of Chauntécleer, the sighte.
But sovereynly dame Pertélotè shrighte,
Ful louder than dide Hasdrubales wyf,
Whan that hir housbond haddè lost his lyf,
And that the Romayns haddè brend Cartáge,—   595
She was so ful of torment and of rage,
That wilfully into the fyr she sterte,

Priam, but of an earlier passage which tells how the Greeks,
having penetrated Ilium with the wooden horse, open the gates
and block the streets: *Æneid* ii. 333:

> stat ferri acies mucrone corusco
> Stricta, parata neci.

A line of drawn swords with flashing blades stands ready for
slaughter.

589. Eneydos: a Greek genitive dependent on *liber* understood, *Æneidos Liber*, the book of Æneas, the Æneid.

592. E. *sodeynly*, Hl. etc. *sovereynly*.

593. Hasdrubales wyf: the wife of Hasdrubal, King of Carthage, at the time when the Romans under the command of the
Scipio who, according to Cicero, saw the *Somnium Scipionis*,
captured and sacked Carthage in 146 B.C. Hasdrubal pleaded
for his life and was allowed to live; but his wife was so indignant
at his weakness that she threw herself into the flames with her
sons rather than live under Roman subjection. Chaucer also
alludes to the story in the Franklin's Tale (F 1399-1404).

Sisam says that Chaucer's source was St Jerome's *Contra
Jovinianum*, bk. i. (43), which seems probable, as this book is
referred to in the prologue of the Wife of Bath's Tale, D 673-5;
but the story was also told by Boccaccio in his *De Casibus
Virorum et Feminarum Illustrium*, bk. v.

594. Hn. Cm. Dd. *ylost*.

595. Hl. *ibrent*.

596. She: Hasdrubal's wife. This Hasdrubal, one might
add, was not the more famous brother of Hannibal, who lived
a century earlier.

And brende hirselven with a stedefast herte.
O woful hennes, right so cryden ye,
As, whan that Nero brendè the citée   (B. 6560)
Of Romè, cryden senatoures wyves   601
For that hir husbonds losten alle hir lyves
Withouten gilt,—this Nero hath hem slayn.
Now wol I tornè to my tale agayn.

    This sely widwe, and eek hir doughtres two,   605
Herden thise hennes crye and maken wo,
And out at dores stirten they anon
And syen the fox toward the grove gon,
And bar upon his bak the cok away,
And cryden, " Out ! harrow ! and weylaway !   610
Ha ! ha ! the fox ! " and after hym they ran,
And eek with staves many another man ;
Ran Colle our dogge, and Talbot and Gerland,
And Malkyn, with a distaf in hir hand ;

600. An allusion to the great fire at Rome in A.D. 64, when
Nero fiddled whilst Rome burned. Chaucer told the story of
Nero in the *Monk's Tale*, B 3653-3740 :

> He Romè brendè for his delicasie ;
> The senatours he slow upon a day
> To heerè how men woldè wepe and crie.

He says there that his source was Suetonius, but the story is also
told by Boethius, *Consolation of Philosophy* ii., met. 6.

  601. Hl. Hn. Cp. *the senatours.*

  604. E. *Now turne I wole.*

  605. E. *This*, Hl. Hn. Cm. Dd. *The* ; Hl. Cp. omit *eek.*

  609. And bar: and bore. A confused construction. It
should be ' And bere ' (and bear).

  613. Colle, Talbot, Gerland: names of dogs. Pollard says
" Colle is a shortened form of Nicholas." Talbot and Gerland
are more distinguished, and sound like the names of hounds.

  614. Malkyn : one of the daughters of the widow, who was
evidently engaged in spinning woollen or linen thread.

Ran cow and calf, and eek the verray hogges,   615
Sóre aferd for berking of the dogges
And shouting of the men and wommen eek;
They ronnë so, hem thoughte hir hertë breek.
They yelleden, as feendes doon in helle;
The dokes cryden, as men wolde hem quelle;   (B. 4580)
The gees, for feerë, flowen over the trees;   621
Out of the hyvë cam the swarm of bees;
So hidous was the noyse, *a ! benedicitee !*
Certes, he Jakkë Straw and his meynee
Ne madë nevere shoutes half so shrille,   625
Whan that they wolden any Fleming kille,
As thilkë day was maad upon the fox.
Of bras they broughten bemes, and of box,
Of horn, of boon, in whiche they blewe and powped,

615. E. Hl. omit *eek*.

616. E. Hn. Dd. *So fered*, Cp. Ln. Pt. *Sore aferde*, Cm. *Forfered*, Hl. *So were they fered*.

618. They ran so (fast), it seemed to them their heart would break (past subjunctive).

619. E. *yolleden*, others *yelleden*.

624. he Jakke Straw: that (notorious) Jack Straw. Jack Straw, together with Wat Tyler and John Ball, was a leader of the Peasants' Revolt in 1381. Chaucer was in London on June 13 when the mob entered the city, and for three days there was riot and disorder. Besides attacking the prisons and the Savoy, the peasants, assisted by the London apprentices, hunted down any Flemings they could find. The Flemings had been encouraged by Edward III to settle in London and Norwich. They were engaged in the cloth trade, and had aroused the antipathy of the English, who accused them of taking the bread out of their mouths.

At the end of the rioting, when court and city once again had the upper hand, Jack Straw was discovered hiding in an old house. He was beheaded, and his head was set on London Bridge, looking over Southwark to the Kent from which he came.

625. E. Ln. Dd. *shille*, Hn. and others *shrille*.

And therwithal they shriked and they howped ;   630
It semed as that heven sholdė falle.

Now, goodė men, I pray you, herkneth alle !
Lo, how Fortúnė turneth sodeynly
The hope and prydė of hir enemy !
This cok, that lay upon the foxes bak,   635
In al his drede unto the fox he spak,
And seydė, ' Sire, if that I were as ye,
Yet sholde I seyn,—as wis God helpė me,—
" Turneth agayn, ye proudė cherles alle !
A verray pestilence upon you falle !   (B. 4600)
Now am I come unto this wodes syde,   641
Maugree your heed, the cock shal heer abyde ;
I wol him ete in feith, and that anon." '

The fox answérde, ' In feith, it shal be don ' ;
And as he spak that word, al sodeynly   645
This cok brak from his mouth deliverly,
And heighe upon a tree he fleigh anon.

And whan the fox saugh that he was ygoon,
' Allas ! ' quod he, ' O Chauntėcleer ! allas !
I have to you,' quod he, ' ydoon trespas,   650
In-as-muche as I maked you aferd
Whan I you hente, and broughte out of the yerd ;

630. E. Hn. *skriked*.

632. Now, goode men : This is probably a truncated line :
ᴗ Nów | good mén | for *cp*. l. 675 where the final -*e* cannot be
sounded ; and, indeed, it is not written in all MSS. Another
instance occurs in l. 670.

634. prydė : The -*e* of pryde is not elided before ' of,' because
it occurs before the pause or cæsura.

638. as wis God helpe me : as certainly as may God help me,
as sure as fate.—E. Dd. *wolde*.

641. Now am I come unto : Now that I have reached.

648. Hl. *igoon*, others *gon, goon*.

652. E. Hn. Dd. *into this*, others *out of the*.

But, sire, I dide it in no wikke entente.
Com doun, and I shal telle you what I mente ;
I shal seye sooth to you, God help me so ! '   655
    ' Nay than,' quod he, ' I shrewe us bothe two,
And first I shrewe myself, bothe blood and bones,
If thou bigyle me any ofter than ones.
Thou shalt namoore, thurgh thy flaterye,
Do me to singe, and winke with myn eye ;   (B. 4620)
For he that winketh, whan he sholde see,   661
Al wilfully, God lat him never thee ! '
    ' Nay,' quod the fox, ' but God yeve hym mes-
        chaunce,
That is so undiscreet of gouvernaunce
That jangleth whan he sholde holde his pees ! '   665
    Lo, swich it is for to be recchelees,
And necligent, and truste on flaterye.
But ye that holden this tale a folye,—
As of a fox, or of a cok and hen,—
Taketh the moralitee, good-men ;   670
For Seint Paul seith that al that writen is,
To our doctrine it is ywrite, ywis ;
Taketh the fruyt, and lat the chaf be stille.

653. E. *of.*
658. Cp. Dd. *ofter,* E. Hl. Hn. *any ofter.*
660. Do me to singe, etc.: Cause me to sing and to close my
eye(s). 'Winke' means in Old and Middle English to blink, to
shut the eyes for a moment, as well as to wink, to close and open
the eyes. Here evidently it means to close the eyes, for when
the cock crowed, he " heeld his eyen cloos," l. 562.
669. As of a fox: about a fox. ' As ' introduces the phrase,
and is meaningless.
671. An allusion to St Paul's *Epistle to the Romans* xv. 4 :
" For whatsoever things were written aforetime were written
for our learning."
673. A proverb from threshing: take the corn and leave the

Now, goodė God, if that it be thy wille,
(As seith my lord), so make us alle good-men   675
And bringe us to his heighė blisse ! *Amen.*

Heere is ended the Nonne Preestes tale.

husks. In other words, hold fast that which is good, and forget
the rest.

674. These last three lines are a prayer. Chaucer frequently
ended a tale with something of this kind, *cf.* the prayer to St
Hugh of Lincoln at the end of the *Prioress's Tale*, and the
Pardoner's absolution at the end of his story (ll. 916-19). One
might add the conclusion of the Man of Law's Tale (B 1160-2) :

> Now Jesu Crist, that of his myght may sende
> Joye after wo, governe us in his grace,
> And kepe us alle that been in this place.

The general sense of this prayer is clear, but the words " As seith
my lord " are difficult to understand. A marginal note in the
Ellesmere MS. occurs also in the Hengwrt MS. : 'Dominus archi-
episcopus Cantuariensis.' This would appear to mean that the
then Archbishop of Canterbury, who from 1381-96 was William
Courtenay, had the habit of qualifying his prayers for salvation
with " if it be Thy will," a habit which, no doubt, would have
met with the approval of Thomas Bradwardine, Archbishop of
Canterbury in 1349.

On the other hand, 'my lord' may stand for my Lord, or
as we should now say " our Lord "; cf. *Prologue*, l. 47, where
' his lordes' seems to mean, from the context, our Lord's. In
this case the allusion is to our Lord's words in *St John* vi. 38-39 :
" For I came down from heaven, not to do mine own will, but
the will of him that sent me.   And this is the Father's will which
hath sent me, that of all which he hath given me I should lose
nothing, but should raise it up again at the last day."

After writing this note I find that Patterson had already
suggested a similar interpretation : " The natural interpretation
of the words 'if that it be thy wille, As seith my lord' is that
they refer to the words of Our Lord, ' Thy will be done,' in the
Lord's Prayer."   I think ' my lord ' means ' Our Lord.'

675. Hl. Ln. Pt. *good*, E. etc. *goode*.

THE PARDONER'S TALE

*The wordes of the Hoost to the Phisicien and
the Pardoner*

OUR Hoostė gan to swere as he were wood ;
' Harrow ! ' quod he, ' by nayles, and by blood !
This was a fals cherl and a fals justise !
As shameful deeth as herte may devyse
Come to thise juges, and hir advocatz !   5
Algate this sely mayde is slayn, allas !
Allas ! too deerė boughtė she beautee !
Wherfore I seye alday, as men may see,
That yiftes of Fortúne or of Natúre
Been cause of deeth to many a creäture.   10
Hir beautee was hir deeth, I dar wel sayn ;
Allas ! so pitously as she was slayn !

1. Ln. *Oste*, others *hoost, ost*.

4. The allusion is to the story of Appius and Virginia which
had just been told by the Doctor of Physic. In this tale the
Roman maiden Virginia is killed by her father to save her from
the unholy grasp of the unjust judge, Appius Claudius, who slew
himself in prison to prevent his trial and condemnation.

5. The rime of *advocatz : allas* implies that the pronunciation
here at any rate, was advocaas—

Instead of ll. 5-6, many MSS. (including Hl. Cp. Ln.) have
these lines :

> So fall upon his body and his bones,
> The devil I bekenne him al at ones.

5. E. *thise false Iuges*.

9. **yiftes of Fortune or of Nature** : gifts of Fortune or Nature,
wealth or beauty.—E. Hn. *and*, others *or*.

11-12. only in Hl. Cp. Ln., others omit.

124

Of bothè yiftes that I speke of now
Men han ful oftè moorè harm than prow.   (C. 300)
　　' But trewèly, myn owenè maister deere,   15
This is a pitous talè for to heere ;
But nathèlees, passe over ; is no fors ;
I pray to God, so save thy gentil cors,
And eek thyn urinals and thy jordanes,
Thyn Ypocras, and eek thy Galianes,   20
And every boyst ful of thy letuarie ;
God blesse hem, and our lady seintè Marie !
So moot I theen, thou art a proprè man,
And lyk a prelat, by seint Ronyan !
Seyde I nat wel ? I kan nat speke in terme ;   25
But wel I woot thou doost myn herte to erme

14. E. *moore for harm.*
17. is no fors : it does not matter.
19. thyn urinals and thy jordanes : your medical vessels and
bottles. A 'jordan' appears to have been originally the name
given to the bottles in which pilgrims brought back water from
the river Jordan, but in the Elizabethan Age it meant a chamber-
pot.
20. Thyn Ypocras, and eek thy Galianes : your Hippocrateses
and your Galens. It will be remembered that the Doctor well
knew (Prologue, l. 431) :

　　　　Olde Ypocras, Haly, and Galien.

Hippocrates and Galen were distinguished physicians of antiquity. Here their names may refer to their works, or to remedies
called after them. ' Ypocras ' was also a name given to spiced
wine.
21. E. Hn. Hl. *boyste*, Cp. Pt. Ln. *box.*
22. E. *seint.*
24. seint Ronyan : This appears to be a popular perversion of
the name of St Ninian. There was a Saint Ronan, a minor
Scottish saint, who lived in the eighth century ; but it is not
likely that his fame had reached the Host of Southwark, or
Chaucer in London.

That I almost have kaught a cardinacle.
By *corpus* bones ! but I have triácle,
Or elles a draughte of moyste and corny ale,
Or, but I heere anon a mirie tale,   30
Myn herte is lost, for pitee of this mayde.
Thou *bel amy*, thou Pardoneer,' he sayde,
' Telle us som mirthe, or japes, right anon ! '
    ' It shal be doon,' quod he, ' by seint Ronyon !
' But first,' quod he, ' heer at this alé-stake   35
I wol bothe drinke and eten of a cake.'   (C. 321)
    And right anon the gentils gonne to crye,
' Nay ! lat him telle us of no ribaudye ;
Telle us som moral thing, that we may leere
Som wit, and thanné wol we gladly heere.'   40
    ' I graunte, y-wis,' quod he, ' but I moot thinke
Upon som honest thing, whil that I drinke.'

Heere folweth the Prologe of the Pardoner's Tale

    ' Lordings,' quod he, ' in chirches whan I preche,
I peyné me to han an hauteyn speche,
And ringe it out as round as gooth a belle,   45
For I kan al by roté that I telle.
My theme is alwey oon, and evere was,—
" *Radix malorum est Cupiditas.*"

27. E. Hn. *cardynacle*, others *cardiacle*.
28. By *corpus* bones : A mixture of two oaths : by Corpus
Domini and by Christes bones.   The Host is not an educated man,
as his malapropism of cardinacle for cardiacle shows.
29. moyste and corny : new and strong.
36. a cake : a loaf, not a cake in the modern meaning of the
word.
43. E. *chirches*, Hl. etc. *chirche*.
45. And speak in a resonant voice continuously, like a bell.

First, I pronounce whennes that I come,
And than my bulles shewe I, alle and some ;   50
Our lige lordes seel on my patente,
That shewe I first, my body to warente,
That no man be so boold, ne preest, ne clerk,
Me to destourbe of Cristes hooly werk ;
And, after that, than telle I forth my tales.   55
Bulles of popes and of cardinales,
Of patriarks and bishoppes I shewe,
And in Latýn I speke a wordes fewe
To saffron with my predicacioun,
And for to stire hem to devocioun ;   60

---

49. I tell first where I come from. The Pardoner came from
Rome, Prologue, l. 671. But he may have been pictured as a
lying impostor with forged credentials. Those interested in
Pardoners should read Jusserand, *English Wayfaring Life in the
Middle Ages*, Part III, ch. ii.

There was another pope at Avignon in this period of the Great
Schism (1378-1417), but in England the French pope was not
recognised. First the Pardoner showed his ' bulls.' These,
presumably, were copies of papal bulls authorising the sale of
indulgences. Then he showed his ' patente' or papal commission, sealed by his " lige lord." His papal commission would
authorise him to sell indulgences on behalf of the convent or
hospital of Rouncival, Charing Cross. The seal referred to might
be the papal seal, which would certainly be attached to the
' patente,' but as a pardoner could only operate in a diocese
with the permission of the local bishop, l. 51 may mean that the
patent contained the bishop's seal, or as ' lige lord ' usually refers
to the king, it may mean that his patent was approved by the
king. Then he showed the edicts of ecclesiastical authorities
on the question of indulgences, and quoted a few words in Latin
in order to flavour his discourse. Then when he had convinced his
congregation that he was an important and authoritative individual, he produced his sham relics.

59. E. *saffron*, Hl. etc. *savore*.
60. E. Hl. Hn. *hem*, others *men*.

16 M

Than shewe I forth my longė cristal stones
Y-crammed ful of cloutes and of bones,—
Reliks been they, as wenen they echoon.
Thanne have I in latoun a sholder-boon
Which that was of an hooly Jewes sheep.   65
    "Good-men," seye I, "taak of my wordes keep ;
If that this boon be wasshe in any welle,
If cow, or calf, or sheep, or oxė swelle
That any worm hath ete, or worm ystonge,
Taak water of that welle and wassh his tonge,   70
And it is hool anon ; and forthermoor
Of pokkes, and of scabbe, and every soor,
Shal every sheep be hool, that of this welle
Drinketh a draughte. Taak kepe eek what I telle :
If that the good-man that the beestes oweth   75
Wol every wyke, er that the cok him croweth,   (c. 362)
Fásting, drinken of this welle a draughte,
As thilkė hooly Jew oure eldres taughte,
His beestes and his stoor shal multiplye.
And, sires, also it heeleth jalousye,   80
For though a man be falle in jalous rage,
Lat maken with this water his potáge,

61. cristal stones : hollow pieces of pure quartz, or glass
flasks, in which the relics were carried, *cf*. Prologue, l. 700 :
" And in a glass he hadde pigges bones."
64. latoun : brass, in a brass box.
66. Hl. Pt. Cm. *Good men*, E. Hn. Cp. *Goode men*.
69. Which has eaten any worm, or a snake has stung. ' Worm '
means snake, cf. *Midsummer Night's Dream* iii. 2, 71 : " Could
not a worm, an adder, do so much ? "
76. er that the cok him croweth : lit. before the cock crows for
him, *i.e.* before cock-crow.
77. E. *drynke*.
80. E. Hn. *sire*, others *sires*, *sirs*.

And never shal he moore his wyf mistriste,
Though he the sooth of hir defaute wiste,—
Al had she taken preestes two or three. 85
   Heer is a mitayn eek, that ye may see ;
He that his hond wol putte in this mitayn,
He shal have multiplying of his grain,
Whan he hath sowen, be it whete or otes,
So that he offre pens, or elles grotes. 90
Good-men and wommen, o thing warne I you,
If any wight be in this chirche now
That hath doon sinne horrible, that he
Dar nat, for shame, of it y-shriven be, (c. 380)
Swich folk shal have no power ne no grace 95
To offren to my reliks in this place ;
And whoso fyndeth hym out of swich blame,
They wol come up and offre in Goddes name,
And I assoille hem by th' auctoritee
Which that by bulle ygraunted was to me." 100
   By this gaude have I wonne, yeer by yeer,
An hundred mark sith I was Pardoneer.
I stonde lyk a clerk in my pulpet,
And whan the lewed peple is doun yset,
I preche so as ye han herd bifore, 105
And telle an hundred false japes moore ;

---

91. E. Hn. *Goode*, others *And*.

95. **have no power ne no grace** : neither be able (of their own strength) nor have favour (from God).

97. **out of** : without, free from.—E. *fame*, others *blame*.

102. A hundred marks was a large income in those days. A mark was valued at 13s. 4d., so that 100 marks would be worth £66. 13s. 4d. A regular clergyman received about £5 a year. We should have to multiply by 30 to translate them into present values, but at that rate the pardoner was earning, not entirely for himself of course, some £2000 a year.

Than peyne I me to strecchè forth my nekke,
And est and west upon the peple I bekke,
As dooth a douvè, sittinge on a berne.
Myn hondes and my tongè goon so yerne,   110
That it is joy to see my bisinesse.
  Of avarice and of swich cursednesse   (C. 400)
Is al my preching, for to make hem free
To yeven hir pens, and namely unto me.
For myn entente is nat-but for to winne,   115
And nothyng for correccioun of sinne.
I rekkè nevere, whan that they been beryed,
Though that hir soules goon a-blakèbéryed !
  For certes, many a predicacioun
Comth oftè tyme of yvel entencioun ;   120
Som for plesaunce of folk and flaterye,
To been avaunced by ipocrisye ;
And som for veynè-glorie, and som for hate.
For whan I dar noon oother weyes debate,
Than wol I stinge him with my tongè smerte   125
In preching, so that he shal nat asterte
To been defamed falsly, if that he
Hath trespased to my bretheren or to me.
For though I tellè noght his proprè name,
Men shal wel knowè that it is the same   130
By signes, and by othere circumstances.
Thus quyte I folk that doon us displesánces ;   (C. 420)
Thus spitte I out my venim under hewe
Of hoolinesse, to semen hooly and trewe.

107. E *the*, Hl. Cm. Cp. Ln. *my, myn*.

117. E. Hl. *whan they been*.

118. Though their souls go a-blackberrying, *i.e.* wander at
will. He means that his concern is only with the living who
have pence to give. Masses for the dead are not his business.

125. him : a member of my congregation.

But, shortly, myn entente I wol devyse,— 135
I preche of no thing but for coveityse;
Therfore my theme is yet, and ever was,
" *Radix malorum est Cupiditas.*"
Thus kan I preche agayn that samė vice
Which that I use, and that is avarice ; 140
But though myself be gilty in that sinne
Yet kan I maken oother folk to twinne
From avarice, and soorė to repente.
But that is nat my principal entente ;
I prechė no thing but for coveityse. 145
Of this mateer it oughte ynough suffise.

Than telle I hem ensamples many oon
Of oldė stories longė tyme agoon :
For lewed peple loven tales olde ;
Swiche thinges kan they wel reporte and holde. 150
What ! trowė ye, the whiles that I may preche,
And winnė gold and silver for I teche, (c. 440)
That I wol live in poverte wilfully ?
Nay, nay, I thoughte it never, trewėly,
For I wol preche and begge in sondry londes ; 155

147. ensamples : examples (of fiction). Books of *exempla*, or
sermon-illustrations, were quite common in the Middle Ages.
One of the first books of this kind was Petrus Alphonsus's
Disciplina Clericalis (*c.* 1110). Robert Holkot's *Libri Sapientiae*
(*c.* 1340) was a famous English book of this kind in Chaucer's age.
Perhaps the most famous of all was the anonymous *Gesta
Romanorum* (*c.* 1300).

151. E. Pt. *the whiles*, Hl. *whiles*, Cp. Ln. *whiles that*, Hn. *that
whiles*, Cm. *that whilis that.*

152. for I teche : because I teach, by my teaching. ' For '
stands for ' for that.'

153. in poverte wilfully : in poverty deliberately, voluntarily
in poverty. As, for example, did the hermits, and the friars in
their early days.

I wol nat do no labour with myn hondes,
Ne makė baskettes, and live therby,
Bicause I wol nat beggen ydelly.
I wol noon of the Apostles countrefete ;
I wol have moneye, wollė, chese and whete,   160
Al were it yeven of the povereste page,
Or of the povereste widwe in a village,
Al sholde hir children stervė for famyne.
Nay, I wol drinkė licour of the vyne,
And have a joly wenche in every toun.   165
    But herkneth, lordings, in conclusioun ;
Your lyking is that I shal telle a tale.
Now have I dronke a draughte of corny ale,
By God, I hope I shal you telle a thing
That shal, by resoun, been at your lyking ;   170
For though myself be a ful vicious man,
A moral tale yet I you tellė kan,   (c. 460)
Which I am wont to prechė, for to winne.
Now hoold your pees, my tale I wol biginne.'

Heere bigynneth the Pardoners Tale

In Flaundres whilom was a compaignye   175
Of yongė folk, that haunteden folýe,

159. The Apostles were sent forth to preach without money
and without food, cf. *St Mark* vi. 7-10.

160. There is a malicious description of the begging of two
friars, accompanied by a strong servant, near the beginning
of *The Summoner's Tale*, D. 1736-1760. They received gifts in
kind. One friar begged, the other wrote down the names of the
donors as if the friars would pray for them—and rubbed them out
afterwards, and their strong henchman carried away the gifts in
a sack. But it is not certain that the Pardoner was a friar. He
might even be a layman. Chaucer does not say.

176. that haunteden folye : who practised folly, who were given
to foolishness.

As riot, hasard, stewes and tavérnes,
Whereas with harpes, lutes and giternes,
They dauncen and pleyen at dees, bothe day and
    nyght,
And eten also, and drinken over hir myght,   180
Thurgh which they doon the devel sacrifyse
Within that develes temple, in cursed wyse,
By superfluitee abhominable.
Hir othes been so grete and so dampnáble
That it is grisly for to heere hem swere.   185
Our blessed Lordes body they to-tére —
Hem thoughte that Jewes rente him noght ynough —
And ech óf hem at otheres sinnë lough.
And right anon than coomen tombesteres
Fetis and smale, and yongë fruytesteres,   190
Singers with harpes, baudes, waferéres,
Whiche been the verray develes officéres,   (c. 480)
To kindle and blowe the fyr of lecherye,
That is annexed unto glotonye.
The hooly writ take I to my witnesse   195

177. E. Hl. *stywes*.
180. over hir myght: lit. above their strength, to excess.
182. that develes temple: that tavern.
183. By means of their abominable excess.
186. They seemed to tear Christ's body in pieces by swearing
by His soul, heart, bones, and body, wounds, nails, etc.; cf.
Parson's Tale, 591.
186. Hl. *blisful*, E. Hn. Cm. Dd. *blissed*.
187. Hl. Cp. Ln. omit *that*.
189. tombesteres: female acrobats or tumblers, though the
word means also dancing girls, because such entertainers performed both dancing and tumbling. The ending *-stere* is an old
feminine ending, which is no longer living, but it still survives in
spinster, and in the personal names Baxter, Webster, etc.
191. wafereres: cake-sellers, sellers of wafers and ginger-bread.

That luxurie is in wyn and dronkenesse.

   Herodes (who-so wel the stories soughte),
Whan he of wyn repleet was at his feeste,
Right at his owenė table, he yaf his heeste
To sleen the Baptist, John, ful giltėlees.   200

   Senek eek seith a good word, doutėlees ;
He seith he kan no differencė fynde
Bitwix a man that is out of his mynde
And a man which that is dronkelewe,
But that woodnesse, yfallen in a shrewe,   205
Persévereth lenger than dooth dronkenesse.

   O glotonyė, ful of cursednesse ;
O causė first of our confusioun ;
O original of our dampnacioun ;   (c. 500)
Till Crist hadde bought us with his blood agayn !   210
Ló, how deerė, shortly for to sayn,
Abought was thilkė cursed vileynye !

196. Cf. *Ephesians* v. 18 : Et nolite inebriari vino, in quo est luxuria ; And be not drunk with wine, wherein is excess.

197. **who-so wel the stories soughte** : if anyone were to search well the histories, if anyone should read the stories about him. The allusion is to the death of John the Baptist, cf. *St Matt*. xiv. 3-12 ; *St Mark* vi. 17-29.

198. E. etc. *was repleet*.

201. Tyrwhitt pointed out first that the " good word " said by Seneca is to be found in his *Epistles*, 83 : Extende in plures dies illum ebrii habitum : numquid de furore dubitabis ? nunc quoque non est minor, sed brevior. Prolong the state of a drunken man for several days, and will you have a doubt about his madness ?   Also his state is not less in degree, only shorter (than madness).—Cp. Ln. *Senek seith eek*, others omit *eek*.

205. Except that madness, when it has befallen a wicked man, lasts longer than drunkenness.—E. Hl. *fallen*, Hn. Cm. *yfallen*.

208. O first cause of our being put to shame. The Pardoner's doctrine is that the eating of the fruit by Eve and Adam was gluttony, and its result was the fall of man.

Corrupt was al this world for glotonye.

    Adam our fader, and his wyf also,

Fro Paradys, to labour and to wo   215

Were driven for that vice, it is no drede,—

For whyl that Adam fasted, as I rede,

He was in Paradys, and whan that he

Eet of the fruyt defended on the tree,

Anon he was outcast to wo and peyne.   220

    O glotonye, on thee wel oughte us pleyne !

O, wiste a man how many maladyes

Folwen of excesse and of glotonyes,

He woldè been the moorè mesurable

Of his dietè, sittinge at his table !   225

Allas ! the shortè throte, the tendrè mouth

Maketh that—est and west and north and south,

In erthe, in eir, in water,—men to swinke

214. The best MSS. here have a marginal note comparing St Jerome's treatise against Jovinian : *Ieronimus contra Iovinianum* : Quamdiu jejunavit Adam, in paradiso fuit : comedit et ejectus est : [ejectus] statim duxit uxorem. So long as Adam fasted, he remained in paradise. He ate and was cast out. Cast out, immediately he took a wife. This book is doubtless what Chaucer had in mind when writing ll. 214-220. Moreover, it was this book, which, says Chaucer, caused the deafness of the Wife of Bath, because when her fourth husband read it aloud, she tore a page out, which so enraged him that he gave her a box on the ear (D. 666-686).

219. the fruyt defended : the forbidden fruit.

226. Alas ! the short throat and tender mouth makes men toil—in every direction, in earth, air, and water—to procure dainty food for a glutton.

227. 'Maketh that' is a confused construction ; maketh that men swinke, and maketh men to swinke. The construction and, I think, the line would be better without 'that.' Skeat avoids the difficulty by reading "to-swinke," which means, he says, "labour greatly." But this is doubtful.

228. E. Hl. *man*, others *men*.

To gete a glotoun deyntee mete and drinke ! (c. 520)
Of this mateere, O Paul, wel kanstow trete !   230
' Mete unto wombe, and wombe eek unto mete,
Shal God destroyen bothe,' as Paulus seith.
Allas ! a foul thing is it, by my feith,
To seye this word, and fouler is the dede
Whan man so drinketh of the white and rede,   235
That of his throte he maketh his privee,
Thurgh thilkè cursed superfluitee.

    Th' Apostel weping seith ful pitously,
' Ther walken many of whiche you toold have I,
I seye it now, wepyng with pitous voys,   240
Thér been enemys of Cristes croys,
Of whiche the ende is deeth, wombe is hir god.'
Ó wombe ! O bely ! O stinking cod !
How greet labóur and cost is thee to fynde !
Thise cookes, how they stampe, and streyne, and
    grynde,

231. A quotation from 1 *Corinthians* vi. 13, as a note in the margin of several MSS. indicates.

235. the white and rede : the white wine and the red.

239. A quotation from *Philippians* iii. 18, as a manuscript note indicates. Chaucer used the passage again in *The Parson's Tale*, 820.

241. Ther been : There are.—Hl. *thay*, others *Ther*.

242. wombe is hir god : their stomach is their god.

243. Hl. *o stynking is thi cod*, E. etc. omit *is thy*.

246. is thee to fynde : it is to provide for thee. Cf. *Nun's Priest's Tale*, l. 63.

247. This passage, as Köppel first noticed, is a recollection of a passage in a book that was very familiar to Chaucer, namely, Pope Innocent III's *De Contemptu Mundi*. The passage is in Bk. ii. 17. " Quaeruntur pigmenta, nutriuntur altilia, capiuntur ob escam quae studiose coquuntur arte coquorum, quae laute parantur officio ministrorum. Alius contundit et colat, alius

And turnen substaunce into accident,
To fulfille al thy likerous talént !   (c. 540)
Out of the hardė bones knokkė they   250
The mary, for they castė naught awey
That may go thurgh the golet softe and swoote.
Of spicerye, of leef, and bark, and roote,
Shal been his sauce ymaked by delyt
To make him yet a newer appetyt ;   255
But certes, he that haunteth swich delices
Is deed, whyl that he liveth in tho vices.

    A lecherous thing is wyn ; and dronkenesse
Is ful of stryving and of wrecchednesse.
O dronkė man ! disfigured is thy face,   260
Sour is thy breeth, foul artow to embrace,
And thurgh thy dronkė nose semeth the soun

confundit et conficit, substantiam convertit in accidens. Flavours are sought for, fowls are fed and taken for food ; they are carefully prepared by the art of cooks and are elegantly prepared by the service of assistants. One man pounds and strains, another mixes and prepares, and turns substance into accident.

248. *And turn substance into accident.* This alludes to a medieval philosophical distinction between the substance, the inner and essential nature of a thing, and its accidents, or outward qualities. The substance was something which could not be perceived : the accidents of form, colour, taste and smell could be distinguished by the human senses. Chaucer means that the art of cookery so changed food that it became a different thing. Its original substance was entirely lost in the new form, colour, taste and smell which the cooks gave it.

249. E. *fulfillen*.

251. E. etc. *noght*.

254. *his* : a gluttonous man's.

257. An adaptation of 1 *Timothy* v. 6, as a note in the margin of some MSS. indicates. " She that liveth in pleasure is dead while she liveth."

As though thou seydest ay, 'Sampsóun! Sampsóun!'
    And yet, God woot, Sampsoun drank never no wyn.
Thou fallest, as it were a stiked swyn ;   265
Thy tonge is lost, and al thyn honeste cure ;
For dronkenesse is verray sepulture
Of mannes wit and his discrecioun ;
In whom that drinke hath dominacioun,   (c. 560)
He kan no conseil kepe, it is no drede.   270
    Now kepe you fro the white and fro the rede,
And namely fro the whitë wyn of Lepe,
That is to selle in Fisshstrete, or in Chepe.
This wyn of Spaignë crepeth subtilly
In otherë wynes, growing fastë by,   275
Of which ther ryseth swich fumositee,
That whan a man hath dronken draughtes three,
And weneth that he be at hoom in Chepe,
He is in Spaigne, right at the toune of Lepe,
Nat at the Rochel, ne at Burdeux toun,   280

263. Sampsoun! Sampsoun: an imitation of the snore heard in the sleep of the drunken man.

264. Samson was a Nazarite, *i.e.* he drank no wine nor strong drink, from his earliest years : *Judges* xiii. 5.

266. and al thyn honeste cure : and all thy care for honourable things, thy regard for decency.

272. Lepe : said to be in the kingdom of Seville, Spain, north-west of Cadiz.   The wine would be a heavy white one of the sherry type, and cheaper than the French wines of La Rochelle and Bordeaux.   The implication is that taverners used it to adulterate other wines.   Chaucer was familiar with the wine trade.   His father, John Chaucer, was a vintner, an importer of wines from France and Spain, who lived in Thames Street, where Cannon Street Station now stands.

273. Fisshstrete, or in Chepe : in Fish Street, off Thames Street, just below London Bridge ; or in Cheapside, at that time one of the principal streets for shops.

280. the Rochel, ne at Burdeux toun : He has a Spanish kind of drunkenness, not a French one, which would remind him of

And thannè wol he seye, ' Sampsóun, Sampsóun ! '
    But herkneth, lordings, o word, I you preye,
That alle the sovereyn actes, dar I seye,
Of victories in the Oldè Testament,
Thurgh verray God that is omnipotent,   285
Were doon in abstinence and in preyere ;
Looketh the Bible, and ther ye may it leere.
    Looke, Attilla, the gretè conquerour,
Deyde in his sleep, with shame and díshonour,   (c. 580)
Bledynge ay at his nose in dronkenesse.   290
A capitayn sholde live in sobrenesse ;
And over al this, avyseth you right wel

the cities from which French wine came. La Rochelle in the
north, and Bordeaux in the south of the Duchy of Aquitaine
were included in the Angevin Empire of Henry II after 1152.
La Rochelle reverted to France in 1224, but was ceded to England
again in 1360. It was recaptured in 1372, and when this tale
was written it was a French port. Bordeaux on the river
Garonne was not recaptured for France until 1451. The Black
Prince held court there for a time, and Richard II was born
there. Bordeaux was, and is, especially famous for the wines
of the district, the clarets and sauternes.

282. E. *lordes*, others *lordyngs, lordinges*.

283. the sovereyn actes : the noble deeds.

288. Attila (*c.* 406-453) was a king of the Huns who conquered the world from the Rhine to the Great Wall of China,
but he was defeated in a most bloody battle fought at Chalons
in 451 by Aetius the Roman general. Attila retreated across
the Rhine, and in 452 invaded Italy, when Rome was only
spared by the intervention of Pope Leo I. He was preparing
for a new invasion of Italy in 453, but he died on the night of
his marriage with a German maiden named Ildico. Rumour
said she murdered him. In the *Volsungasaga* he dies thus by
the hand of his wife Gudrun. Chaucer follows the historical
version of the story, as given by Jordanes and Paul the Deacon,
that, after a debauch, he broke a blood-vessel and died of
bleeding at the nose.

What was comaunded unto Lamuel,—
Nat Samuel, but Lamuel, seye I ;
Redeth the Bible, and fynde it expresly   295
Of wyn-yevyng to hem that han justise.
Namoore of this, for it may wel suffise.

    And now that I have spoken of glotonye,
Now wol I you defenden hasardrye.
Hasard is verray mooder of lesynges,   300
And of deceite, and cursed forswerynges,
Blaspheme of Crist, manslaughtre, and wast also
Of catel and of tyme ; and forthermo
It is repreeve and contrarie of honour
For to ben holde a commune hasardour :   305
And ever the hyer he is of estaat,
The moore is he holden desolaat.
If that a prince useth hasardrye,
In alle governaunce and policye   (c. 600)
He is, as by commune opinioun,   310

293. **Lamuel :** the king to whom the last chapter of *Proverbs*
is ascribed ; cf. *Proverbs* xxxi. 4 : " It is not for kings, O Lemuel,
it is not for kings to drink wine, nor for princes strong drink ;
Lest they drink, and forget the law, and pervert the judgment
of any of the afflicted."

296. **that han justise :** that administer justice, that have (the
prerogative of) justice.

298. E. Hl. *And now I*.

299. **you defenden hasardrye :** forbid gambling for you.
' You ' is the ethic dative.

300. An adaptation of a saying in John of Salisbury's *Polycraticus* i. 5 : Mendaciorum et perjuriarum mater est alea ;
Gambling is the mother of lies and false oaths : as a note in the
margins of some MSS. indicates. The stories of Stilbon and
Demetrius, which follow, come from the same chapter on
gambling.

302. E. *Blasphemynge*, others *Blaspheme*.

305. **a commune hasardour :** a public gambler.

Yholde the lasse in reputacioun.

   Stilbon, that was a wys embassadour,
Was sent to Corinthe in ful greet honour
Fro Lacidomïe to máken hir álliáunce ;
And whan he cam, him happedè *par chaunce*   315
That alle the gretteste that were of that lond
Pléyinge attè hasard he hem fond ;
For which, as soonè as it myghtè be,
He stal him hoom agayn to his contree,
And seydè, ' Ther wol I nat lese my name,   320
N' I wol nat táke on me so greet defame,
You for t' allye unto none hasardours ;
Séndeth otherè wise embassadours ;
For, by my trouthè, me were levere dye,
Than I you sholde to hasardours allye ;   325
For ye that been so glorious in honours
Shul nat allyen you with hasardours,
As by my wil, ne as by my tretee ! '
This wisè philosóphrè thus seyde he.   (C. 620)

   Looke, eek, that to the kyng Demetrius,   330

---

312. Stilbon: The story is told in John of Salisbury's *Polycraticus* i. 5, where, however, the Lacedæmonian ambassador is called Chilon. Stilbon means in Greek, shining, and is a name for the planet Mercury.

314. Lacidomie: Lacedæmon or Sparta, the most southerly state of ancient Greece.

315. E. Hn. Pt. *happed*, Hl. Cm. Cp. *happede.*

321. E. etc. *Ne I*, Hn. *Ny*, Cm. *Nay*, Hl. *I nyl not.*

322. E. etc. *for to allie.*

330. Demetrius: The story follows immediately after the last in John of Salisbury's *Polycraticus* i, 5. Skeat says: " What Demetrius this was, we are not told ; perhaps it may have been Demetrius Nicator, king of Syria, who was defeated and taken prisoner by the Parthians, 138 B.C., and detained in captivity by them for ten years."—E. Hl. omit *to.*

The king of Parthes, as the book seith us,
Sente him a paire of dees of gold, in scorn,
For he hadde used hasard ther-biforn ;
For which he heeld his glorie or his renoun
At no value or reputacioun.　　　　　　　　335
Lordes may fynden oother maner pley
Honeste ynough to dryve the day awey.

　　Now wol I speke of othes false and grete
A word or two, as oldè bookes trete.
Greet swering is a thing abhomináble,　　　340
And fals sweryng is yet moore reprèváble.
The heighè God forbad sweryng at al,—
Witnesse on Mathew ; but in special
Of swering seith the hooly Jeremýe,
' Thou shalt seye sooth thyn othes, and nat lye,　345
And swere in doom, and eek in rightwisnesse ' ;
But ydel swering is a cursednesse.

　　Bihoold and see, that in the firstè table
Of heighè Goddes heestes honurable,　　　(c. 640)

___

331. The king of Parthes : the king of the Parthians. Parthia
was northern Persia. The Parthians were Scythians who came
under the influence of Greek civilisation, and became an imperial
race from the second century B.C. until the second century A.D.,
with their capital at Ctesiphon.

343. Witnesse on Mathew : see the Gospel according to St
Matthew. The allusion is to *S. Matthew* v. 34. " Swear not at
all," as a marginal note in several MSS. indicates.

344. the hooly Jeremye : the holy Jeremiah, the prophet
Jeremiah. The allusion is to *Jeremiah* iv. 2 : and " thou shalt
swear . . . in truth, in judgment, and in righteousness " ; as
a marginal note in several MSS. indicates.

347. ydel swering : swearing in vain, useless swearing.

348. the firste table : The ten commandments fall naturally
into two halves or ' tables.' The first table teaches our duty to
God : the second table teaches our duty to our neighbours.

How that the seconde heeste of hym is this :   350
' Take nat my name in ydel, or amiss ' ;
Lo, rather he forbedeth swich swerýng
Than homicyde, or many a cursed thing ;
I seye that, as by ordrė, thus it stondeth.
This knowen, that his heestes understondeth,   355
How that the seconde heeste of God is that ;
And forther-over, I wol thee telle, al plat,
That vengeance shal nat parten from his hous
That of his othes is too outrageous.
' By Goddes precious herte,' and ' By his nayles,'   360
And ' By the blood of Crist that is in Hayles,'
' Sevene is my chaunce, and thyn is cynk and treye,

350. **the seconde heeste :** the second commandment. The Catholic Church considers what Protestants call the first two commandments to be the first ; and Chaucer's second command-ment is therefore what Protestants call the third : " Thou shalt not take the name of the Lord thy God in vain." The tenth commandment was divided into two, so that both Catholics and Protestants recognise ten commandments in *Exodus* xx.

352. **rather :** earlier, in an earlier place. For the command-ment against swearing comes earlier than those against murder and other sins against our fellows.

353. Hl. Hn. Cm. *many a,* E. *any,* Cp. Pt. Ln. *eny other.*

355. They who understand His commandments know this, namely, that the second commandment of God is that.

358. The pardoner is quoting *Ecclesiasticus* xxiii. 11 : " A man that useth much swearing shall be filled with iniquity, and the plague shall never depart from his house."

361. At Hales Abbey in Gloucestershire there was kept as a relic a vial containing a portion of what was generally regarded as the blood of Christ.

362. My chance is seven. Thine is five and three. The caster at a game of hazard is supposed to be speaking. The game of hazard is now forgotten in England, but it is still played by the negroes, and possibly by others, in the United States under the name of Craps, so-called from the name of the lowest

16 N

By Goddes armes, if thou falsly pleye,
This dagger shal thurghout thyn hertè go ! '—
This fruyt cometh of the bicched bones two,　　365
Forsweryng, irè, falsnesse, homicyde.
Now, for the love of Crist that for us dyde,
Leveth youre othes, bothè grete and smale.
But, sirs, now wol I tellè forth my tale.　　(C. 660)

　　Thise riotoures three, of which I telle,　　370
Long erst er prymè rong of any belle,
Were set hem in a tavern for to drinke ;
And, as they sat, they herde a bellè clinke
Biforn a cors,—was caried to his grave.
That oon of hem gan callen to his knave :　　375
' Go bet,' quod he, ' and axè redily
What cors is this, that passeth heer forby,
And look that thou reporte his namè weel.'
　　' Sire,' quod this boy, ' it nedeth never-a-deel ;
It was me toold, er ye cam heer, two houres.　　380
He was, *pardee*, an old felawe of youres,

throw, two aces ; whence our phrase " to turn out crabs,"—to
end in failure.

365. bicched: accursed. The meaning is conjectural ; the
derivation of the word is probably from the word bitch. E. Cp.
Hl. *bicched*, Ln. *becched*, Hn. Cm. *bicche*.

368. E. Hn. *Lete*, others *Leueth*.

371. Long before any bell rang for the service of prime. The
time implied is between 6 o'clock and 9 in the morning.

372. Hl. Cp. Pt. *for to drynke*, E. etc. omit *for*.

373. The sexton rang a hand-bell in front of the corpse as the
funeral procession went to the church-yard ; and the faithful,
when they heard it, said a prayer for the departed soul.

375. That oon of hem: one of them.

376. Go bet : " lit. go better, *i.e.* go quickly ; a term of en-
couragement to dogs in the chase " (Skeat).

378. Hl. omits *that*.

And sodeynly he was yslayn to-nyght,
Fordronke, as he sat on his bench upright.
Ther cam a privee theef, men clepeth Deeth,
That in this contree al the peplé sleeth,　　　　385
And with his spere he smoot his herte a-two,
And wente his wey withouten wordes mo.
He hath a thousand slayn this pestilence ;
And, maister, ere ye come in his presence,　　(c. 680)
Me thinketh that it werè necessárie　　　　390
For to be war of swich an adversárie.
Beth redy for to meete him everemoore ;
Thus taughtè me my dame ; I seye namoore.'
　'By seintè Marie ! ' seyde this taverneer,
'The child seith sooth, for he hath slayn this yeer　395
Henne over a mile, withinne a greet village,
Bothe man and womman, child, and hyne, and page.
I trowe his habitacioun be there ;
To been avysed, greet wisdom it were,
Er that he dide a man a dishonóur.'　　　　400
　'Ye, Goddes armes ! ' quod this riotour,
'Is it swich peril with him for to meete ?
I shal him seke, by wey and eek by strete,
I make avow to Goddes dignè bones !
Herkneth, feláwes, we three been al ones,　　405
Lat ech of us holde up his hand til oother,

382. **to-nyght :** last night. It can also have the modern
meaning, but not here.
383. **upright :** The word usually means lying on his back, face
upwards ; but here it may have the meaning of erect. The man
died of plague, *cf.* l. 388.
393. **my dame :** my mother.
403. **by wey and eek by strete :** on every road. A street was
a paved road ; a way was a track, unpaved and rutted.
405. **we three been al ones :** we three are all of one (mind).

And ech of us bicomen otheres brother,
And we wol sleen this false traytour, Deeth ;
He shal be slayn, which that so many sleeth,   (c. 700)
By Goddes dignitee, er it be nyght ! '   410

    To-gidres han thise three hir trouthes plight
To live and dyen ech of hem for oother,
As though he were his owene borne brother.
And up they stirte, al dronken, in this rage ;
And forth they goon towardes that villáge   415
Of which the taverner had spoke biforn.
And many a grisly ooth than han they sworn ;
And Cristes blessed body they to-rente,—
Deeth shal be deed, if that they may him hente.

    Whan they han goon nat fully half a mile,   420
Right as they wolde han troden over a stile,
An old man and a poure with hem mette.
This olde man ful mekely hem grette,
And seyde thus : ' Now, lordes, God you see ! '
    The proudeste of thise riotoures three   425
Answérde agayn, ' What ! carl, with sory grace,

---

407. They were to become sworn-brothers by plighting their troth to each other. They made a guild or fraternity for the purpose of killing Death.

409. He that slays so many shall be slain before nightfall.— E. etc. *which that.*

413. E. *yborn*, Pt. *born*, Hn. Dd. *ybore*, Cm. *bore*, Hl. Cp. Ln. *sworne.*

418. They swore in the way indicated by the Pardoner in l. 360. See note to l. 182.

419. Death shall die if they can catch him.

422. The olde man is the Wandering Jew.

424. God you see ! : may God look upon you = God bless you.

426. with sory grace : with ill luck, who bringest ill fortune. Almost equivalent to ' hang you ! ' It is not a reference to the face or ' cheere ' of the old man, or to his expression as in the modern sense of these words.

Why artow al forwrapped, save thy face ?
Why livestow so longe in so greet age ? '
   This oldė man gan looke in his viságe,   (c. 720)
And seydė thus : ' For I ne kan nat fynde   430
A man, though that I walked into Ynde,
Neither in citee, nor in no villáge,
That woldė chaunge his youthė for myn age ;
And therfore moot I han myn agė stille,
As longė tyme as it is Goddes wille ;   435
Ne Deeth, allas ! ne wol nat han my lyf.
Thus walke I, lyk a restėlees caityf.
And on the ground, which is my moodres gate,
I knokkė with my staf, both erly and late,
And seyė : " Leevė mooder, leet me in !   440
Lo, how I vanisshe, flessh and blood and skin ;
Allas ! whan shul my bones been at reste ?
Móoder, with you wolde I chaunge my cheste
That in my chambrė longė tyme hath be,
Ye, for an hayrė-clout to wrappė me ! "   445
But yet to me she wol nat do that grace,
For which ful pale and welked is my face.
   ' But, sires, to you it is no curteisye
To speken to an old man vileynye,   (c. 740)
But he trespasse in word, or elles in dede.   450

431. **into Ynde :** into India, as far as India.

439. E. Hn. Cm. Dd. *bothe erly*.

440. **Leeve mooder :** dear mother Earth.

443. I would exchange my chest with you, mother, even for a shroud to wrap me in. The chest, in which one's valuables were stored, was wardrobe, bookcase and strong-box. The old man is willing to exchange his chest, that has stood for a long time in his bedroom, for a shroud of sack-cloth (a hayre-clout).

445. E. etc. *heyre-clout*.

448. **to you it is no curteisye :** it is no courtesy for you, it is discourteous of you.

In Hooly Writ ye may yourself wel rede,
" Agayns an old man, hoor upon his heed,
Ye sholde arise " ; wherfore I yeve you reed,
Ne dooth unto an old man noon harm now,
Namoorè than ye wolde men dide to you   455
In agè, if that ye so longe abyde :
And God be with you, wher ye go or ryde ;
I moot go thider as I have to go.'
    ' Nay, oldè cherl, by God, thou shalt nat so ! '
Séyde this oother hasardour anon ;   460
' Thou partest nat so lightly, by seint John !
Thou spak right now of thilkè traytour, Deeth,
That in this contree alle our freendes sleeth ;
Have heer my trouthe, as thou art his espye,
Telle where he is, or thou shalt it abye,   465
By God and by the hooly sacrement !
For soothly, thou art oon of his assent
To sleen us yongè folk, thou falsè theef ! '
    ' Now, sirs,' quod he, ' if that ye be so leef (c. 760)
To fyndè Deeth, turne up this croked wey,   470
For in that grove I lafte him, by my fey,
Under a tree, and there he wole abyde ;
Noght for your boost he wole him nothing hyde.
See ye that ook ?   Right there ye shal him fynde.
God savè you, that boughte agayn mankynde,   475
And you amende ! ' thus seyde this oldè man ;

    452. An allusion to *Leviticus* xix. 32 ; " Thou shalt rise up
before the hoary head, and honour the face of the old man," as
the marginal note in several MSS. indicates.
    455. E. Hn. *than that ye*, Hl. Cm. Pt. Ln. *than ye*.
    457. wher ye go or ryde : whether you walk or ride, however
you go. ' Wher ' is here a contracted form of ' whether,' and not
the adverb ' where.'
    465. Hl. *or elles thou schalt dye*.
    469. E. Cm. *ye*, Hl. Hn. *yow*.

And everich of thise riotoures ran
Til he cam to that tree, and there they founde,
Of florins fyne, of gold ycoyned rounde,
Wel ny an eightė busshels, as hem thoughte.   480
No lenger thannė after Deeth they soughte,
But ech of them so glad was of that sighte,
For that the florins been so faire and brighte,
That doun they sette hem by this precious hoord.
The worste of hem he spak the firstė word.   485
    'Bretheren,' quod he, 'taak kepė what I seye ;
My wit is greet, though that I bourde and pleye.
This tresor hath Fortúne unto us yeven
In mirthe and jolitee our lyf to liven ;   (c. 780)
And lightly as it comth, so wol we spende.   490
Ey, Goddes precious dignitee ! who weende
To-day, that we sholde han so fair a grace ?
But myghte this gold be caried fro this place
Hoom to myn hous, or elles unto youres,—
For wel ye woot that al this gold is oures,—   495
Than werė we in heigh felicitee.

478. E. Hn. Dd. *he*, others *they*.
479. florins : Gold florins were so called because they were
first coined at Florence in 1252. Edward III coined English
'florins' of gold in 1344 : worth 6s. They were almost immediately withdrawn from circulation, and a new coin, the
'noble,' worth 6s. 8d., issued. A gold florin of Chaucer's time
was a large gold coin 1¼ inches in diameter, and was worth in
modern equivalent something like £10 in paper money. A conti-
nental florin was a smaller coin, worth half as much.
480. Hl. Cp. Pt. *seuen*, E. etc. *eighte, an viij*.
486. Hl. *what I schal*, Hn. Dd. *what that*.
489. E. *Ioliftee*, Hn. etc. *jolitee*.
490. Alluding to the proverb : 'Lightly come, lightly go.'
491. who weende : who would have thought. Past subjunctive.

But trewėly, by daye it may nat be ;
Men woldė seyn that we were theves stronge,
And for our owenė tresor doon us honge.
This tresor moste ycaried be by nyghte   500
As wisely and as slyly as it myghte.
Wherfore, I rede that cut among us alle
Be drawe, and lat see wher the cut wol falle ;
And he that hath the cut, with hertė blythe,
Shal rennė to the towne, and that ful swythe,   505
And bringe us breed and wyn ful privėly,
And two of us shul kepen subtilly
This tresor wel ; and, if he wol nat tarie,
When it is nyght, we wol this tresor carie   (c. 800)
By oon assent where-as us thinketh best.'   510
    That oon of hem the cut broughte in his fest,
And bad hem drawe, and looke where it wol falle ;
And it fil on the yongeste of hem alle,
And forth toward the toun he wente anon ;
    And also soonė as that he was gon,   515
That oon of hem spak thus unto that oother :

---

498. 'Thieves' because they would be in possession of a treasure to which they had no legal right.   In England, treasure belonged to the crown.

499. doon us honge : lit. make us hang=have us hanged.

501. As prudently and as cunningly as possible.

502. cut . . . be drawe : A number of straws, sticks, or pieces of grass was collected by one of the revellers, and each selected one.   The person who drew either the longest or the shortest piece " was the one on whom the lot fell.   The fatal straw was the *cut* " (Skeat).

505. Hl. Cp. *the*, E. etc. omit.

507. kepen subtilly : cunningly watch.

511. That oon : the one.   Similarly *That other*, which still survives in the dialect phrase *the tother*, meaning the other, occurs in l. 525.

512. E. *hym.*

' Thou knowest wel thou art my swornė brother ;
Thy profit wol I tellė thee anon ;
Thou woost wel that our felawe is agon,
And heer is gold, and that ful greet plentee,   520
That shal departed been among us three ;
But nathėlees, if I kan shape it so
That it departed were among us two,
Hadde I nat doon a freendes turn to thee ? '

   That oother answérde, ' I noot how that may be ; 525
He woot wel that the gold is with us tweye ;
What shul we doon ? what shul we to him seye ? '

   ' Shal it be conseil ? ' seyde the firstė shrewe,
' And I shal tellen in a wordes fewe   (C. 820)
What we shal doon, and bringen it wel aboute.'   530

   ' I grauntė,' quod that oother, ' out of doute,
That by my trouthe I wol thee nat biwreye.'

   ' Now,' quod the firste, ' thou woost wel we be tweye,
And two of us shul strenger be than oon.
Looke whan that he is set, and than anoon   535
Arys, as though thou woldest with him pleye,

517. E. Hn. Pt. *sworn*, Hl. Cp. Ln. *sworne*, Cm. *swore*.

524. **Hadde I nat doon?** : Should I not have done ? or as
modern English demands : Shall I not have done ?

526. E. *how*, Hl. Cp. Pt. *wel*, Hn. etc. omit.

528. **Shal it be conseil?** : shall it be a secret ? let it be a
secret.

529. The Harleian MS. 7334 only reads ' shal tellen thee.'

532. E. *shal*, others *wol*, *wil*.

535. This and the following line are a crux. The MSS. read
' Looke ' and ' Arise.' They can only be imperatives, I think,
though ' Looke whan ' has been interpreted as an adverbial
conjunction meaning whenever. The reading of E. Hn. Cm.
and Dd., ' that right anoon,' I take to mean : when he is sitting
down, see that immediately you arise, etc. ; but if so, there is
a confused construction, and instead of ' Arys ' there should be

And I shal ryve him thurgh the sydes tweye,
Whil that thou strogelest with him as in game,
And, with thy dagger, looke thou do the same ;
And than shal al this gold departed be,   540
My deerė freend, bitwixen me and thee.
Than may we bothe our lustės all fulfille,
And pleye at dees right at our owenė wille.'
And thus acorded been thise shrewes tweye,
To sleen the thridde, as ye han herd me seye.   545

    This yongeste, which that wente unto the toun
Ful ofte in herte he rolleth up and doun
The beautee of thise florins newe and brighte.
' O Lord,' quod he, ' if so were, that I myghte (c. 840)
Have al this tresor to myself allone,   550
Ther is no man that liveth under the trone
Of God, that sholdė live so murie as I ! '
And attė laste the feend, our enemy,
Putte in his thought that he sholde poyson beye,
With which he myghtė sleen his felawes tweye ;   555
For-why the feend foond hym in swich livynge,
That he hadde levė hym to sorwė bringe,
For this was outrėly his fulle entente
To sleen hem bothe and never to repente.

Arysest. ' Aryse ' would be plural, which would be curious after
the singular imperative ' Looke.'

    It seems better to me to take the reading of the Corpus MS.,
' and thanne anon.' It may not be what Chaucer wrote, but
at least its meaning is clear. ' Set ' is the p.p. of *sette*(*n*), to set,
or to sit down. I would translate : Notice when he has sat
down, and then immediately get up as if you wanted to tease
him, and I will run him through.—E. Hn. Cm. Dd. *that right
anoon*, Hl. Pt. Ln. *and that anoon*, Cp. *and thanne anoon*.

    537. E. etc. *ryve*, Cp. Ln. *renne*.

    541. E. etc. *me and thee*, Hl. Hn. Cp. Pt. *thee and me*.

    547. in herte : in his mind.

And forth he gooth, no lenger wolde he tarie,   560
Into the toun, unto a pothecárie,
And preyede hym that he him woldė selle
Som poyson, that he myghte his rattės quelle ;
And eek ther was a polcat in his hawe,
That, as he seyde, his capouns hadde yslawe ;   565
And fayn he woldė wreke hym, if he myghte,
On vermin, that destroyed hym by nyghte.

The pothecarie answérde, ' And thou shalt have
A thing that,—also God my soulė save !—   (c. 860)
In al this world ther is no creäture,   570
That eten or dronke hath of this confiture,
Noght but the mountance of a corn of whete,
That he ne shal his lyf anon forlete ;
Ye, sterve he shal, and that in lassė while
Than thou wolt goon a-páas nat-but a mile ;   575
This poyson is so strong and violent.'

This cursed man hath in his hond yhent
This poyson in a box, and sith he ran
Into the nextė strete unto a man,
And borwed of him largė botels three,   580

562. Cm. *preyede*, Hn. *preyed*, E. etc. *preyde*.
567. **that destroyed hym**: that disturbed him, cf. *Summoner's Tale*, D. 1847 :

> The body is ay so redy and penyble
> To wake, that my stomak is destroyed.

569. **also God my soule save** : God bless my soul. ' Also ' is used simply to introduce a wish, and is meaningless.
570. E. Hn. Cm. *is*, Hl. Cp. *nys*.
575. **goon a-paas nat-but** : walk at an easy pace only, etc. Cf. *Prologue*, l. 534.
576. Hl. Hn. Cm. Dd. *The*, E. etc. *This*.
580. **borwed of him** : borrowed from him. All MSS. omit ' of,' and the line then means : borrowed for himself—where ' him ' is ethic dative. The objection to this reading is that without ' of ' the line does not scan.—All omit *of*.

And in the two his poyson poured he ;
The thridde he keptė clene for his owenė drinke ;
For al the nyght he shoop him for to swinke
In caryinge of the gold out of that place.
And whan this riotour, with sory grace,   585
Had filled with wyn his gretė botels three,
To his felawes agayn repaireth he.
    What nedeth it to sermone of it moore ?
For right as they hadde cast his deeth bifoore, (c. 880)
Right so they han him slayn, and that anon,   590
And whan that this was doon, thus spak that oon :
' Now lat us sitte and drinke, and make us merie,
And afterward we wol his body berie ' ;
And with that word it happed hym, *par cas*,
To take the botel ther the poyson was,   595
And drank, and yaf his felawe drinke also,
For which anon they storven bothė two.
    But certes, I suppose that Avicen
Wroot never in no Canon, n'in no fen,
Mo wonder signes of empoisonyng   600
Than hadde thise wrecches two, er hir endyng.

582. E. only, *his owene*, others omit *owene*.
585. with sory grace : with ill favour, with evil intention.
588. to sermone of it moore : to make a longer sermon of it.
589. E. *right so as*, others omit *so*.
591. Hl. *whan this was idon then spak*.
598. **Avicen** : a Persian (Arab) physician named Ibn Sina
(980-1037). Avicenna wrote the Canon of Medicine, a famous
medieval text-book of medicine which was translated into Latin
as the *Canon Medicinae*. Canon means a rule, and is not only
the title of the whole work, but is the name for his ' rules for
curing,' or prescriptions. The work is divided into books, and
the books are divided into ' fens ' or parts.
599. Avicenna never wrote in any rule nor in any part (of the
Canon of Medicine).
600. **signes** : symptoms.—E. Hn. Cm. *signes*, Hl. Cp. Ln. *sorwes*.

Thus ended been thise homicydes two,
And eek the false empoisonere also.

   O cursed sinne of allè cursednesse !
O traytorous homicyde ! O wikkednesse !   605
O glotonye, luxúrie, and hasardrye !
Thou blasphemour of Crist with vileynye,
And othes grete, of usage and of pride !
Allas ! mankyndè, how may it bityde   (c. 900)
That to thy Creätour, which that thee wroughte, 610
And with his precious hertè-blood thee boughte,
Thou art so fals and so unkynde, allas ' !

   Now, good-men, God foryeve you your trespás,
And ware yow fro the sinne of avarice.
Myn hooly pardoun may you alle waríce,   615
So that ye offrè nobles or sterlynges,
Or elles silver broches, spoones, ringes.
Boweth youre heed under this hooly bulle !
Cometh up, ye wyves, offreth of youre wolle !
Your names I entre heer in my rolle anon ;   620

604. E. Hn. Cm. *of alle*, Hl. Cp. Ln. *ful of*, Pt. *ful of al*.
605. E. etc. *traytours*.
608. of usage and of pride : both from habit and from insolence.
The distinction is that an ' oath of usage ' is said unconsciously,
whereas an ' oath of pride ' is a deliberate sin.
    615. My sacred indulgences can benefit you all, if, etc.
    616. nobles or sterlynges: great coins or small, *cf.* l. 639,
" Nobles or pens." A noble was a gold coin worth 6s. 8d., something like £10 in modern paper money. A ' sterlynge ' was a
silver penny, equivalent to half a crown to-day. Coined money
was not plentiful enough in the Middle Ages, and hence offerings
were often made in kind. But the pardoner does not invite
gifts of wares, he wants silver, though he is prepared to accept wool
from the women.
    619. E. *Com*, others *Cometh*.
    620. This was a habit of the friars. See note on l. 160.—
E. Hl. *names*, others *name*.

Into the blisse of heven shul ye gon ;
I you assoillè by myn heigh powéer,—
You that wol offre,—as clene and eek as cleer
As ye were born ; and lo, sirs, thus I preche,
And Jhesu Crist, that is our soules leche,   625
So grauntè you his pardoun to receyve ;
For that is best ; I wol you nat deceyve.

  ' But, sires, o word forgat I in my tale ;
I have relíks and pardoun in my male   (c. 920)
As faire as any man in Engèlond,   630
Whiche were me yeven by the Popes hond.
If any of yóu wole, of devocioun,
Offren, and han myn absolucioun,
Cometh forth anón, and kneleth heer adoun,
And mekèly receyveth my pardóun ;   635
Or elles taketh pardoun as ye wende,
Al newe and fressh, at every miles ende,—
So that ye offren, alwey newe and newe,
Nobles or pens, whiche that be goode and trewe.
  It is an honour to everich that is heer   640
That ye mowe have a suffisant Pardoneer
T' assoillè you in contree as ye ryde,
For áventúres whiche that may bityde.
Paraventure ther may fallen oon or two
Doun of his hors, and breke his nekke a-two ;   645
Looke which a seuretee ís it to you alle,
That I am in your felaweshipe yfalle,

634. E. Hn. *Com*, others *Cometh*.

637. E. Hn. Cm. *myles*, others *tounes*.

639. E. Hn. *or*, others *and*.

644. Paraventure : peradventure, perhaps. The word was
probably pronounced paraunter.

646. which a seuretee : what a security, what a blessing.

That may assoillè yow, bothe moore and lasse,
Whan that the soule shal fro the body passe. (c. 940)
I redè that our Hoost heer shal biginne, 650
For he is moost envóluped in sinne !
Com forth, sire Hoost, and offrè first anon,
And thou shalt kisse the relikes everichon,—
Ye, for a grote ! Unbokele anon thy purs.'
  ' Nay, nay,' quod he, ' than have I Cristes curs ! 655
Lat be,' quod he, ' it shal nat be, so theech !
Thou woldest make me kissè thyn oldè breech
And swere it were a relik of a seynt.
  This Pardoneer answérdè nat a word ;
So wrooth he was, no word ne wolde he seye. 660
  ' Now,' quod our Hoost, ' I wol no lenger pleye
With thee, ne with noon oother angry man.'
But right anon the worthy Knyght bigan,— (c. 960)
Whan that he saugh that al the peple lough,—
  ' Namoore of this, for it is right ynough ! 665
Sir Pardoneer, be glad and mirie of cheere ;
And ye, sir Hoost, that been to me so deere,
I prey you that ye kisse the Pardoneer ;
And Pardoneer, I prey thee, drawe thee neer,
And, as we diden, lat us laughe and pleye.' 670
Anon they kiste and riden forth hir weye.

Heere is ended the Pardoners tale.

648. bothe moore and lasse : both great and small, gentle folk
and commoners.
  650. E. and Cm. only, *heere*, query *Hooste.*
  653. E. *my*, Cm. *myne*, others *the.*
  656. so theech : so thee ich = as I hope to thrive, lit. so thrive
I : where ' so ' merely introduces a sentence containing a wish,
and is meaningless, and ' thee ' is present subjunctive.—Hn. *thee
ich*, others *theech.*
  665. right ynough : quite enough.

ABBREVIATIONS

The following abbreviations are used:

adj.	.	adjective
adv.	.	adverb
cf.	.	compare (a related word)
comp.	.	comparative
conj.	.	conjunction
dat.	.	dative case
def.	.	definite form (after *the, his,* etc.)
fem.	.	feminine
gen.	.	genitive case
imp. s.	.	imperative singular
imp. pl.	.	imperative plural
impers.	.	used impersonally
indef. art.		indefinite article
int.	.	interjection
intr.	.	intransitive
lit.	.	literally
masc.	.	masculine
n. pl.	.	neuter plural
neut.	.	neuter
pl.	.	plural
poss.	.	possessive case
pron.	.	pronoun
p.p.	.	past participle
pr. p.	.	present participle
prep.	.	preposition
pr. s.	.	present tense singular
pr. pl.	.	present tense plural

p.t.	.	past tense
s.	.	substantive
st.	.	strong verb
subj.	.	subjunctive mood
sup.	.	superlative
trans.	.	transitive
v.	.	verb
A.Fr.	.	Anglo-French (Old Norman French)
Fr.	.	French
Ger.	.	German
Germ.	.	of Germanic origin
Gk.	.	Greek
L.	.	Latin
LL.	.	non-classical Latin
M.H.G.	.	Middle High German
O.E.	.	Old English
O.Fr.	.	Old French
O.H.G.	.	Old High German
O.N.	.	Old Norse (Old Icelandic)
Kent.	.	Kentish or South-eastern form (with *e* for O.E. *y*)
þ	.	O.E., O.N., *th*, in 'thin'
ð	.	O.E., O.N., *th*, in 'then'

GLOSSARY

A, the letter A

A, *int.,* ah! oh!

A, *prep.,* on, in; a Goddes name, in God's name. Weakened (unemphatic) form of O.E. *on* (on, in)

A, An, *indef. art.,* a, an; *adj.,* one. O.E. *ān* (one)

Abbay, *s.,* abbey. O.Fr. *abeie,* Fr. *abbaye,* LL. *abbatia*

Abbey-orlogge, *s.,* abbey-clock. O.Fr. *orloge,* Fr. *horloge,* L.Gk. *horologium* (sun-dial)

Abhominable, *adj.,* abominable, detestable. O.Fr. *abominable,* L., *abōminabilis.* Connected with L. *ōmen* (sign, omen), not with *hŏmo* (man). The *h* is due to false etymology

A-blakeberyed, *adv.,* a blackberrying, astray. Cf. O.E. *blæce* (black) and *berie* (berry). The ending in *-ed* is due to confusion of the ending of the verbal substantive in *-aþ* with *-ed,* the ending of the weak past participle

Able, *adv.,* able, fit. O.Fr. *hable,* L. *habilis* (handy)

Aboute, *adv., prep.,* about, around, round about. O.E. *onbūtan, abūtan* (on the outside)

Above(n), *adv.,* above, upwards, O.E. *abufan*

Abreyde(n), *v.,* wake up, start up; **Abrayde,** *p.t. s.,* started up. O.E. *a-bregdan* (to alarm)

Absolucioun, *s.,* absolution. L. *absolutio-nem*

Abyde(n), *v.,* abide, dwell; wait, stay. O.E. *abīdan*

Abye, *v.,* pay for; **Abought,** *p.p.,* paid for. O.E. *ā-bycgan* (pay for, redeem)

Accident, *s.,* that which is accidental, the outward appearance. L. *accidens, accidentem* (happening)

Accord, *s.,* agreement, harmony. O.Fr. *acord.* See **Acorde**

Accorde, *v.,* agree. See **Acorde**

Achaat, *s.,* buying. O.Fr. *achat*

Achatour, *s.,* buyer. O.Fr. *achateor,* Fr. *acheteur.* Cf. LL. *accaptare* (buy), *accaptātor* (buyer)

Acordaunt, *adj.,* according

Acorde, *s.,* accord, agree; **Acorded,** *p.t. s.,* it agreed. O.Fr. *acorder,* LL. *accordare* (harmonize)

Actes, *s.pl.,* deeds, chronicles. L. *acta* (things done)

Acursed, *p.p.,* accursed, wicked

Adoun, *adv.,* down, downwards. O.E. *of dūne, adūne*

Adrad, *p.p.,* afraid. O.E. *of-drǣdd*

Adversitee, *s.,* adversity. L. *adversitas, -atem*

Advocatz, *s. pl.,* advocates, L. *advocātos, pl.*

Aferd, *p.p.,* afraid. O.E. *ā-fǣred* (frightened)

Afferme, *v.,* affirm, support. O.Fr. *afermer,* L. *affirmare.* Cf. L. *firmus* (strong)

Affraye, *v.,* terrify; **Affrayed,**

p.p., afraid. O.Fr. *esfreier*, LL. *exfridare* (break the peace). Cf. O.H.G. *fridu*, O.E. *friþ* (peace)

Affyle(n), *v.*, sharpen, put an edge on. O.Fr. *affiler*. Cf. L. *filum* (thread)

Afright, *adj.*, frightened. O.E. *ā-fyrht*

After, *adv.*, afterwards: *prep.*, after, according to; after **hir mete**, for her food; after **oon**, according to one standard, alike; after his felawe, for his friend. O.E. *æfter*

Agast, *adj.*, aghast, afraid. O.E. *a*+*gǣsted* (terrified). Cf. *gǣstan* (to terrify)

Agaste(n), *v.*, terrify. Cf. O.E. *gǣstan*

Agayn, *adv.*, again, back; turne agayn, return: *prep.*, against, towards; agayn the sonne, towards the sun, in the sunshine; agayn the day, towards morning, just before day. O.E. *on-gegn*

Agayns, *prep.*, before, in presence of

Ago, Agon, Agoon, *p.p.*, gone away, departed, ago; longe tyme agon, a long time ago. O.E. *ā-gān*, *p.p.*

Agrief, *adv.*, ill, amiss. *a*+Fr. *grief* (grievous), L. *gravis* (heavy)

Ague, *s.*, fever with alternate cold and hot fits. O.Fr. *ague*, L. *acuta* (sharp)

Al, *adj.*, all; **Alle**, *pl.*, all; **Aller**, *gen. pl.*, of all; at oure aller cost, at the cost of us all; **Alle and some**, one and all; **Al**, *adv.*, only, quite; **al ones**, quite united; **Al**, *conj.*, although; al speke he, although he speak; al were it, although it were; al be that, although;

although, although. O.E. *eall, all*

Alday, *adv.*, every day, continually

Alderbeste, *adj.*, best of all. O.E. *ealra betsta*

Alderman, *s.*, alderman, warden, head of a guild. O.E. *ealdor-mann* (ruler, nobleman)

Ale-stake, *s.*, inn-sign, a horizontal stake supporting a bush or garland. O.E. *ealu* +*staca*

Aley, *s.*, alley, narrow street. O.Fr. *alee*, Fr. *allée*. Cf. Fr. *aller* (to go)

Algate, *adv.*, always, at any rate. Cf. O.N. *alla gōtu*, always

Alighte(n), *v.*, alight, descend; **Alighte**, *p.t. s.*, alighted; **Alyght**, *p.p.*, alighted. O.E. *ālihtan*

Allas, *int.*, alas! O.Fr. *alas* (ah! wretched). Fr. *hélas*. Cf. L. *lassus* (weary)

Aller, *adj. gen. pl.*, of all; oure aller cok, the awakener of us all; hir aller, of them all. O.E. *ealra*

Alliaunce, *s.*, alliance, confederation. O.Fr. *aliance*. Cf. L. *alligare* (to bind)

Allone, *adj.*, alone. O.E. *eall* (all) +*āna* (alone)

Allye(n), *v.*, ally. O.Fr. *alier*, L. *alligare* (bind)

Alma Redemptoris Mater: kind Saviour's mother; a Latin hymn beginning with these words

Al ones, *adv.*, all of one mind. O.E. *eall*+*ānes* (of one)

Als, Also, *adv.*, as, so, just as, also, besides; *conj.*, as; also wel, as well; also siker as, as sure as; also soone as that, as soon as; Also is used to express a hope or wish; also God my soule save, may God save my soul. O.E. *ealswā, alswā*

Altercacioun, *s.*, altercation, dispute. L. *altercationem*

Alwey, Alway, Alweys, *adv.*, always; alwey oon, ever the same; alweys after oon, always of one standard; alwey newe and newe, continually. O.E. *ealneweg*

Alyghte(n), *v.*, to alight, descend; Alighte, *p.t. s.*, alighted; Alyght, *p.p.*, alighted (from our horses). O.E. *ālihtan*

Amblere, *s.*, an ambling horse, literally a walker. Fr. *ambler* (to amble), L. *ambulare* (to walk)

Amende(n), *v.*, to improve, make better. Fr. *amender*, O.Fr. *esmender*, L. *emendare*

Amiable, *adj.*, kind, courteous. O.Fr. *amable*, Fr. *aimable*, L. *amabilis* (lovable)

Amor vincit omnia: Love conquers all things. Cf. Virgil, Éclogue X, 69, *Omnia vincit Amor*

Amorwe, *adv.*, on the morrow, next morning. O.E. *on morgene*

Anhanged, *p.p.*, hanged. O.E. *anhangen, p.p.* of *anhōn* or *onhōn*

Anlaas, *s.*, two-edged knife, or dagger, carried on the belt by men of the middle class

Annexed, *p.p.*, bound. Cf. L. *annexum* (bound)

Anon, Anoon, *adv.*, at once, immediately; right anon, immediately. O.E. *on ān* (forthwith)

Anoye, *v.*, annoy, vex, weary. O.Fr. *anuier*, LL. *inodiare*

Answere, *v.*, answer; Answerde, *p.t.*, answered. O.E. *andswerian*

Antem, *s.*, anthem, hymn. O.E. *antefne*, LL. *antifona*, from Greek

Antiphoner, *s.*, hymn-book, containing Latin hymns and canticles

A-nyght, *adv.*, at night. O.E. *on nihte*

A-pass, *adv.*, at an easy pace. M.E. *a*+Fr. *pas* (pace)

Apaye, *v.*, please; yvel apayd, ill-pleased. O.Fr. *apaier*, LL. *appacare* (quieten)

Apoplexye, *s.*, apoplexy; n'apoplexye shente, nor did apoplexy injure. L.Gk., *apoplēxia*

Apothecaries, *s.*, druggists. LL. *apothecarius*. Cf. Greek *apothēkē* (store-house)

Appetyt, *s.*, desire. O.Fr. *apetit*, L. *appetītus*

Aproche(n), *v.*, approach. O.Fr. *aprochier*, LL. *appropiāre*. Cf. L. *prope* (near)

Apyked, *p.p.*, ornamented, embroidered. Cf. O.E. *pīcian* (to prick)

Aqueyntaunce, *s.*, acquaintance. Cf. O.Fr. *acointance*, LL. *accognitantia*

Areeste, *s.*, arrest; maad areest, seized

Areste(n), *v.*, detain, stop; bigan areste, did stop; maad areest, seized. O.Fr. *arester*, LL. *arrestare* (halt)

Arette(n), *v.*, impute; That ye n'arette it nat, that you do not attribute it (to). O.Fr. *areter*, L. *ad+reputare*

Aright, *adv.*, truly, wholly, certainly. O.E. *on-riht*

Armee, *s.*, army, expedition. Fr. *armée*, L. *armāta* (armed)

Array, *s.*, dress. A.Fr., cf. O.E. *gerǣdu* (equipment)

Arrayed, *p.p.*, equipped. A.Fr. *arayer* (to be ready). Germ.

Arrerage, *s.*, arrears; bringe hym in arrerage, accuse him of being behindhand. O.F. *arere* (behind) +-*age*

Arreste(n), *v.*, arrest: do thilke carte arresten, stop that cart. See Areste(n)

Art, *s.*, art, practical knowledge, practice. L. *ars, artem*

Artow, art thou. 2 *pers. sing.* of Be. O.E. *eart þu*

Arwe, *s.*, arrow. O.E. *arwe*

Aryght, *adv.*, rightly, regularly

Aryse(n), *v.*, arise; Arys, *imp. s.*

As, *adv.*, as, whilst; often introducing an adverbial phrase: as nouthe, now, at present; as of, in, considering, about; as of so litel space, in so short a time; as by, with; as by his facultee, with his position; as by way of kynde, in the natural course of things; as after, according to; as after my konnynge, to the best of my power; as touching, concerning; as for that nyght, for that night. O.E. *ealswā, alswā.* See Als, Also

As, *conj.*, as, like, as if, since. (As is a shortened form of also, als.) As that, as, as if; as it were, like; as it were right, just like; as he kouthe, as best he could; as man that, like one who; as men wolde, as if one wanted; As wel . . . as, both . . . and; As . . . ne as, neither . . . nor. O.E. *ealswā, alswā.* As is also used to introduce sentences expressing a wish: as taak som laxatyf, take some aperient medicine; as evere mote I, as sure as ever I hope; as wis God helpe me, as sure as may God help me

Ascendent, *s.*, ascendant, rising; that degree of the imaginary celestial circle representing the sun's orbit—or of the parallel belt known as the zodiac, through which the sun and planets move— which is rising above the eastern horizon at any given moment (such as birth, or commencement of illness). L. *ascendens, ascendentem*

Ascensioun, *s.*, ascension; celestial longitude. L. *ascensio-nem* (ascent)

Asonder, *adv.*, asunder. O.E. *on-sundran* (apart)

Assent, *s.*, assent, party; by oon assent, by general agreement

Assente, *v.*, assent, agree to. L. *assentire*

Assoiling, *s.*, absolution

Assoille(n), *v.*, absolve, pardon. O.Fr. *assoille, pr. subj.* of *assoudre*, L. *absolvere* (unbind)

Asterte, *v.*, escape from. O.E. *styrtan*, Kent. *stertan*

Astored, *p.p.*, stored, provided. See Stoor

Astronomye, *s.*, astrology. L., Gk. *astronomia*

Asure, *s.*, sky blue. O.Fr. *azur*, Arabic

At, *prep.*, at, of; at the best, of the best kind; at your lyking, to your liking. O.E. *æt*

Attamed, *p.p.*, begun, *lit.* broached. O.Fr. *atamer*, Fr. *entamer* (cut into). Cf. L. *intaminātus* (undefiled), LL. *intaminare* (to contaminate)

Atte, *prep.*, at the; atte beste, in the best manner; atte fulle, fully, completely; atte laste, at the last

Attempree, *adj.,* moderate, temperate. O.Fr. *atempré,* L. *attemperātus* (adjusted)

A-two, *adv.,* in twain. O.E. *on twā,* into two

Auctoritee, *s.,* authority. L. *auctoritas*

Auctour, *s.,* author. L. *auctor*

Audience, *s.,* hearing, audience. L. *audientia*

Auditour, *s.,* auditor, one who examines accounts. L. *audītor*

Aungel, *s.,* angel. L., Gk. *angelus* (messenger)

Auter, *s.,* altar. O.Fr. *auter,* Fr. *autel,* L. *altarium*

Availle, *v.,* avail, help. Cf. O.Fr. *vaille, pr. subj.* of *valoir* (avail). L. *valēre* (be worth)

Avaunce, *v.,* cause to advance, profit; **Avaunced,** *p.p.,* profited. O.Fr. *avancier* (advance), LL. *ab-anti-are*

Avaunt, *s.,* boast. Cf. O.Fr. *vanter* (to boast), L. *vanitas* (vanity)

Avauntour, *s.,* boaster, braggart

Ave Marye : a Latin prayer to the Blessed Virgin

Aventure, *s.,* luck, chance; adventure; *pl.* adventures. O.Fr. *aventure,* LL. *adventura* (a happening)

Avisioun, *s.,* vision. O.Fr. *avision,* L. *ad-visio-nem*

Avow, *s.,* vow, proclamation. Cf. O.Fr. *vou,* L. *votum*

Avoy, *int.,* alas ! O.Fr. *avoï !* (exclamation of astonishment)

Avys, *s.,* advice, deliberation. O.Fr. *avis,* LL. *ad-visum*

Avyse, *v.,* consider; **Avysed,** *p.p.* careful

Await, *s.,* waiting, ambush. Cf. A.Fr. *waite,* O.Fr. *gaite* (sentinel), Germ. *wahta* (watchman)

Awey, *adv.,* away. O.E. *onweg*

Axe(n), *v.,* ask ; **Axe,** *imp.* ask. O.E. *āscian, axian*

Ay, *adv.,* aye, ever ; yes ; **ay biforn,** always ahead

Bacheler, *s.,* young man ; candidate for knighthood, or a master's degree. O.Fr. *bacheler* (young man), LL. *baccalārius, baccalāris* (farmer)

Bad, *p.t. s.,* begged, bade. See **Bidde(n)**

Bak, *s.,* back. O.E. *bæc*

Bake(n), *p.p.,* baked ; **bake mete,** meat pies, or perhaps roast meat. O.E. *(ge)-bacen*

Balled, *adj.,* bald

Bane, *s.,* slayer, death, cause of death. O.E. *bana*

Bar, Baar, *p.t. s.,* bore. See **Bere(n)**

Bare, *adj.,* bareheaded. O.E. *bær*

Bargaynes, *s. pl.,* bargains, buying and selling. O.Fr. *bargaine,* perhaps from L. *barca* (a kind of small boat)

Barge, *s.,* bark, a cargo-boat. O.Fr. *barge.* Cf. L. *barca* (small boat)

Barres, *s. pl.,* ornamental bands, or perhaps clasps, on a girdle

Baskettes, *s. pl.,* baskets

Bataille, battle ; *pl.* **Batailles.** O.Fr. *bataille,* LL. *battualis, battualia, n. pl.* (battle)

Batailled, *adj.,* indented, crenellated, like the parapet of a fortified wall. O.Fr. *bataillé* (turreted)

Bathe, *v.,* to bathe ; **to bathe hir,** to bathe herself, to bask. O.E. *baðian*

Baud, *s.,* jester, blasphemer, obscene person

Bawdrik, *s.,* baldric, belt crossing from shoulder to hip.

Cf. M.H.G. *balderich* (girdle).
O.Fr. *baudrei*

Be, Been, *v.*, be; Art, 2 *pr. s.*,
art; Is, 3 *pr. s.*, is; Been,
Beth, *pr. pl.*, are; Be, *pr. s.*,
subj., be; Was, *pt. s.*, was;
Were(n), *pt. pl.*, were; Beth,
imp. pl., be; Be, Been,
Ybeen, *p.p.*, been; be it,
whether it be; ne beth nat,
be not. O.E. *bēon*

Beautee, *s.*, beauty. O.Fr.
beauté. Cf. L. *bellus*, pretty

Bedes, *s. pl.*, beads. O.E.
(ge-)*bedu*, prayers

Beem, *s.*, beam, perch; Bemes,
pl., beams. O.E. *bēam* (tree)

Been. See Be, Been

Beer(e), *s.*, bier. O.E. *bǣr*,
(bier). Cf. *beran* (bear)

Beer, *p.t. s.*, carried. See
Bere(n)

Beest, *s.*, beast. O.Fr. *beste*,
L. *bestia*

Beggere, *s. masc.* beggar

Beggestere, *s. fem.*, beggar, *lit.*
beggar-woman

Bekke, *v.*, nod. O.E. *bēacnian*.
Cf. *bēacen* (beacon)

Bel amy: fair friend. O.Fr.
bel ami

Belle, *s.*, bell. O.E. *belle*

Beme, *s.*, trumpet; Bemes, *pl.*,
trumpets. O.E. *bīeme*

Bene, *s.*, bean. O.E. *bēan*

Benedicitee : bless us, *lit.* bless
ye (the Lord); probably
pronounced with three syllables as ' bendistee '

Benefice, *s.*, church-living, appointment. L. *beneficium*
(benefit)

Benignitee, *s.*, benignity,
graciousness ; of thy b., in
thy graciousness. L. *be-
nignitas*

Benygne, *adj.*, benign, kind.
O.Fr. *benigne*, L. *benignus*
(kind)

Berd, *s.*, beard. O.E. *beard*

Bere, *s.*, bear. O.E. *bera*

Bere(n), *v.*, bear, carry; Bereth
him, 3 *pr. s.*, behaves; Bar,
Baar, Beer, *p.t. s.*, bore,
carried; sang; Baren us,
p.t. pl., behaved ourselves;
Boren, Born(e), Y-bore(n),
p.p., born, borne, carried.
O.E. *beran, bær, boren*

Berie, *v.*, bury; Beryed, *p.p.*,
buried. O.E. *byrgan*, Kent.
bergan

Berking, *s.*, barking. Cf. O.E.
beorcan (bark)

Bern, *s.*, barn. O.E. *berern,
bern* (barley-store)

Berye, *s.*, berry. O.E. *berie*

Beste, *adj.*, best ; for the beste,
for your advantage. O.E. *betst*

Bet, *adv.*, better ; go bet, go
quickly. O.E. *bet*

Bete, *v.*, beat ; Beten, *p.p.*,
beaten. O.E. *bēatan*

Beth : are, be. See Be, Been

Bettre, *adj.*, *adv.*, better. O.E.
betera

Bevere, *adj.*, made of beaver.
Cf. O.E. *befer* (beaver)

Beye, *s.*, buy. O.E. *bycgan*,
Kent. *becgan*. See Bye

Bicched, *adj.*, accursed; bicched bones, accursed bones,
i.e. dice

Bicomen, *v.* become. O.E.
becuman

Bidde(n), *v.*, bid, ask; Bit,
3 *pr. s.*, bids, commands;
Bad, *p.t. s.*, bade, begged.
O.E. *biddan* (ask), confused
with *bēodan* (command)

Bifalle(n), *v.*, happen, befall ;
Bifil, Bifel, Bifell, *p.t. s.*, it
happened ; Bifalle, *p.p.*, happened. O.E. *be-feallan, fēoll,
feallen*

Bifore(n), Bifoore, Biforn, *adv.*,
before, in front ; he was ay
biforn, he was always ahead :

prep., before, in the presence of. O.E. *be-foran*

Biginne(n), *v.*, begin; Bigan, *p.t. s.*, began; Bigonne, *p.p.*, begun. As auxiliary verb, Bigan, *p.t. s.*, did. O.E. *beginnan, gan, gunnen*

Bigyle(n), *v.*, beguile; Bigyle, 2 *pr. s. subj.* Cf. O.Fr. *guile* (deceit), O.E. *wil* (wile)

Biknowe, *v.*, confess; Biknewe, *p.t. pl.*, confessed. O.E. *becnāwan* (know)

Binethe, *adv.*, downwards. O.E. *beneoðan*

Binne, *s.*, bin, stock of corn. O.E. *binn*

Bisette(n), *v.*, employ; Bisette, *p.t. s.*, employed. O.E. *besettan* (beset, set about)

Bisily, *adv.*, diligently

Bismotered, *p.p.*, stained, smudged. Cf. G. *schmutz* (dirt)

Bisy, *adj.*, busy, occupied; bisy thought, anxious thought; Bisier, *comp.*, busier. O.E. *bysig*, comp., *bysigra*

Bisyde, Bisydes, *prep.*, beside, near; it bisyde, near it; him bisydes, near him; of bisyde Bathe, from near Bath; where ... bisyde, near which. O.E. *be sīdan* (at the side)

Bisynesse, *s.*, business, work

Bit, 3 *pr. s.*, bids, commands. See Bidde

Bithinke, *v.*, imagine, think of; Bithought, *p.p.*, I am right now bithought, I have just thought. O.E. *be-þencan*

Bitwix, Bitwixe, Bitwixen, *pret.*, betwixt, between; bitwix ... and of, between ... and. O.E. *betwix, betweoxn*

Bityde, *v.*, happen. O.E. *be + tīdan* (happen)

Biwaille, *v.*, bewail. Cf. O.N. *væla* (to wail)

Biwreye(n), *v.*, reveal; Biwreyest, 2 *pr. s.*, revealest. O.E. *be + wrēgan* (accuse)

Blak, *adj.*, black; Blake, *pl.* O.E. *blæc*

Blankmanger, *s.*, chicken stewed with milk, honey, and rice. O.Fr. *blanc manger* (white food)

Blaspheme, *s.*, blasphemy. Fr. *blasphème*. Gk. *blasphēmia* (profane language)

Blasphemour, *s.*, blasphemer

Blede(n), *v.*, bleed; Bledde, *p.t. s.*, bled; Bledynge, *pres. p.* O.E. *blēdan*

Blesse(n), *v.*, bless. O.E. *bletsian* (consecrate)

Blew, *adj.*, blue. O.Fr. *bleu*, Germ.

Blisful, *adj.*, happy, blessed, holy. O.E. *blisfull*, confused with Blesse(n)

Blowe, *v.*, blow; Blewe, *p.t. pl.*, blew. O.E. *blāwan, blēow*

Blythe, *adj.*, blithe, glad. O.E. *bliþe* (happy)

Boille, *v.*, boil. O.Fr. *boillir*, L. *bullire* (to bubble)

Bokler, *s.*, buckler, small round shield. O.Fr. *boucler* (shield). Cf. L. *buccula* (boss on a shield)

Bole, *s.*, bull. Cf. O.N. *boli*

Boold, *adj.*, bold. O.E. *beald, bāld*

Boon, *s.*, bone; Bones, *pl.* O.E. *bān*

Boost, *s.*, boasting, loud talk

Boot, *s.*, remedy, redress. O.E. *bōt* (help)

Bootes, *s. pl.*, boots. O.Fr. *bote*, Fr. *botte* (boot)

Boras, *s.*, borax. O.Fr. *boras*, Arabic

Bord, *s.*, table (originally of boards on trestles); He had the bord bigonne, he had been an honoured guest. O.E. *bord* (board)

Boren, Born(e), *p.p.*, born.

Borwe(n), *v.*, borrow; **Borwed,**
p.p. O.E. *borgian*

Botel, *s.*, bottle. O.Fr. *bouteille,* LL. *buticula*

Boterflye, *s.*, butterfly. O.E.
buttor-fleoge

Bothe, *adj., adv.*, both; **bothe
blood and bones,** utterly;
bothe moore and lasse, both
great and small. O.N.
bāðir

Botme, *s.*, bottom, hull. O.E.
botm

Bountee, *s.*, goodness. O.Fr.
bonté, LL. *bonitas.* Cf. L.
bonus (good)

Bour, *s.*, bedroom. O.E. *būr*
(bower)

Bourde, *v.*, jest. O.Fr. *bourdir*
(jest), Fr. *bourder* (deceive)

Bowe, *s.*, bow. O.E. *boga*

Bowen, *v.*, bow, bend; **Boweth,**
imp. O.E. *būgan*

Box, *s.*, boxwood. L. *buxus*
(boxwood)

Boyst, *s.*, box. O.Fr. *boiste,*
Fr. *boîte.* Cf. L. Gk. *pyxis,
pyxidem* (box)

Bracer, *s.*, arm-guard of leather
worn on the left forearm.
O.Fr. *brasseure.* Cf. L.
brachium (arm), Fr. *bras*

Brak, *p.t. s.*, broke. See Breke

Brast, *p.t. s.*, burst, broke. O.N.
brast, from *bresta* (to burst)

Brawn, *s.*, muscle. O.Fr. *braon*
(flesh). Germ.

Breech, *s.*, breeches. O.E.
brēc, pl., like ' feet ' and
' teeth '; ' breeches ' is a
double plural. Cf. children

Breed, *s.*, bread. O.E. *brēad*

Breek, *p.t. s. subj.*, would break

Breem, *s.*, bream, a fish. O.Fr.
bresmel, Fr. *brême.* Germ.

Breeth, *s.*, breath; **his swete
breeth,** his pleasant air.
O.E. *brǣð*

Breke, *v.*, break; **Brak,** *p.t. s.,*
broke; **Breek,** *p.t. s. subj.,*
would break. O.E. *brecan,
brǣc, brǣce*

Bren, *s.*, bran. O.Fr. *bren*

Brenne(n), *v.*, burn; **Brende,**
p.t. s., burned; **Brennynge,**
pres. p., burning; **Brend,**
p.p., burnt. O.N. *brenna*

Brest, *s.*, breast. O.E. *brēost*

Bretful, *adj.*, brim-full. O.E.
brerdful, with loss of *r.* Cf.
Swedish, *bräddfull*

Bretherhed, *s.*, brotherhood, religious guild. Cf. O.E. *brōðer,
dat. s.* of *brōðor* (brother)

Brid, *s.*, bird. O.E. *brid*

Brimstoon, *s.*, sulphur, sulphur-
ointment. O.E. *bryne* (burning) and *stān* (stone)

Bringe(n), *v.*, bring; **Broghte,
Broughte(n),** *p.t.* brought.
O.E. *bringan; brohte*

Broche, *s.*, brooch. O.Fr. *broche*
(spit, pin). Cf. L. *broccus*
(projecting, like teeth)

Brode, *adv.*, broadly, plainly,
coarsely

Brood, *adj.*, broad, large. O.E.
brād

Brouke, *s.*, enjoy. O.E. *brūcan.*
Cf. Ger. *brauchen* (use)

Broun, *adj.*, brown, sunburnt.
O.E. *brūn*

Brustle, *s.*, bristle. O.E.
byrst (burst) +*el* (diminutive)

Brydel, *s.*, bridle. O.E. *brīdel,*
Cf. *bregdan* (pull)

Bryghte, *adj.*, bright. O.E.
beorht, bryht

Bulle, *s.*, papal bull, edict. L.
bulla (seal)

Bulte, *v.*, bolt, sift; **bult it to
the bren,** sift the flour from
the bran. O.Fr. *bulter,* LL.
burra (red cloth)

Burdoun, *s.*, bass; **bar a
burdoun,** sang an accompani-

ment (in a deep bass voice). Fr. *bourdon*, LL. *burdo-nem* (drone)

Burgeys, *s.*, burgess, man of substance. O.Fr. *burgeis* (burgher), Fr. *bourgeois*. Germ.

Burie(n), *v.*, bury. Cf. O.E. *byrgan*. A Southern form

Burnissht, *p.p.*, burnished. O.Fr. *burnir*, *burniss-ant*. Germ. Cf. O.H.G., *brūn* (brown)

Busshel, *s.*, bushel. O.Fr. *boissel*. Cf. O.Fr. *boiste* (box)

But, *adv.*, but, only; but a litel, only a little; But, *conj.*, but, except, unless; but it were, but were there. O.E. *būtan*

But if, *conj.*, unless

Butiller, *s.*, butler, servant in charge of the wine. A.Fr. *bouteillier*. Cf. O.Fr. *bouteille* (bottle). Germ.

By, *adv.*, besides; *prep.* by; by weste, in the west. O.E. *bī*

Bycause that, *conj.*, because. Fr. *cause*, L. *caussa*

Byde, *v.*, wait. O.E. *bīdan*

Bye, *v.*, buy; Boughte, *p.t. s.*; boughte agayn, redeemed; Bought, *p.p.* O.E. *bycgan*, *bohte*

Bying, *s.*, buying

Byte, *v.*, bite, smart. O.E. *bītan*

Caas, Cas, *s.*, case, chance, mischance; in this caas, on this occasion; Caas, *pl.*, law-cases. O.Fr. *cas*, L. *cāsus* (fall, occasion)

Cacche(n), *v.*, catch; Caughte, *p.t. s.*, took; Kaught, *p.p.*, caught, taken. A.Fr. *cachier*, LL. *captiare* (to hunt)

Caityf, *s.*, prisoner, captive. A.Fr., *caitif*, L. *captivus* (captive)

Cake, *s.*, flat, round loaf of bread. Germ.

Calf, *s.*, calf (of leg). O.N. *kálfī*

Canon, *s.*, rule; the *Canon Medicinae*, a book by Avicenna. L. Gk. *Canon* (rule, standard). Cf. *canna* (cane)

Capitayn, *s.*, captain. O.Fr. *capitain*. Cf. L. *caput*

Capoun, *s.*, cock, fowl. O.E. *capun*. L. Gk.

Cappe, *s.*, cap, skull-cap; sette hir aller cappe, befooled them all. O.E. *cæppe*, from L. *cappa* (cape)

Cardinacle, *s.*, the host's perversion of cardiacle, palpitation of the heart. O.Fr. *cardiaque* (cardiac). Cf. Gk. *kardia* (heart)

Cardinales, *s. pl.*, cardinals, members of the Pope's council, so called because originally they were in charge of important (cardinal) churches. L. *cardinalis*. Cf. L. *cardo* (hinge)

Carf, *p.t. s.*, carved. See **Kerve**

Carie(n), *v.*, carry; Caried, Ycaried, *p.p.*, carried. A.Fr. *carier*. Cf. L. *carrus* (car)

Carl, *s.*, man, fellow. O.N. *karl* (churl)

Carpe(n), *v.*, chatter, prate. O.N. *karpa* (brag)

Cas, *s.*, case. See **Caas**

Caste(n), *v.*, cast; Caste, *p.t. s.*, threw; caste up, lifted up, raised; casten hem, resolved, Cast, *p.p.*, planned. O.N. *kasta*

Castel, *s.*, castle. O.E. and A.Fr. *castel*, from L. *castellum*, diminutive of L. *castrum* (fort)

Casuelly, *adv.*, by chance. Cf. Fr. *casuel*

Catel, *s.*, wealth, property; cattle. A.Fr. *catel*, L. *capitale* (chief property). Now 'cattle,' and a doublet of 'chattle'

Cause, *s.*, cause, reason for; cause first, first cause. O.Fr. *cause*, L. *caussa*

Ceint, *s.*, belt, girdle. O.Fr. *ceint*, L. *cinctum* (girded)

Celle, *s.*, small monastic house. L. *cella* (a small room)

Centaure, *s.*, lesser centaury, a plant

Certein, Certeyn, *adj.*, a certain, some; **Certeyn, Certeinly**, *adv.*, certainly, indeed. O.Fr. *certain*. Cf. L. *certus* (decided)

Certes, *adv.*, certainly. Cf. L. *certes*. Cf. L. *a certis* (from sure grounds)

Ceruce, *s.*, white lead, lead carbonate. L. Gk. *cērussa*

Chace, *v.*, chase, drive. O.F. *chacier*. L.L. *captiare* (to hunt); doublet of cacche(n), *q.v.*

Chambre, *s.*, room. Fr. *chambre*. L. *camera* (vaulted room)

Champioun, *s.*, wrestler, prize-fighter. O.Fr. *champion*, L. *campio-nem*. Cf. L. *campus* (field, camp)

Chaped, *adj.*, tipped with 'chapes' (*i.e.* metal caps) on the scabbard-point, capped. Fr. *chape* (cope, cape, cap). L. *capa*. Doublet of 'cap' and 'cape'

Chapeleine, *s.*, secretary, *lit.* chaplain. O.Fr. *chapelain*. Cf. LL. *cappella* (chapel)

Chapitre, *s.*, chapter. Fr. *chapitre*, L. *capitulum*

Chapman, *s.*, dealer, merchant. O.E. *céap-man*

Charge, *s.*, load, power. O.Fr. *charge* (burden)

Charitable, *adj.*, kind. O.Fr *charitable*. Cf. L. *cārus* (dear)

Charitee, *s.*, charity, love; for seinte charitee, for holy charity, in the name of charity. O.Fr. *charité*, L. *caritatem*. Cf. L. *cārus* (dear)

Chastitee, *s.*, chastity. O.Fr. *chasteté*; L. *castitas, castitatem* (purity)

Chaunce, *s.*, chance. O.Fr. *cheance*. L. *cadentia* (falling)

Chaunge(n), *v.*, change, exchange. O.Fr. *changer*. Cf. L. *cambire* (to exchange)

Chaunterie, *s.*, chapel or altar endowed for a priest to say mass for founder's soul. O.Fr. *chanterie*. Cf. Fr. *chanter* (chant), L. *cantāre* (sing)

Cheere, *s.*, face; behaviour, style; mirth, gladness. O.Fr. *chere*, L. *cara* (face)

Cherl, *s.*, churl, peasant. O.E. *ceorl*. Doublet of 'carl'

Cherubyn, *s.*, angelic being, gifted with divine knowledge; **Cherubynnes**, *poss.* Fr. *cherubin*, from Hebrew

Chese, *s.*, cheese. O.E. *cīese* or *cēse*, L. *cāseus*

Chevisaunce, *s.*, dealing for profit, borrowing or lending at interest. O.Fr. *chevissance*. Cf. O.Fr. *chevir*, Fr. *achever* (to complete); cf. L. *caput* (head)

Child, *s.*, child, boy; **Children**, *pl.*; children an heep, a number of boys. O.E. *cild, cildru, pl.*

Childhede, *s.*, childhood

Chirche, *s.*, church; **Chirchedore**, *s.*, church-door. O.E. *cirice*

Chivachye, *s.*, cavalry raid; in chivachye, on raids. O.Fr.

chevauchiée (cavalry). Cf. L. *caballus* (horse)

Chivalrye, *s.*, knightly conduct, adventure. O.Fr. *chevalerie*. Cf. L. *caballarius* (horse-soldier)

Choys, *s.*, choice; free choys, free will. O.Fr. *chois*. Cf. *choisir* (choose). Germ.

Chuk, *int.*, chuck! the call of a fowl

Chukketh, 3 *pr. s.*, chucks, clucks

Chyde, *v.*, chide, reproach. O.E. *cīdan*

Citee, *s.*, city. O.Fr. *cité*, L. *cīvitas, cīvitatem*

Clad, *p.p.*, clothed. See Clothen

Clappe(n) *v.*, chatter, talk noisily. O.N. *klappa* (to pat)

Clause, *s.*, sentence; in a clause, shortly, briefly. Fr. *clause*, L. *clausa* (conclusion)

Cleer, *adj.*, clear, bright. O.Fr. *cler*, Fr. *clair*, L. *clārus*

Cleere, Cleerly, *adv.*, clearly

Clene, *adj.*, *adv.*, clean, pure, finely, entirely. O.E. *clǣne*

Clennesse, *s.*, purity

Clense, *v.*, cleanse, make clean. O.E. *clǣnsian*

Clepe(n), *v.*, call, name; men clepen, men clepeth, people call; Cleped, ycleped, *p.p.*, called. O.E. *cleopian*

Clergeon, *s.*, chorister. O.Fr. *clerjon* (little cleric or scholar). Cf. O.Fr. *clerc*, LL. *clericus* (clergyman)

Clerk, *s.*, cleric, *i.e.* clergyman or scholar; Clerkis, *pl.* O.Fr. *clerc*, L.Gk. *clericus* (clergyman)

Clinke, *v.*, tinkle; Clinking, *s.*, tinkling

Cloisterer, *s.*, one who lives in a cloister

Cloistre, *s.*, cloister. O.Fr. *cloistre*. L. *claustrum* (barrier)

Cloke, *s.*, cloak. O.Fr. *cloque*, LL. *cloca* (bell-shaped cape)

Clokke, *s.*, clock. Cf. M.Dutch *clocke*, LL. *cloca* (bell)

Clomben, *p.p.*, climbed. See Clymben

Cloos, *adj.*, closed, shut. Fr. *clos*, *p.p.* of *clore*, L. *claudere*

Clooth-makyng, *s.*, cloth-manufacture

Clos, *s.*, yard. Fr. *clos*, L. *clausum* (shut in)

Clothe(n), *v.*, clothe; Clothed, Clad, *p.p.*, clothed, covered. O.E. *clāðian*

Clout, *s.*, cloth, piece of clothing. O.E. *clūt*

Clymben, *v.*, climb; Clomben, *p.p.*, ascended. O.E. *climban, clumben, p.p.*

Cod, *s.*, bag, stomach. O.E. *codd* (bag). Cf. *pease-cod* (pea-pod)

Cofre, *s.*, coffer, strong-box. O.Fr. *cofre*, L. Gk. *cophinus* (basket)

Cok, *s.*, cock; Cokkes, *poss.*; our aller cok, the rouser of us all. O.E. *cocc*. Hence cok! cok! the call of a fowl when startled

Cold, *adj.* (1) cold; (2) disastrous (N.P. Tale, 486). (1) O.E. *ceald, cāld*. (2) O.N. *kaldr*

Colere, Colera, *s.*, the choleric humour, bile, anger. L. *cholera* (bile). Cf. Gk. *kholē* (bile)

Colerik, *adj.*, bilious, bad tempered

Col-fox, *s.*, a fox with black markings. O.E. *col* (coal) + *fox*

Colpons, *s. pl.*, shreds, strips; by colpons, in locks. O.Fr. *colpon*. Cf. O.Fr. *colper* (hit); cf. L. Gk. *colaphus* (a blow)

Come, *v.*, come; Comth, *pr. s.*,

comes; Cam, *p.t. s.*, came; **Coomen**, *p.t. pl.*, came; in coomen, came in; **Comen**, **ycome(n)**, *p.p.*, come; was **come(n)**, had come; **Com**, *imp. s.*; Cometh, *imp. pl.*, come. O.E. *cuman*, *cōm-on*, *cumen*

Commissioun, *s.*, commission, royal warrant conferring authority. L. *commissionem*

Commune, *adj.*, common, general, public; as in commune, in common, commonly. O.Fr. *commun(e)*, L. *communis*

Compaignable, *adj.*, companionable, sociable

Compaignye, *s.*, company, fellowship. O.Fr. *compaignie*. Cf. L. *panis* (bread)

Compeer, *s.*, friend, comrade. O.Fr. *comper*. Cf. L. *par* (equal)

Compleet, Complet, *adj.*, completed, finished. L. *complētus* (filled)

Compleyne, *v.*, complain; **Compleyned**, *p.t. s.* O.Fr. *complaindre*, *complaignant*, L. *com-plangere* (bewail)

Complexioun, *s.*, temperament; **Compleccions**, *pl.*, combination of humours. L. *com-plexio-nem* (combination)

Composicioun, *s.*, agreement. L. *compositio* (placing together)

Comynge, *s.*, coming

Conclusioun, *s.*, decision, judgment; as for conclusioun, in conclusion, finally. L. *con-clūsio-nem*

Concubyn, *s.*, concubine, secondary wife. L. *concubīna*

Confiture, *s.*, preparation (of drugs). Fr. *confiture* (jam)

Confort, *s.*, comfort; **doon you confort**, amuse you. O.Fr. *confort*. Cf. L. *fortis* (strong)

Congregacioun, *s.*, crowd, assembly. Fr. *congrégation*. Cf. L. *grex* (flock)

Conjure, *v.*, entreat, appeal solemnly (to). O.Fr. *conjurer*, L. *con-jurare* (swear an oath)

Conscience, *s.*, disposition, considerateness; conscience. L. *con-scientia* (knowledge, feeling)

Conseil, *s.*, counsel, secret, intention; **shal it be conseil**, let it be a secret. O.Fr. *conseil*, L. *con-silium* (consultation)

Conseille, *v.*, to counsel

Construe, *v.*, translate. L. *con-struere* (build)

Contek, *s.*, strife, quarrel. O.Fr. *contec*

Contenaunce, *s.*, appearance. O.Fr. *contenance* (aspect, behaviour). L. *continentia* (restraint)

Contour, *s.*, assistant tax-collector or auditor. O.Fr. *conteor* (lawyer). Cf. L. *com-putare* (reckon)

Contree, *s.*, country, district. O.Fr. *contrée*. LL. *contrata* (land lying *contra* (opposite)). Cf. Ger. *Gegen-d*

Coomb, *s.*, comb. O.E. *cāmb*

Cop, *s.*, top. O.E. *cop*

Cope, *s.*, cope, cape. L. *capa* (cape)

Coppe, *s.*, cup. O.E. *cuppa*

Corage, *s.*, heart; mood, spirit; **Corages**, *pl.*, natures. O.Fr. *corage*. Cf. L. *cor* (heart)

Cordial, *s.*, cordial, medicine that stimulates the heart. Cf. L. *cor* (heart)

Corny, *adj.*, strong in corn or malt. Cf. O.E. *corn* (corn)

Corpus, *s.*, body; **Corpus bones**, a nonsensical oath on the

analogy of L. *corpus domini*, body of the Lord. L. *corpus* (body)

Correccioun, *s.*, correction, admonishing. L. *correctio-nem*

Cors, *s.*, body, corpse. O.Fr. *cors*, L. *corpus*

Cosin, *s.*, cousin; **Cosin**, *adj.*, akin to, related to. O.Fr. *cosin*, L. *consobrinus* (cousin, relation)

Cost, *s.*, expense. O.Fr. *cost*. Cf. L. *constāre* (to agree, cost)

Cote (1), *s.*, cottage. O.E. *cot*, *cote*

Cote (2), *s.*, coat, gown. O.Fr. *cote*, Fr. *cotte* (petticoat), LL. *cotta*

Countrefete, *v.*, imitate. O.Fr. *contrefet*, *contrefait*, *p.p.* of *contrefaire*. Cf. L. *contra* (against); *facere* (make)

Courtepy, *s.*, short coat. M. Dutch, *korte pie* (short coat)

Coveityse, *s.*, covetousness. O.Fr. *coveitise*. Cf. L. *cupīdo* (desire)

Covent, *s.*, convent, monastery. A.Fr. *covent*, L. *conventus* (assembly)

Coverchief, *s.*, kerchief, headdress. O.Fr. *couvrechief* (head-cover)

Covyne, *s.*, trickery, fraud. A.Fr. *covine*, O.Fr. *couvine* (agreement), LL. *convenium* (agreement)

Coy, *adj.*, quiet, shy. Fr. *coi*, L. *quietus*

Craft, *s.*, skill; art, trade; O.E. *cræft*

Crepe, *v.*, creep. O.E. *crēopan*

Cristal, *adj.*, crystal, transparent; cristal stones, flasks. O.Fr. *cristal*, L. *crystallum*, Gk. *krustallos* (ice, crystal)

Cristemasse, *s.*, Christmas

Cristen, *adj.*, Christian. O.E. *cristen*

Cristendom, *s.*, Christian lands. O.E. *cristen-dōm* (Christianity)

Croked, *adj.*, crooked. O.N. *krōkr* (hook)

Cronicle, *s.*, chronicle. A.Fr. *cronicle*, LL. *chronica*. Cf. Gk. *khronos* (time)

Crop, *s.*, sprout, top; **Croppes**, *pl.*, tops of plants, new leaves. O.E. *cropp*

Crowe(n) *v.*, crow; him crow-eth, crows. O.E. *crāwan*

Croys, *s.*, cross. O.Fr. *crois*, L. *crux*, *crucem*

Crul, *adj.*, curly; **Crulle**, *pl.*

Crye, *v.*, cry, cry out; **Cryde(n)**, *p.t.* O.Fr. *crier*, L. *quiritare* (call for help). Cf. L. *Quir-ītes* (Romans)

Cryke, *s.*, creek, mouth of river

Curat, *s.*, one who has a 'cure' or parish, parish priest. L. *curātus*. Cf. L. *cura* (care)

Cure, *s.*, care, heed; took cure, took care; thyn honeste cure, thy care for honourable things. O.Fr. *cure*, L. *cura* (care)

Curious, *adj.*, careful, skilful; beautiful, elaborately made. O.Fr. *curios*, L. *curiosus* (careful)

Curs, *s.*, excommunication, curse. O.Fr. *curs*

Curse(n), *v.*, excommunicate; **Cursed**, *p.p.*, *adj.*, accursed, wicked, abominable. O.E. *cursian*

Cursednesse, *s.*, wickedness

Cursing, *s.*, excommunication

Curteis, *adj.*, courteous. O.Fr. *corteis*. Cf. O.Fr. *cort* (court) L. *cohortem* (cohort)

Curteisye, *s.*, courtesy, courteous manners. O.Fr. *cortesie*. See Curteis

Cut, *s.*, lots, cut-straw. Cf. Welsh, *cwt* (a lot)

Cynk, *num. adj.*, five; **cynk and treye,** five and three. O.Fr. *cinq* (5), O.Fr. *trei(s)* (3)

Daliaunce, *s.*, small talk, conversation; **dooth he daliaunce,** he makes conversation. Cf. O.Fr. *dallier* (to converse), Germ.

Damoysele, *s.*, damsel, young lady; O.Fr. *damoisele,* L. *dominicella*

Dampnable, *adj.*, damnable. O.Fr. *damnable,* L. *damnābilis* (harmful)

Dampnacioun, *s.*, condemnation. L. *damnātiō-nem*

Dar, *v.*, dare; **Dorste,** *p.t. s.*, durst, might venture (to). O.E. *dearr, dorste*

Daun, *s.*, sir, master, a title of respect given to clerics. O.Fr. *dan,* L. *dominus*

Daunce, *s.*, dance; **the olde daunce,** the old game, all that was to be known. O.Fr. *dance.* Germ.

Dauncen, *v.*, dance. O.Fr. *danser,* Germ.

Daunger, *s.*, power; peril, danger; **in daunger,** in his power. O.Fr. *dangier* (dominion), LL. *dominiārium* (lordship). Cf. L. *dominus* (lord)

Daungerous, *adj.*, domineering, difficult. O.Fr. *dangeros*

Daweninge, *s.*, dawn. O.N. Cf. Danish, *dagning* (dawn)

Day, *s.*, day; **on a day,** one day; **dayes lyght,** daylight. O.E. *dæg*

Dayerye, *s.*, dairy. Cf. O.E. *dæge* (dairy-woman)

Dayesye, *s.*, daisy. O.E. *dæges ēage* (day's eye)

Debate, *v.*, contend, quarrel.

O.Fr. *de-batre* (strike). L. *de* (down)+*bat(u)ere* (beat)

Debonaire, *adj.*, gracious, of good manners. O.Fr. *deboneire* (of good stock). Fr. *débonnaire* (gentle). Cf. L. *ārea* (site, place)

Deceyve, *v.*, deceive. O.Fr. *decevoir* or *deceivre,* L. *decipere*

Declare, *v.*, make clear, make known. L., *dēclārāre* (make clear). Cf. L. *clārus* (clear)

Dede, *s.*, deed, action; **in dede,** indeed. O.E. *dēd* or *dēd*

Deed, *adj.*, dead; **Dede,** *def.* O.E. *dēad* ; **Were deed** : died

Deef, *adj.*, deaf. O.E. *dēaf*

Deel, *s.*, deal, share; **a ful greet deel,** a very great deal; **never a deel,** not a bit. O.E., *dēl*

Deelen, *v.*, to deal, be friendly with. O.E. *dēlan* (divide)

Deere, *adj.*, dear; *adv.*, dearly. O.E. *dēore*

Dees, *s. pl.*, dice (*sing.,* **Dee**). O.Fr. *dē, des, pl.,* L. *datum, data, pl.* (given thing)

Deeth, *s.*, death; **the Black Death** (plague). O.E. *dēaþ*

Defame, *s.*, dishonour. O.Fr. *defame* (dishonour). Cf. L. *fāma* (rumour)

Defaute, *s.*, fault; sin. O.Fr. *defaute.* Cf. L. *fallere* (deceive)

Defende(n), *v.*, forbid; **wol I you defenden hasardrye,** I will forbid gambling for your benefit (*Ethic Dative*) ; **Defended,** *p.p.* as *adj.,* forbidden. O.Fr. *défendre,* L. *defendere* (defend)

Degree, *s.*, rank, position; degree of circular measure. O.Fr. *degré.* Cf. L. *gradus* (step)

Deigne, *v.*, deign; **him deigned**

nat, *p.t. impers.*, he disdained. O.Fr. *deigner*, L. *dignarī*

Deitee, *s.,* Deity, God. Fr. *déité*, L. *deitas*. Cf. L. *de-us* (God)

Delices, *s. pl.,* delights, pleasures. Fr. *délices*, L. *deliciae*

Deliver, *adj.,* nimble, agile, deft. O.Fr. *delivre* (free). Cf. L. *liber* (free)

Delve, *v.,* dig. O.E. *delfan*

Delyt, *s.,* delight; *pleyn delyt*, complete happiness. O.Fr. *delit*. Cf. O.Fr. *delitier*, L. *delectare* (to delight)

Departe(n), *v.,* part, divide; **Departed,** *p.p.,* divided. O.Fr. *departir*. Cf. L. *partire* (divide)

Depe, *adv.,* deeply. O.E. *dēope*

Desdeyn, *s.,* disdain, contempt. O.Fr. *desdeign*. Cf. O.Fr. *desdeigner*, LL. *dis-dignare* (despise); cf. L. *dignarī* (to be worthy)

Deserve, *v.,* deserve; *wol deserve*, wishes to be entitled to, asks for. O.Fr. *deservir*, L. *de-servire* (serve devotedly)

Desolaat, *adj.,* desolate, abandoned; *holden desolaat*, thought to be abandoned. L. *desolātus* (forsaken). Cf. L. *sōlus*, alone

Despitous, *adj.,* arrogant, cruel. O.Fr. *despiteus*. Cf. O.Fr. *despire*, L. *de-spicere* (despise)

Desport, *s.,* cheerfulness, amusement. O.Fr. *desport*. Cf. O.Fr. *deporter* or *desporter* (amuse); L. *disportare* (carry away)

Despyt, *s.,* contempt, disdain; *in your despyt,* in spite of you, in contempt of you. O.Fr. *despit,* L. *despectus* (contempt)

Destinee, *s.,* fate, destiny. O.Fr. *destiné,* L. *destinātum* (design)

Destourbe, *v.,* disturb; **to destourbe of,** to disturb in. O.Fr. *destorber.* Cf. L. *turba* (crowd)

Dette, *s.,* debt. O.Fr. *dete* or *dette,* L. *dēbitum* (debt)

Dettelees, *adj.,* free from debt

Devel, *s.,* devil. O.E. *dēofol*

Devys, *s.,* devise, direction; **at his devys,** according to his will. O.Fr. *devis,* L. *divīsus* (distribution)

Devyse, *v.,* devise; relate, tell; describe; **ther as I you devyse,** to that place which I mention to you. O.Fr. *deviser,* L. *divisare* (share)

Deye, *s.,* dairy-woman. O.E. *dǣge* (farm-woman)

Deye(n), *v.,* to die; **Deyde,** *p.t. s.,* died. O.N. *deyja*

Deyinge, *s.,* death

Deyntee, *s.,* dainty, delicacy. O.Fr. *daintié,* L. *dignitas* (worthiness)

Deyntee, *adj.,* dainty, rare, good

Deys, *s.,* dais, place of the high table in hall. O.Fr. *deis,* L. *discus* (dish, table)

Dich, *s.,* ditch. O.E. *dic* (ditch, dyke)

Dide, *p.t. s.,* did. See *Do*

Diete, *s.,* diet, usual food. O.Fr. *diete.* L. Gk. *diæta* (mode of living)

Diffye, *v.,* defy, challenge. O.Fr. *defier,* LL. *diffidare* (distrust), L. *diffidere.* Cf. *fīdus* (trusty)

Digestyves, *s. pl.,* substances aiding digestion

Digne, *adj.,* worthy, honourable; proud, haughty. Fr. *digne,* L. *dignus* (worthy)

Diocise, *s.,* diocese. O.Fr. *diocise,* L. Gk. *diœcēsis*

Dischevelee, *adj.*, dishevelled, with untidy hair. O.Fr. *deschevelé*. Cf. O.Fr. *chevel* (hair), L. *capillus*

Discrecioun, *s.*, prudence, judgment. O.Fr. *discrecion*, L. *dis-cretio-nem* (discernment). Cf. L. *cernere* (sift)

Disese, *s.*, discomfort, pain. O.Fr. *desaise*

Dishonour, *s.*, harm, injury. O.Fr. *deshonor*. Cf. L. *honor* (honour)

Dispence, *s.*, spending, expenditure. O.Fr. *dispens(er)* (to distribute), L. *dispensare* (to weigh out)

Displese, *v.*, displease. O.Fr. *desplaisir*, L. *dis+placēre* (please)

Displesance, *s.*, annoyance, displeasure; *doon us displesances*, annoy us

Disport, *s.*, sport, amusement. O.Fr. *desport(er)*, L. *disportare* (to carry away)

Disputisoun, *s.*, dispute, argument. O.Fr. *desputoison* (debate), A.Fr. *desputeison*. Cf. L. *dis-putare* (argue)

Dissimulour, *s.*, dissembler. Cf. L. *dissimulātor*

Distaf, *s.*, distaff, winding-stick (for wool). O.E. *distæf*

Divyne, *adj.*, divine. L. *divīnus*

Divyne, *v.*, guess, suppose. L. *divinare* (predict)

Doctour, *s.*, doctor, physician; theologian. O.Fr. *doctour*, L. *doctor* (teacher)

Doctrine, *s.*, learning, instruction. L. *doctrīna* (instruction)

Doke, *s.*, duck. O.E. *duca(m.)*, *duce* (*f.*)

Dokked, *p.p.*, docked, cut short

Dominacioun, *s.*, dominion. L. *dominatio-nem*. Cf. *dominus* (lord)

Dong, *s.*, dung; **Dong-carte**, dung-cart. O.E. *dung*

Donge(n), *v.*, dung, manure

Do, Doon, *v.*, do, make; cause; *do my labour, do my task*; *do my diligence, do my best*; *doon us honge, have us hanged*; *do no fors*, pay no heed; **Doth, Dooth**, 3 *pr. s.*, does, makes; **Dide**, *p.t. s.*, did; *men dide*, one should do; **Diden**, *p.t. pl.*, did; **Ydoon**, *p.p.*, done. O.E. *dōn, dyde, gedōn*

Doom, *s.*, judgment, decision. O.E. *dōm*

Dore, *s.*, door; *out at dores*, out of doors. O.E. *duru*

Dorste, *p.t.*, durst, might venture (to). See Dar

Doughter, *s.*, daughter; **Doughtres, Doughtren**, *pl.* O.E. *dohtor, dohtru, pl.*

Doumb, *adj.*, dumb. O.E. *dūmb*

Doun, *adv.*, down; *up and doun*, backwards and forwards. O.E. *dūne*

Doute, *s.*, doubt; *out of doute, doutelees*, doubtless, indeed. O.Fr. *doute*. Cf. *douter*, L. *dubitare* (doubt)

Douve, *s.*, dove. O.N. *dūfa*

Drawe(n), *v.*, draw, attract; *he dide hem drawe*, he had them drawn; **Drough**, *p.t. s.*, drew, approached; **Drawe, ydrawe(n)**, *p.p.*, drawn; **Draweth**, *imper. pl.*, draw. O.E. *dragan*

Drecche, *v.*, vex; **Drecched**, *p.p.*, vexed, troubled. O.E. *dreccean* (afflict)

Drede, *s.*, dread, fear; *it is no drede*, without a doubt, doubtless

Drede(n), *v.*, dread, fear; *intrans.*, to be afraid; *no dremes for to drede*, not to be afraid of dreams; Dredeth, *imp. pl.*, fear. O.E. *on-drǣdan*

Dreem, *s.*, dream; Dremes, *pl.* O.E. *drēam* (joy), influenced in meaning by O.N. *draumr* (dream)

Dremynges, *s. pl.*, dreams

Drenche(n), *v.*, drown; Dreynt, *p.p.*, drowned. O.E. *drencean* (to cause to drink)

Dresse(n), *v.*, prepare, set in order. O.Fr. *dresser*, LL. *directiare* (to set in order). Cf. *directus* (straight)

Dreynt, *p.p.*, drowned. See Drenche(n)

Drinke(n), *v.*, drink; Drank, *p.t. s.*, drank; Dronken, *p.t. pl.*, drank; Dronke(n), *p.p.*, drunk. O.E. *drincan*; *dranc*, *druncon*; *druncen*

Drinke, *s.*, drink, strong drink. O.E. *drinc(e)*

Drogges, *s. pl.*, drugs. Fr. *drogue*

Dronke(n), *p.p.* as *adj.*, drunken. See Drinke(n)

Dronkelewe, *adj.*, habitually drunken. O.E. *druncenlǣwe* (betrayed by drink)

Dronkenesse, *s.*, drunkenness. O.E. *drunce(n)ness*

Drough, *p.t.s.*, drew, approached. See Drawe(n)

Drouped, *p.t. s.*, drooped, fell short. O.N. *drūpa* (droop)

Dryve(n), *v.*, drive; to dryve the day awey, to wile away the time; Driven, *p.p.*, driven. O.E. *drīfan*

Duzeyne, *s.*, dozen, twelve. O.Fr. *dozeine*; L. *duodecim* (O.Fr. *doze*)+*ēna*

Dwelle(n), *v.*, dwell, remain, linger; Dwelte, *p.t. s.*; Dwellinge, *pr. p.* O.E. *dwellan* (lead astray, dwell)

Dye(n), *v.*, die; Dyde, *p.t. s.*,

died; Dyed, *p.p.* Another form of Deye(n), *q.v.*

Dyere, *s.*, dyer. Cf. O.E. *dēag* (dye)

Dyke(n), *v.*, dig ditches or drains. O.E. *dīcian*

Ecclesiaste, *s.*, preacher, from the Old Testament book, 'Ecclesiastes, or the Preacher'

Ech(e), *adj.*, each. O.E. *ǣlc*

Echon, Echoon, *s.* and *pron.*, each one; everyone; echon the Jewes, every one of the Jews

Eek, *adv.*, eke, also, moreover. O.E. *ēac*

Eet, *p.t. s.*, ate. See Ete(n)

Effect, *s.*, result, reality; in effect, in fact, in reality. O.Fr. *effect*, L. *effectus*

Eir, *s.*, air. Fr. *air*, L.Gk. *aer*

Elder, *adj.*, older; Eldres, *s. pl.*, forefathers

Ellebor, *s.*, black hellebore or Christmas Rose

Elles, *adv.*, else, otherwise; somewhat elles, something else. O.E. *elles*

Elleswhere, *adv.*, elsewhere. O.E. *elles-hwǣr*

Elvish, *adj.*, elfish, strange, like a creature from another world. O.E. *ælf*+*ish*

Embassadour, *s.*, ambassador. O.Fr. *ambassader* (to negotiate). Cf. L. *ambactus* (servant)

Embrouded, *p.p.*, *adj.*, embroidered. O.Fr. *embroder*

Emeraude, *s.*, emerald. O.Fr. *esmeraude*, L.Gk. *smaragdus*

Empoisonere, *s.*, poisoner

Empoisonyng, *s.*, poisoning. O.Fr. *empoisoner* (to poison). Cf. L. *pōtio-nem* (poison)

Enbrace, *v.*, embrace. O.Fr. *embracer*. Cf. L. *bracchium* (arm)

16 P

Encombre, *v.*, encumber; **Encombred,** *p.p.*, encumbered, stuck fast. O.Fr. *encombrer*

Encreese(n), *v.*, increase. O.Fr. *encreistre*, L. *increscere* (grow)

Endyng, *s.*, ending, death. O.E. *endung*

Endyte, *v.*, dictate; compose. O.Fr. *enditer*, L. *indictare* (dictate, compose)

Engendre(n), *v.*, beget, be produced; **Engendred,** *p.p.*, produced. O.Fr. *engendrer*, L. *ingenerare* (generate)

Engyned, *p.p.*, tortured, racked. Cf. O.Fr. *engin* (artifice), L. *ingenium* (invention)

Enoynt, *p.p.*, anointed. O.Fr. *enoint*, L. *inunctum* (*p.p.*), (oiled)

Ensample, *s.*, example. A.Fr. *ensample*, O.Fr. *essample*, L. *exemplum*

Entencioun, *s.*, intention, purpose. L. *intentio* (exertion)

Entente, *s.*, desire, intention; set was his entente, his heart was fixed. O.Fr. *entente*, L. *intentus*

Entraille, *s.*, entrails, bowels. O.Fr. *entraille*, L. *interānea* (entrails, *lit.* ' inwards ')

Entre, *v.*, enter, set down in writing. O.Fr. *entrer*, L. *intrare* (to go within)

Entuned, *p.p.*, intoned, chanted. Cf. Fr. *ton*, L.Gk. *tonus* (tone, tune)

Envoluped, *p.p.*, enveloped, involved. O.Fr. *envoleper* or *envoluper* (to wrap up)

Envyned, *adj.*, stocked with wine. O.Fr. *enviné* (mellowed with wine). Cf. L. *vinum* (wine)

Equinoxial, *s.*, line of the equator on the celestial globe, celestial equator. L. *aequinoctialis* (pertaining to the equinox)

Er, *adv.*, *conj.*, *prep.*, before; **Er that,** before. O.E. *ǣr*

Erchedeken, *s.*, archdeacon. O.E. *ǣrcediacon*

Ere, *s.*, ear. O.E. *ēare*

Erly, *adv.*, early. O.E. *ǣrlice*

Erme(n), *v.*, grieve. O.E. *earmian*

Erst, *adv.*, first, at first; before; at erst, for the first time; long erst er, long before. O.E. *ǣrest* (first of all)

Erthe, *s.*, earth, land. O.E. *eorþe*

Eschaunge, *s.*, exchange. A.Fr. *eschaunge*, O.Fr. *eschange*. Cf. LL. *excambiare* (to exchange)

Eschewe, *v.*, avoid; **Eschewed,** *p.p.* O.Fr. *eschiver*, *eschuer*. Germ.

Ese, *s.*, ease, comfort; **do you ese,** give pleasure to you; wel at ese, very comfortable. O.Fr. *aise*

Ese(n), *s.*, ease; entertain; **Esed,** *p.p.*, entertained, made comfortable

Esily, *adv.*, at ease, comfortably

Espye, *s.*, spy. O.Fr. *espie* (a spy). Germ.

Espye, *v.*, catch sight of, see; finally gan so fer espye, did at last discover. O.Fr. *espier*. Germ.

Est, *s.*, east. O.E. *ēast*

Estaat, Estat, *s.*, state, condition; rank. O.Fr. *estat*, L. *status*

Estatlich, *adj.*, stately, imposing

Esy, *adj.*, easy; kind, moderate; but **esy of dispense,** only slow to spend money. O.Fr. *aisié* (*p.p.*)

Ete(n), *v.*, eat; **Eet,** *p.t. s.*, ate; **Ete(n),** *p.p.*, eaten; **Ete,** *imp. s.*; ete hem in, eat them up. O.E. *etan*; *ǣt, ǣton* (*pl.*); *eten*

Even(e), *adj.*, even; of evene lengthe, of average height. O.E. *efen*

Even-song, *s.*, evensong. O.E. *æfensang*

Even-tyde, *s.*, evening. O.E. *æfen-tid*

Ever, *adv.*, ever, always; ever in oon, continually. O.E. *æfre*

Everemoore, Everemo, *adv.*, evermore, continually

Everich, Every, *adj.*, every, each one. O.E. *æfre-ælc* (ever-each)

Everichon, *pron.*, every one

Everydeel, *adv.*, every bit, entirely

Expoun(d)e, *v.*, expound, explain. L. *exponere* (to lay down)

Expresly, *adv.*, expressly, definitely stated

Ey, *s.*, egg. O.E. *æg*; *ægru*, *pl.*

Ey, *int.*, eh! what!

Eye, *s.*, eye; **Eyen**, *pl.*, eyes. O.E. *ēage*; *eagan*, *pl.*

Eyle, *v.*, ail. O.E. *eglian*

Eyther, *adj.*, *pron.*, each, both. O.E. *ægþer*

Facultee, *s.*, faculty, profession; as by his facultee, with his licence as limitour, with his position. L. *facultas* (ability)

Fader, *s.*, father; **Fader, Fadres**, *poss.*, father's; fader kin, ancestors. O.E. *fæder*

Faille(n), *v.*, fail. O.Fr. *faillir*. Cf. L. *fallere* (deceive)

Fair, *adj.*, pretty, beautiful; good, excellent; a fair for the maistrye, an exceedingly good one. O.E. *fæger*

Faire, *adv.*, well, honestly, courteously. O.E. *fægre*

Fairnesse, *s.*, beauty of life, goodness, gentleness

Falding, *s.*, coarse cloth

Falle(n), *v.*, fall; befall, happen; gan fallen in suspecioun, became suspicious; as it wolde falle, just as luck would have it; **Fel, Fell, Fil**, *p.t. s.*, fell, happened; him fil, there happened to him; **Falle, Fallen, Yfalle**, *p.p.*, fallen, befallen, happened. O.E. *fallan*, *fēoll*, *fallen*

Fals, *adj.*, false; fals sweryng, perjury. O.E. *fals*, L. *falsus*

Falsnesse, *s.*, falsehood

Famulier, *adj.*, servile, on friendly terms. Confusion of L. *famularis* (servile) with L. *familiaris* (familiar)

Famyne, *s.*, famine, hunger. O.Fr. *famine*. Cf. L. *fames* (hunger)

Fare(n), *v.*, fare, go; behave; **Faren**, *p.p.*, fared, gone. O.E. *faran* (go)

Farsed, *p.p.*, stuffed. Fr. *farcir*, L. *farcire*

Faste, *adv.*, fast; hard; faste by, near; ful faste, quickly. O.E. *fæste*

Faste(n), *v.*, fast; **Fastynge**, *pres. p.* O.E. *fæstan* (keep a fast)

Faught, *p.t. s.*, fought. See **Fighten**

Fayn, *adv.*, gladly. O.E. *fægen* (fain)

Fecche(n), *s.*, fetch; **Fet**, *p.p.*, fetched. O.E. *fetian, feccean*

Fede(n), *v.*, feed; **Fedde**, *p.t. s.*, fed. O.E. *fēdan*. Cf. O.E. *fōda* (food)

Feelynge, *s.*, feeling, emotion. Cf. O.E. *fēlan* (to feel)

Feend, *s.*, fiend, devil. O.E. *fēond* (enemy)

Feer(e), *s.*, fear. O.E. *fær*

Fee-simple, *s.*, estate which can be bequeathed at the pleasure of the owner, absolute property. Cf. O.Fr. *fee* (salary), *fief* (feudal estate or appointment), LL. *feudum* (feudal estate)

Feeste, *s.*, feast, banquet. O.Fr. *feste*, L. *festa*

Feith, *s.*, faith. O.Fr. *feid, fei*, L. *fides*

Felawe, *s.*, fellow; a good felawe, a great rascal, a disreputable scoundrel. O.N. *félagi* (partner)

Felaweship, *s.*, company, companionship

Fele(n), *v.*, feel; Felte, *p.t. s.* O.E. *fēlan*

Felicitee, *s.*, felicity; felicitee parfyt, the chief good of life, *lit.* perfect felicity. L. *fēlicitas*

Felonye, *s.*, crime. O.Fr. *felonie* (violence). Cf. O.Fr. *fel* (cruel), L. *fel* (bile, anger)

Fen, *s.*, section of Avicenna's *Canon Medicinae*. Arabic, *fann* (a part of a science)

Fer, *adv.* far; fer by weste, far in the west; fer in a yeerd, a long way down a yard; Ferre, Ferrer, *comp.*, farther; Ferreste, *sup.*, farthest. O.E. *feorr; fierra; fierresta*

Ferme, *s.*, fixed payment. O.Fr. *ferme*, LL. *firma* (fixed payment)

Fern, *adj.*, ancient, distant; Ferne, *pl.* O.E. *fyrn* (old). Kent

Ferther, *adj.*, *adv.*, farther, further

Ferthing, *s.*, bit, small portion. O.E. *feorðung* (fourth part)

Fest, *s.*, fist. O.E. *fȳst*, Kent. *fēst*

Festne(n), *v.*, fasten. O.E. *fæstnian*

Fet, *p.p.*, fetched. See Fecche(n)

Fetis, *adj.*, pretty, neat, well

formed. O.Fr. *faitis*, LL. *facticius* (artificial)

Fetisly, *adv.*, prettily, neatly

Fey, *s.*, faith. O.Fr. *fei*, L. *fides*

Feyne, *v.*, feign; Feyned, *p.p.*, O.Fr. *feindre, feign-ant* (pretend), L. *fingere* (to shape)

Fighte(n), *v.*, fight; Faught, *p.t. s.*, fought; Foughten, *p.p.*, fought. O.E. *feohtan; feaht; fohten*

Figure, *s.*, shape, figure of speech. L. *figūra*. Cf. L. *fingere* (to shape)

Fil, *p.t. s.*, fell, happened. See Falle(n)

Finch, *s.*, small bird; pulle a finch, cheat a dupe. O.E. *finc*

Fithele, *s.*, fiddle. O.E. *fiðele*. Cf. L. *vitula* (calf)

Flaterye, *s.*, flattery. O.Fr. *flaterie*. Cf. *flater* (make flat or smooth). Germ.

Flatour, *s.*, flatterer

Flee(n) (1), *v.*, fly; Flough, 2 *p.t. s.*, flewest; Fleigh, 3 *p.t. s.*, flew; Flowen, *p.t. pl.*, flew. O.E. *flēogan; flēah, flugon; flogen*

Flee(n) (2), *v.*, flee, escape; Fled, *p.t.* O.E. *flēon, st.*

Fleigh, *p.t. s.*, flew. See Flee(n) (1)

Flessh, *s.*, flesh, meat. O.E. *flǣsc*

Flex, *s.*, flax. O.E. *fleax*

Flok, *s.*, flock, band. O.E. *flocc*

Florins, *s. pl.*, florins, gold coins worth 6s.

Flough, 2 *p.t. s.*, flewest. See Flee(n) (1)

Flour, *s.*, flower; Flour-de-lys, *s.*, fleur-de-lis, the white lily (so called) of the coat-of-arms of France. O.Fr. *flour*, L. *flos, florem*; O.Fr. *lis*, L. *lilium* (lily)

Flowen, *p.t. pl., flew.* See Flee(n) (1)

Floytinge, *s.,* whistling. Cf. O.Fr. *flaüter* (play the flute)

Folowe(n), Folwen, *v.,* follow. O.E. *folgian*

Folye, *s.,* folly, ridiculous thing. O.Fr. *folie.* Cf. O.Fr. *fol* (fool), L. *follis* (bellows, windbag)

Fond, Foond, *p.t. s.,* found. See **Fynde**

Foo, *s.,* foe, enemy; **firste foo,** chief enemy. O.E. *(ge)-fā.* Cf. *fāh* (hostile)

Foot-mantel, *s.,* overskirt, riding petticoat

For, *prep.,* for, because of; against; **for me, as for me;** **for anything,** in spite of anything, at all events; **for traison,** against treason; **for to daunce,** from dancing; **for my prymer,** for neglecting my primer; **For to** (followed by infinitive), to, in order to, so as to; **for to telle,** to tell; **gan for to pace,** did pass. O.E. *for*

For, *conj.,* for, because, so that; **For that,** because; **so worldly for,** so worldly as; **for ye shall not,** so that you shall not; **but for men speke of singing,** but since singing is mentioned. O.E. *for*

Forbede(n), *v.,* forbid; **Forbedeth,** 3 *pr. s.,* forbids; **Forbad,** *p.t. s.* O.E. *forbēodan*

Forby, *adv.,* by, past (that place); **oght forby,** past it all

Fordronke(n), *pp. adj.,* very drunk. O.E. *fordruncen*

Foreward, *s.,* agreement, bargain. O.E. *foreweard*

Forewiting, *s.,* foreknowledge. Cf. O.E. *forewitan* (to foreknow)

Forewoot, *pr. s.,* foreknows. O.E. *forewāt* (foreknows)

Forgat, *p.t. s.,* forgot. See Foryete(n)

Forheed, *s.,* forehead. O.E. *forhēafod*

Forked, *adj.,* forked, branching. Cf. O.E. *forca,* L. *furca* (fork)

Forlete(n), *v.,* lose, give up. O.E. *forlǣtan*

Forme, *s.,* form; **in forme,** formally. O.Fr. *forme,* L. *forma*

Forncast, *p.p.,* forecast, seen in advance, foretold; **by heigh imaginacioun forncast,** by deep imagination aforethought, or foreordained. O.E. *foran* (before) + O.N. *kasta* (cast)

Forneys, *s.,* furnace. O.Fr. *fornais,* L. *fornax*

Forpyned, *p.p.,* tortured, tormented. O.E. *for-pīnian,* L. *poena* (punishment)

Fors, *s.,* force; **no fors, no** matter; **ne do no fors of dremes,** pay no heed to dreams. O.Fr. *force* (strength), L. *fortia* (strong things)

Forslewthe(n), *v.,* waste (by sloth). Cf. O.E. *slǣwþ* (sloth)

Forster, *s.,* forester. O.F. *forestier.* Cf. LL. *forestis* (hunting-ground), L. *foris* (out of doors)

Forsweryng, *s.,* perjury, false swearing. Cf. O.E. *forswerian* (to swear falsely)

Forthermo, Forthermoor(e), *adv.,* moreover. O.E. *furðor* (further) + *mā, māra* (more)

Forther over, *adv.,* moreover

Fortunen, *v.,* make lucky; happen; **wel koude he fortunen th' ascendant of his images,** he well knew how to say that the rising of the planet corresponding to his talismans was favourable. O.Fr. *fortuner*, L. *fortunare* (make fortunate)

For-why, *conj.*, why, because. O.E. *forhwy* (why)

Forwrapped, *adj.*, wrapped up, closely wrapped

Foryete(n), *v.*, forget; Forgat, *p.t. s.*, forgot. O.E. *forģietan*. The *g* in 'forgat' is due to the influence of O.N. *geta*, *gat*. O.E. *ge-*, *ģie-* became *ye*

Foryeve(n), *v.*, forgive. O.E. *forģiefan*

Fother, *s.*, cart-load. O.E. *fōðer* (fodder, cart-load)

Foughten, *p.p.*, fought. See Fighte(n)

Foul, *adj.*, stinking, dirty; sinful, vile. O.E. *fūl*

Founde(n), *p.p.*, found. See Fynde(n)

Fowel, *s.*, bird; Fowel (*collective pl.*), Fowles, *pl.* O.E. *fugol*

Frankeleyn, *s.*, freeholder, small landowner. Cf. O.Fr. *franc* (free)

Fraternitee, *s.*, fraternity, religious guild. L. *fraternitas* (brotherhood)

Frayne(n), *v.*, ask, enquire. O.E. (*ge*)*fraġnian*

Frēdom, *s.*, liberality, generosity. O.E. *frēodōm* (freedom)

Free, *adj.*, free, voluntary; liberal, generous; noble; for it was free, for it was a thoroughfare. O.E. *frēo*

Freend, *s.*, friend. O.E. *frēond*

Frere, *s.*, friar. O.Fr. *frere*, L. *frater* (brother)

Fressh, *adj.*, fresh; merry. O.E. *fersc*, O.Fr. *freis* (*m.*), *fresche* (*f.*)

Fresshe, Freshly, *adv.*, newly

Fro, *prep.*, from; fro . . .

ward, coming from. O.N. *frá*

Fruyt, *s.*, fruit. O.Fr. *fruit*, L. *fructus*

Fruytesteres, *s. pl.* fruit-girls, sellers of fruit

Frye(n), *v.*, to fry. O.Fr. *frire*, L. *frigĕre* (roast)

Ful, *adj.*, full; Ful, *adv.*, fully, very, quite; atte fulle, completely; ful wo, much woe; ful ofte, very many. O.E. *ful(l)*

Fulfille(n), *v.*, fulfil, satisfy; Fulfilled, *p.p.* filled (full). O.E. *ful-fyllan*

Fume, *s.*, vapours, spleen. O.Fr. *fume*, L. *fumus* (smoke)

Fumetere, *s.*, fumitory, a plant. O.Fr. *fumeterre* (earth-smoke)

Fumositee, *s.*, vapour, headiness. O.Fr. *fumosité* (vapour). Cf. L. *fumosus* (smoky)

Fustian, *s.*, fustian, a kind of cotton-cloth. O.F. *fustaigne*, perhaps from *Fostat*, a suburb of Cairo (cf. worsted)

Fy, *int.*, fie. O.Fr., L. *fi* (exclamation of disgust)

Fyn, *adj.*, fine; Fyne, *pl.*; Fyneste, *sup.*, finest. O.Fr. *fin* (delicate)

Fynde(n), *v.*, find; provide for; is thee to fynde, it is to provide for thee; fyndeth him out, finds himself guilty; Fond, Foond, Founde, *p.t. s.*, found, provided for; Founde, *p.t. pl.*; Founde(n), Yfounde, *p.p.* found. O.E. *findan*; *fand* or *funde*, *fundon*; *funden*

Fyr, *s.*, fire. O.E. *fȳr*

Fyr-reed, *adj.*, red as fire

Gabbe, *v.*, deceive, boast. O.N. *gabba* (mock)

Gadere(n), *v.*, gather; Gadrede, *p.t. s.*, gathered. O.E. *gæderian*

Gaitrys beryes, *s. pl.,* the berries of the 'goat tree,' perhaps common buckthorn. O.E. *gāte-hrīs* (goat's branch)

Galingale, *s.,* an aromatic root, perhaps ginger. O.Fr. *galingal.* Arabic

Game, *s.,* game, sport, fun. O.E. *gamen*

Gamed, *p.t. s.,* it pleased (him)

Gan, *p.t. s.,* began; also auxiliary verb meaning 'did'; **gan preye,** prayed; gan for to pace, did pass. See Ginne

Gape(n), *v.,* gape, stare with the mouth open; gaping upright, on his back, staring with his mouth open. O.N. *gapa*

Gargat, *s.,* throat. O.Fr. *gargatte* (throat). Cf. 'gargle' and 'gargoyle'

Garleek, *s.,* garlic. O.E. *gār-lēac* (spear-leek)

Gat-tothed, *adj.,* either (1) with the two upper middle front teeth wide apart. O.E. *geat* (gate) or O.N. *gat* (hole)+ *tōð* (tooth): or (2) having teeth like a goat, O.E. *gāt* (goat)+*tōð* (tooth). Cf. 'buck-tooth' (projecting tooth)

Gaude, *s.,* trick. Cf. L. *gaudium* (joy)

Gauded, *adj.,* having 'gauds' or large beads. L. *gaudia* (joys)

Geere, *s.,* gear, equipment; utensils, accessories; hir geere apyked was, their equipment was ornamented. O.N. *gervi* (gear). Cf. O.N. *gera* (to make)

Gees, *s. pl.,* geese. O.E. *gōs, gēs (pl.)*

Gelding, *s.,* gelded horse. O.N. *geldingr*

Gemme, *s.,* gem. L. *gemma* (jewel)

Gentil, *adj.,* **gentle,** refined; good-natured, pleasant; **Gentils,** *s.,* gentlefolk. O.Fr. *gentil* (noble), L. *gentīlis* (of good family)

Gentilesse, *s.,* gentleness, kindness, nobility. O.Fr. *gentilesse*

Gerland, *s.,* garland, wreath. O.Fr. *garlande* (circlet). Germ.

Gerner, *s.,* garner, granary. O.Fr. *grenier,* L. *granarium*

Gesse(n), *v.,* guess, suppose; I gesse, I imagine, feel sure

Gete(n), *v.,* get, obtain; **Gat,** *p.t. s.,* got, **Geten,** *p.p.,* got, obtained. O.N. *geta; gat; getinn*

Gilt, *s.,* guilt. O.E. *gylt*

Giltelees, *adj.,* innocent

Ginglen, *v.,* jingle (imitative)

Ginne, *v.,* begin; **Gan,** *p.t. s.,* began; did; gan preye, prayed; gan for to pace, did pass; **Gonne,** *p.t. pl.,* began. O.E. *(on)ginnan; -gan; -gunnon*

Gipoun, *s.,* short, tight surcoat, or tunic. O.Fr. *jupon,* Arabic *djubbah* (vest)

Gipser, *s.,* large hanging purse. O.Fr. *gibecier* (game-bag)

Girles, *s. pl.,* young people, boys or girls

Girt, *p.p.,* girded. O.E. *gyrd; gyrdan (inf.)*

Giterne, *s.,* lute, cithern. O.Fr. *guiterne.* Cf. Fr. *guitare* (guitar); cf. Gk. *kithara* (harp)

Glade, *v.,* gladden, cheer. O.E. *gladian*

Gladly, *adv.,* willingly

Gladsom, *adj.,* delightful

Glaringe, *pr. p.,* shining, staring. Cf. O.E. *glæren* (glassy)

Glas, *s.,* glass. O.E. *glæs*

Glotonye, *s.,* the sin of gluttony, excessive eating and drink.

ing. O.Fr. *gloutonie*. Cf. L. *glūto-nem* (glutton)

Gobet, *s.*, piece, morsel. O.Fr. *gobet* (little mouthful). Cf. Irish *gob* (mouth)

Golet, *s.*, gullet, throat. O.Fr. *goulet*. Cf. L. *gula* (throat)

Goliardeys, *s.*, glutton ; boaster, jester. O.Fr. *gouliardois*. Cf. L. *gula* (throat, gluttony)

Gonne, *p.t. pl.*, began. See Ginne

Good, *adj.*, good ; Good, *s.*, goods, property ; by his propre good, upon the yield of his own estate, within his income. O.E. *gōd*

Goodly, *adj.*, *adv.*, kindly, excellent

Good-man, *s.*, good man, master ; Good-men, *pl.*, good men ; masters, gentlemen

Goon, Gon, *v.*, go, walk ; Gooth, Goth, 3 *pr. s.*, goes ; Goon, Gon, *pr. pl.*, go ; *p.t.* see Wende(n) ; Go, *imp.* ; go bet, go quickly ; Gon, Ygo(n), *p.p.*, gone. O.E. *gān*, *gegān* (*p.p.*)

Goost, *s.*, spirit ; Holy Ghost ; yaf up the goost, died. O.E. *gāst*

Goot, *s.*, goat. O.E. *gāt*

Goute, *s.*, gout. O.Fr. *goute*, L. *gutta* (drop)

Go(u)vernaunce, *s.*, management, government ; behaviour. O.Fr. *gouvernance*

Governe, *v.*, control. O.Fr. *governer*, L. *gubernāre* (steer, govern)

Governour, *s.*, leader, umpire. O.Fr. *governeur*, L. *gubernātor* (helmsman, governor)

Governyng, *s.*, management

Grace, *s.*, favour, good opinion ; luck, fortune ; his lady grace, his lady's favour ; large grace, great fortune ; so fair a grace, such good luck ; with sory grace, with ill-luck. O.Fr. *grace*, L. *grātia* (favour)

Grammeere, *s.*, grammar. L. *grammatica*. Cf. Gk. *gramma* (letter)

Graunt, *s.*, concession

Graunte(n), *v.*, grant, agree to ; promise. A.Fr. *graunter*, O.Fr. *creanter* or *granter*, LL. *crēdentare* (guarantee)

Graunt merci, *dat.*, gramercy, thank you. O.Fr. *grant merci*

Grece, *s.*, grease. O.Fr. *gresse*, L. *crassus, adj.* (fat)

Greet, *adj.*, great, fine ; a greet, a great one ; Grete, *def.* and *pl.* O.E. *grēat*

Grehoundes, *s.*, greyhounds

Grene, *adj.*, green. O.E. *grēne*

Grete(n), *v.* greet ; Grette, *p.t. s.*, greeted. O.E. *grētan*

Gretter, *adj.*, *comp.*, greater ; Gretteste, *adj.*, *sup.*, greatest. O.E. *grētra*, *grētest*

Greye, *adj.*, grey. O.E. *grēg*

Greyn, *s.*, grain. O.Fr. *grain*, L. *granum* (corn)

Grisly, *adj.*, horrible, terrible. O.E. *grislic*

Grone(n), *v.*, groan. O.E. *grānian*

Grope, *v.*, test, question. O.E. *grāpian* (grasp, grope)

Grote, *s.*, a small coin worth 4d., a groat

Ground, *s.*, ground, floor ; foundation, texture. O.E. *grund*

Grounded, *p.p.*, grounded, well instructed

Grove, *s.*, grove, wood. O.E. *grāf*

Gruf, *adv.*, face downwards. O.N. *á grúfu*. Cf. O.N. *grúfa* (to grovel)

Grynde(n), *v.*, grind. O.E. *grindan*

Grys, *s.,* grey (fur). O.Fr. *gris* (grey). Germ.

Gyde, *s.,* guide, leader. Italian, *guida,* Fr. *guide*

Gyde(n), *v.,* guide; **Gydeth,** *imp.* Italian, *guidare,* Fr. *guider,* Germ. *witan* (to know)

Gyse, *s.,* guise, manner; at his **owene gyse,** in his own way. O.Fr. *guise,* Germ. *wīsa* (manner)

Haberdasshere, *s.,* haberdasher, dealer in small wares

Habergeoun, *s.,* light hauberk, coat of mail. O.Fr. *haubergeon,* Germ. *hals* (neck) + *bergan* (to cover)

Habundant, *adj.,* abundant. O.Fr. *abundant,* L. *ab-undans* (overflowing). The *h* is due to confusion with L. *habēre* (have)

Hadde, *p.t. s.,* had. See **Have(n)**

Halle, *s.,* hall, the central room of a house, open to the rafters, and containing a fire-place; the living-room. O.E. *heall, healle* (*acc.*)

Halse(n) *v.,* entreat, implore. O.E. *healsian* (to clasp round the ' hals ' or neck)

Halwe, *s.,* saint; shrine. O.E. *halga* (holy one)

Han, *v.,* have. See **Have(n)**

Hange(n), Honge(n), *v., trans. and intr.,* hang; **Heng, Heeng,** *p.t. s.,* hanged, hung; **Henge,** *p.t. pl.;* **Hanged,** *p.p.* O.E. *hangian* (*intr.*); *hōn* (*trans.*), *hēng* (*p.t.*)

Happe, *v.,* happen; **happed,** it happened; **him happede,** there happened to him. Cf. O.N. *happ* (luck)

Hardely, *adv.,* boldly; certainly, without doubt

Hardy, *adj.,* bold. O.Fr. *hardi*

(bold), originally *p.p.* of *hardir* (harden), Germ. *hardjan*

Harlot, *s.,* servant; scoundrel, vagabond. O.Fr. *(h)arlot*

Harlotrye, *s.,* roguery, villainy; **Harolotries,** *pl.,* knavish tricks, dirty tales

Harm, *s.,* harm, injury; pity. O.E. *hearm*

Harneised, *p.p.,* equipped; ornamented. O.Fr. *harnaschier* (to equip)

Harr, *s.,* hinge; of harre, from its hinges. O.E. *heor*

Harrow, *int.,* help! a cry of distress. O.Fr. *haro* !

Hasard, *s.,* a game of dice; gambling. O.Fr. *hasard.* Arabic

Hasardour, *s.,* gambler

Hasardrye, *s.,* gambling; playing the game of hazard

Hast, *s.,* haste. O.Fr. *haste,* Germ. *hai(f)sti* (strife). Cf. O.E. *hǣst* (violence)

Haunt, *s.,* habitual use, practice; skill; district. O.Fr. *hant* (frequentation)

Haunte(n), *v.,* practise, habitually use. O.Fr. *hanter* (to frequent)

Hauteyn, *adj.,* haughty, arrogant. O.Fr. *hautain* (lofty). Cf. L. *altus,* with *h* from Germ. *hauh* (high)

Have(n), Han, *v.,* have; **Hath,** 3 *pr. s.,* has; **Have, Han,** *pr. pl.,* have; the whiche han of hir propretee by kynde, which have as their natural property (the power); **Hadde, Hade, Had,** *p.t. s.,* had; **Have,** *imp.,* have good day, goodbye; have heer my trouthe, I promise thee. O.E. *habban,* with *v* from *hafaþ,* or *hæfþ* (hath)

Haven, *s.,* haven, harbour.

Haven-syde, shore of a harbour. O.E. *hæfen*

Hawe, *s.*, hedge; enclosure, garden. O.E. *haga* (hedge)

Hayre-clout, *s.*, shroud of sackcloth. O.Fr. *haire* (sackcloth), Germ. *harja*+O.E. *clūt* (cloth)

He, *pron.*, he; if he gaf, if one gave. Him, *acc. dat.*, him; him thoughte, it seemed to him; **His,** *poss. adj.*, his. O.E. *hē, him* (*dat*), *his* (*poss.*)

Heed, *s.*, (1) heed. Cf. O.E. *hēdan* (to heed). (2) head, O.E. *hēafod*

Heeld, *p.t. s.*, held. See Holde(n)

Heelen, *v.*, heal. O.E. *hǣlan*

Heeng, *p.t. s.*, hanged, hung. See Hange(n)

Heep, *s.*, heap; crowd, host. O.E. *hēap*

Heer (1), *adv.*, here. O.E. *hēr*

Heer (2), *s.*, hair. O.E. *hǣr*

Heere(n), *v.*, hear; Herde(n), *p.t.*, heard; Herd, *p.p.*, heard. O.E. *hīeran* or *hēran*

Heeste, *s.*, behest, commandment. O.E. *hǣs*

Heet, *p.t. s.*, was named. O.E. *hātan* (to call); *hēt, p.t.*

Heeth, *s.*, heath. O.E. *hǣþ*

Hegge, *s.*, hedge. O.E. *hecg*

Heigh, Hy, *adj.*, high; great; in heigh and low, in all things, wholly. O.E. *hēah*, or *hēh*

Heighe, Hye, *adv.*, high, aloft; proudly. O.E. *hēah*, or *hēh*

Hele, *s.*, health. O.E. *hǣlo*

Hele(n), *v.*, hide, conceal; Heled, *p.p.*, hidden. O.E. *helan*

Helle, *s.*, hell. O.E. *hell*

Helpe(n), *v.*, help, be of use; cure; Holpen, *p.p.*, helped, cured; Help, *imp. s.*, O.E. *helpan*; *holpen* (*p.p.*)

Hem, *pron., pl., acc.* and *dat.*, them. O.E. *heom*

Heng, *p.t. s.*, hanged, hung. See Hange(n)

Henne, Hennes, *adv.*, hence; henne over a mile, more than a mile away. O.E. *heonan* (+*adv. -es*)

Hente(n), *v.*, catch, seize; get; Hente, *p.t. s.*, caught, seized; Hent, Yhent, *p.p.*, caught, seized. O.E. *hentan*; *hente*; (*ge-*)*hent*

Herbe, *s.*, herb, plant; to herbes techen you, direct you to plants. L. *herba* (grass)

Herbergage, *s.*, lodging, accommodation. O.Fr. *herbergage*, Germ. *here* (army)+*berga* (shelter)+*age* (abstract suffix)

Herberwe, *s.*, harbour; lodging, inn. O.N. *her-bergi.* Cf. preceding word

Herbive, *s.*, a weed, probably crowfoot or marsh trefoil. O.Fr. *herbe yve*

Herd, Herde(n), *p.p.* and *p.t.*, heard. See Heere(n)

Herde, *s.*, herd, herdsman. O.E. *hierde* or *herde*

Herie(n), *v.*, praise. O.E. *herian*

Herkne(n), *v.*, hearken, listen; Herkneth, *imp. pl.* O.E. *hercnian*

Herte, *s.*, heart; of herte, from the heart; herte-blood, blood. O.E. *heorte*

Hertelees, *adj.*, heartless; *s.*, coward

Hertely, *adv.*, heartily, cordially

Heryinge, *s.*, praise, praising. Cf. O.E. *herian* (to praise)

Hethen, *s.*, heathen, pagan. O.E. *hǣðen*

Hethenesse, *s.*, heathendom, pagan lands

Heve(n), *v.*, heave, lift. O.E. *hebban, hef þ*

Heven, *s.,* heaven; **Hevene,** *poss.* heaven's. O.E. *heofon*

Hevinesse, *s.,* sadness. O.E. *hefig* (heavy) +*nes*

Hewe, *s.,* hue, colour; appearance, pretence. O.E. *hīew* or *hīw*

Hewed, *adj.,* coloured

Hider, *adv.,* hither. O.E. *hider*

Hidous, *adj.,* hideous. O.Fr. *hideus,* or *hidos*

Highte, *p.t. s.,* is (or was) named. O.E. *hātan* (call); *heht, p.t.,* confused with *hatte,* (*passive*) (is or was called)

Himselve(n), *pron.,* himself. O.E. *him selfan* (*dat.*)

Hipes, *s. pl.,* hips. O.E. *hype, hypas* (*pl.*)

Hir, *pron., acc.* and *dat.,* her; *poss. adj.,* her. O.E. *hire:* *poss. adj., pl.,* their; O.E. *hira*

Hire, *s.,* hire, pay; reward. O.E. *hȳr*

Hirselve(n), *pron.,* herself. O.E. *hire selfan* (*dat.*)

His, *poss. adj.,* his (*m.*), its (*n.*). O.E. *his* (*masc.* and *neut.*)

Ho, *int.,* stop! hold!

Hogges, *s. pl.,* pigs

Hold, *s.,* keeping, possession. O.E. *heald*

Holde(n), Hoolde(n), *v.,* hold, keep; think, esteem; holde his pees, hold his peace, be silent; **Heeld,** *p.t. s.,* held, went; **Holden,** *pr. pl.,* think; **Holde(n), Yholde,** *p.p.,* held, esteemed; **Hoold,** *imp.,* hold. O.E. *healdan* or *hāldan; hēold; healden*

Holpen, *p.p.,* helped. See **Helpe(n)**

Holt, *s.,* wood. O.E. *holt*

Holwe, *adj., adv.,* hollow, empty. O.E. *holh* (*s.*)

Homicyde, *s.* (1) murderer. L. *homicīda.* (2) murder. L. *homicīdium*

Hond, *s.,* hand; at the hond, at the cuff. O.E. *hand* or *hond*

Honest, *adj.,* honourable, respectable; decent, seemly. O.Fr. *honeste.* L. *honestus*

Honge(n), *v. intrans.,* be hanged; doon us honge, make us hang, have us hanged. O.E. *hangian* (*intrans.*). See **Hange(n)**

Honurable, *adj.,* honourable. O.F. *honorable,* L. *honorābilem.* See **Onour**

Hool, *adj.,* whole, sound. O.E. *hāl*

Hoold, *s.,* custody; keeping; she hath the herte in hoold, she has the heart (of C.) in her keeping. O.E. *ge-heald* or *ge-hāld*

Hoolly, *adv.,* wholly

Hooly, *adj.,* holy. O.E. *hālig*

Hoom, *s.,* home. O.E. *hām*

Hoomly, *adv.,* simply, in a homely style

Hoomward, *adv.,* homeward, coming home

Hoor, *adj.,* hoary, white-haired. O.E. *hār*

Hoord, *s.,* hoard, treasure. O.E. *hŏrd*

Hoost(e), *s.,* host, landlord. O.Fr. *hoste,* L. *hospes, hospitem* (*acc.*) (guest, host)

Hoot, *adj.,* hot; **Hoote,** *adv.,* hotly, fervently. O.E. *hāt* (*adj.*), *hāte* (*adv.*)

Hors *s.,* horse; **Hors,** *pl.,* horses. O.E. *hors* (*s. pl.*)

Hose, *s.,* hose, long stocking; **Hosen,** *pl.,* stockings, O.E. *hosa(n)*

Hostelrye, *s.,* hostelry, inn; **Hostiler,** *s.,* innkeeper. O.Fr. *hostel* (inn) + *-er* (agent, suffix). Cf. L. *hospitalis* (hospitable)

Hous, *s.,* house; monastic house, friary. O.E. *hūs*

Housbond, *s.,* husband. O.N. *húsbóndi*

Housbondrie, *s.,* careful management

Housholdere, *s.,* householder, head of household

How, How that, *adv.,* how, in what way. O.E. *hū*

Howped, *p.t. pl.,* whooped, shouted. O.Fr. *houper*

Humblesse, *s.,* humility, meekness. O.Fr. *humblesse* or *humblece,* L. *humil(is)* (meek) +*-itia*

Humour, *s.,* one of the four vital fluids of the body (melancholy, phlegm, blood, bile) in medieval medicine. L. *humor* (liquid)

Hy, *adj.,* high; **Hye,** *adv.,* high, aloft; proudly. O.E. *hēah* or *hēh*

Hyde(n), *v.,* hide; **Hid,** *p.p.* hidden. O.E. *hȳdan*

Hyer, *comp. adj.,* higher, upper. O.E. *hīehra* or *hīerra*

Hym, *pron.,* him. O.E. *him* (*dat.*)

Hymselve(n), Hymself, *pron.,* himself. O.E. *him selfan* (*dat.*)

Hyndreste, *sup. adv.,* hindmost, last. O.E. *hinder* (behind) +*este*

Hyne, *s.,* hind, servant. O.E. *hīna,* originally *gen. pl.* of *hīwan* (servants)

Hyre, *s.,* hire, payment; sette to hyre, let for profit. O.E. *hȳr*

Hyre(n), *v.,* hire, rent; engage. O.E. *hȳrian, hȳran*

Hyve, *s.,* hive. O.E. *hȳf(e).* (*fem.*)

If that, *conj.,* if; if so were that, if. O.E. *gif,* O.N. *ef, if*

Ilke, *adj.,* same, very; thilke, that, that same. O.E. *ilca*

Image, *s.,* image (used as a charm), talisman. L. *imago, imaginem*

Imaginacioun, *s.,* imagination, the image-forming faculty; foresight. L. *imaginationem*

In, *prep.,* in; in dede, indeed; in comen, came in. O.E. *in*

Infect, *adj.,* invalid, illegal. L. *infectus* (undone)

Iniquitee, *s.,* iniquity, unfairness. L. *inīquitas.* Cf. L. *aequus* (just)

Inn, *s.,* lodging, house, inn. O.E. *inn*

Inne, *adv.,* in. O.E. *inne*

In principio: "In the beginning," St John i. 1

Inspired, *p.p.,* blown upon, quickened. L. *inspīrare* (to breathe upon)

Ipocrisye, *s.,* hypocrisy. O.Fr. *ypocrisie,* L. *hypocrisis* (acting). Cf. L.Gk. *hypocrites* (actor)

Ire, *s.,* anger. O.Fr. *ire,* L. *īra*

Iren, *s.,* iron. O.E. *īren*

It, *pron.,* it; as it were, as if there were. O.E. *hit, him* (*dat.*), *his* (*poss.*)

Jade, *s.,* poor horse

Jalous, *adj.,* jealous. O.Fr. *jalous,* L. *zēlōsus* (zealous). Cf. Gk. *zēlos* (zeal)

Jalousye, *s.,* jealousy

Jangle(n), *v.,* quarrel, chatter. O.Fr. *jangler.* Germ.

Janglere, *s.,* quarrelsome man, chatterer, mocker

Jape, *s.,* jest, trick; **Jape(n),** *v.,* to jest

Jeet, *s.,* jet. O.Fr. *jaiet,* L.Gk. *gagātes*

Jet, *s.,* fashion, style. O.Fr. *giet,* or *jet,* L. *jactus* (cast)

Jewerye, *s.,* Jewry, Jews' quarter. O.Fr. *juerie*

Jolif, Joly, *adj.,* jolly, merry; delightful. O.Fr. *jolif, joli.* Cf. O.N. *jól* (Yule, Christmas)

Jolitee, *s.,* jollity; sport, amusement. O.Fr. *joliveté,* or *jolieté*

Jordanes, *s. pl.,* alchemists' bottles

Juge, *s.,* judge. O.Fr. *juge,* L. *judex, judicem*

Juggement, *s.,* judgment, decision. O.Fr. *jugement*

Juste(n), *v.,* joust, engage in a tournament. O.Fr. *juster,* L. *juxtare* (to meet). Cf. L. *juxta* (near)

Justise, *s.,* justice; (1) judgment; (2) judge. L. *justitia* (justice)

Kan, *v., pr. s.,* can; know, knows; possesses; **Kan I noon but,** I only know; **kan by rote,** know by heart; **Kanstow,** 2 *pr. s.,* canst thou; **Konne,** *pr. pl.,* can; **Koude,** *p.t. s.,* could, knew, understood; **Kouthe,** *p.t. s.,* could, knew how; **Kowthe,** *p.p.* and *adj.,* couth, known; **Konne,** *inf.,* know, learn. O.E. *can, cunnon (pl.); cūþe (p.t.); cūþ (p.p.); cunnan (inf.)*

Katapuce, *s.,* caper-spurge, an acrid plant. Fr. *catapuce,* Ital. *catapuzza*

Kaught, *p.p.,* caught. See **Cacche(n)**

Kene, *adj.,* keen, sharp. O.E. *cēne*

Kepe, Keep, *s.,* heed; **taak kepe,** take keep, take heed. O.E. *cēp(an)* (keep)

Kepe(n), *v.,* keep, take care of, guard; **Kepte,** *p.t. s.,* kept, watched, took care of; **Kept,** *p.p.,* guarded. O.E. *cēpan*

Kepere, *s.,* keeper, prior

Kerve(n), *v.,* carve; **Carf,** *p.t. s.,* carved; **Ycorven,** *p.p.,* cut. O.E. *ceorfan*

Kille(n), *v.,* kill

Kin, *s.,* kindred, family. O.E. *cynn*

Kisse(n), *v.,* kiss; **Kiste,** *p.t. pl.,* kissed. O.E. *cyssan*

Kitte, *p.t. s.,* cut; **Kut,** *p.p.,* cut. Germ.

Knarre, *s.,* knot in wood; **a thikke knarre,** a thickset fellow

Knave, *s.,* servant. O.E. *cnafa*

Knele(n), *v.,* kneel; **Kneleth,** *imp. pl.* O.E. *cneowlian.* Cf. *cnēow* (knee)

Knobbes, *s. pl.,* pimples. Germ.

Knok, *s.,* knock. Germ.

Knokke(n), *v.,* knock, hit. O.E. *cnocian*

Knowe(n), *v.,* know, recognize; **Knowen,** *pr., pl.,* know; **Knew,** *p.t. s.,* knew; **Yknowe,** *p.p.,* known. O.E. *cnāwan; cnēow; (ge-)cnāwen*

Knowes, *s. pl.,* knees. O.E. *cnēow; cnēowas (pl.)*

Knyf, *s.,* knife; **Knyves,** *pl.* O.E. *cnīf,* O.N. *knífr*

Knyght, *s.,* knight; **knyght of the shire,** representative of the county in Parliament. O.E. *cniht* (servant)

Konne, *v.,* know, learn. See **Kan**

Konning, *s.,* skill. O.E. *cunnung* (testing)

Koude, *p.t. s.,* could, knew. See **Kan**

Kouthe, *p.t. s.,* could, knew how. See **Kan**

Kowthe, *p.p.* and *adj.,* known. See **Kan**

Kut, *p.p.,* cut. See **Kitte**

Kyn, *s. pl.,* cows; *s.,* cow. O.E. *cū; cȳ (pl.) +en (pl.)*

Kynde, *s.,* nature; **by kynde,** by instinct, by nature, naturally. O.E. *cȳnd*

Kynde, *adj.,* kind. O.E. *cȳnde*

Laas, *s.*, lace, cord. O.Fr. *laz, las,* L. *laqueus* (noose)

Lafte, *p.t. s.*, left. See Leve(n)

Lak, *s.*, lack, want. Germ.

Lakke(n), *v., impers.*, lack, be wanting; him lakkede, he lacked

Langage, *s.*, language. O.Fr. *langage.* Cf. L. *lingua* (tongue)

Lappe, *s.*, lap, fold of a garment. O.E. *læppa*

Large, *adj.*, large, great; wide. O.Fr. *large,* L. *largus*

Large, *adv.*, freely

Lasse, Lesse, *adv.*, less. O.E. *læssa (adj.)*

Laste, *adj.*, last; atte laste, at last, lastly. O.E. *latost* (latest)

Laste(n), *v.*, last, endure; Laste *p.t. s.*, lasted. O.E. *læstan* (fulfil, perform)

Lat, *imp. s.*, let. See Lete(n)

Late, *adv.*, lately. O.E. *late*

Latoun, *s.*, brass, an alloy of copper and tin or zinc. O.Fr. *laton*

Latyn, *adj.*, Latin (language). L. *latīnus*

Laude, *s.*, praise. O.Fr. *laude,* L. *laudem, acc.* of *laus* (praise)

Laughe(n), *v.*, laugh; lough, *p.t. s.,* laughed. O.E. *hliehhan* or *hlæhhan*; *hlōh (p.t. s.)*

Lawe, *s.*, law; by the law, as the law decreed. O.E. *lagu*

Lawriol, *s.*, spurge-laurel. L. *laureola*

Laxatyf, *adj.* and *s.*, laxative, medicine to purge the bowels. L. *laxatīvus.* Cf. *laxus* (slack)

Lazar, *s.*, leper. Cf. *Lazarus* in *St Luke* xvi. 10

Leche, *s.*, physician. O.E. *læce* (healer)

Lecherous, *adj.*, wanton, lustful. Cf. O.Fr. *lecheur* (glutton)

Lechery, *s.*, love of luxury, gluttony, debauchery. O.Fr. *lecherie.* Germ.

Lede(n), *v.*, to lead; **Ladde,** *p.t. s.*, led. O.E. *lædan*

Leed, *s.*, lead (metal), a large vessel made of lead. Cf. a 'copper.' O.E. *lēad*

Leef (1), *adj.*, lief, dear; **Leve, Leeve,** *def.*; so lief, so desirous. O.E. *lēof* (dear)

Leef (2), *s.*, leaf. O.E. *lēaf.*

Leene, *adj.*, lean, thin. O.E. *hlǣne*

Leere(n), *v.*, learn. O.E. *lǣran* (teach)

Leet, *p.t. s.*, let, left. See Lete(n)

Leeve, Leve, *def. adj.*, dear. See Leef

Legende, *s.*, life (of a saint). L. *legenda* (things to be read)

Lekes, *s. pl.*, leeks. O.E. *lēac*

Lemes, *s. pl.*, flames. O.E. *lēoma*

Lene, *adj.*, lean, thin. See Leene

Lene(n), *v.*, lend. O.E. *lǣnan.* Cf. O.E. *lǣn,* O.N. *lān* (loan)

Lenger, *adj., adv.*, longer. O.E. *lengra (adj.)*

Leoun, *s.*, lion. L. *leōnem, acc.* of *leo* (lion)

Lerne(n), *v.*, learn; **Lerned,** *p.p.* and *adj.*, learned. O.E. *leornian, leornod*

Lerninge, *s.*, learning, study. O.E. *leornung*

Lese(n), *v.*, lose; lorn(e), *p.p.*, lost. O.E. *lēosan*; *loren (p.p.)*

Lessoun, *s.*, lesson. O.Fr. *leçon,* L. *lectiō-nem*

Lest, *s.*, pleasure, delight

Lest, *pr. s. impers.*, it pleases; as him lest, as it pleases him; **Leste,** *p.t. s.*, it pleased; us leste, it pleased us; as him leste, as it pleased him; right as hem leste, just as it pleased them. O.E. *lystan* (please), Kent. *lestan*. See List

Lesyng, *s.*, lie, falsehood. O.E. *léasung*

Lete(n), *v.*, let, leave; **Leet**, *p.t. s.*, let, left; leet he bynde, he caused to be bound; **Lat**, **Let**, **Leet**, *imp.*, let; Lat see, let us see; Lat be, let be, stop; Lat maken, make; lat this man have place, make room for this man. O.E. *lǽtan* (let)

Lette(n), *v.*, hinder, delay; tarry; ne lenger wolde he lette, no longer would he tarry, without delay; **Lette**, *p.t. s.*, hindered. O.E. *lettan* (hinder)

Letuarie, *s.*, electuary, paste, medicinal powder mixed with honey. LL. *electuarium*

Leve, *s.*, leave, permission. O.E. *léaf*

Leve(n) (1), *v.*, leave, cease; **Lafte**, *p.t. s.*, left, ceased; **Leveth**, *imp. pl.*, leave. O.E. *lǽfan* (leave)

Leve(n) (2), *v.*, grant, only in God leve us, God grant us. O.E. *líefan* or *léfan* (allow). Cf. O.E. *léaf* (leave)

Levere, *comp. adj.*, liefer, rather; me were levere, I had rather; him was levere, he had rather. O.E. *léofra* (dearer). See Leef

Lewed, *adj.*, ignorant, uneducated; base. O.E. *lǽwede*

Leye(n), *s.*, lay; lay a wager, bet; **Leyde**, *p.t. s.*, laid; **Leyd**, *p.p.*, laid; **Ley**, *imp. s.*, lay; ley hond to, bear a hand, begin. O.E. *lecgan*

Licenciat, *s.*, licentiate, the holder of a licence which enabled a friar to hear con-

fession in parishes. LL. *licentiatus*

Licour, *s.*, liquor, juice, sap. O.Fr. *licour*, L. *liquor* (liquid)

Lief, *adj.* and *s.*, dear (one), lover. See Leef

Lige, *adj.*, liege, feudal; lige lord, king; lige man, vassal. O.Fr. *lige*. Cf. G. *ledig* (free)

Liggen, *v.*, lie. O.E. *licgan*, O.N. *liggja*

Lighte(n) (1), *v.*, alight, descend. O.E. *lihtan* (make light)

Lighte(n) (2), *v.*, illuminate, fill with light; **Lighte**, *p.t. s.*, enlightened. O.E. *líehtan*. Cf. *léoht* (light)

Lightly, *adv.*, lightly, easily, quickly. O.E. *lihtlíce*

Likerous, *adj.*, lickerish, wanton, lustful. A.Fr. variant of *lecherous* (*q.v.*)

Lilie, **Lilye**, *s.*, lily; lilye-flour, madonna lily, Virgin Mary. O.Fr. *lilie*, L. *lilium*

Limitour, *s.*, a limitary friar, one licensed to practice within certain bounds. Cf. L. *límes*, *límitem* (boundary)

Lipsed, *p.t. s.*, lisped. O.E. *wlispian* (to lisp)

List, *pr. s. impers.*, it pleases; as hym list desire, as it may please him to wish; **Liste**, *p.t. s.*, it pleased; him liste, it pleased him; Nothyng ne liste him thenne, in no wise then did it please him. O.E. *lystan*

Litarge, *s.*, litharge, ointment from oxide of lead. O.Fr. *litarge*, Gk. *litharguros* (silver-stone)

Litel, **Lite**, *adj.*, *adv.*, little. O.E. *lýtel*, *lýt*

Lith, *s.*, limb, member of the body. O.E. *lið*

Live(n), *v.*, live; **Livestow**, 2

pr. s., livest thou. O.E. *libban* or *lifian*

Liveree, s., livery, distinctive gown and hood of a guild. O.Fr. *livrée* (allowance)

Livynge, s., manner or state of life

Lodemenage, s., steersmanship. A.Fr. *lodmanage.* Cf. O.E. *lādmann* (guide, leader)

Logge, s., lodge, abode. O.Fr. *loge* (bower of leaves)

Logge(n), v., to lodge; **Logged, Ylogged,** *p.p.,* lodged. O.Fr. *logier, loger*

Logging, s., lodging

Logyk, s., logic, the science of reasoning. L.Gk. *logica*

Loken, *p.p.,* locked, held fast; **loken in every lith,** bound in every limb. O.E. *locen, p.p.* of *lūcan* (to lock)

Lokkes, s. *pl.,* locks of hair. O.E. *locc,* sing

Lond, s., land, country; **of a lond,** in the land; **upon lond,** in the country; **in londe,** away. O.E. *land* or *lond*

Long(e), adj., long. O.E. *lang* or *long*

Longe, adv., long; **longe ygo,** long gone, a long while devoted himself. O.E. *lange, longe*

Longe(n), v., to long (for), desire. O.E. *longian*

Looke(n), v., look; **Looked,** *p.t.* s.; **Look, Looke,** *imp.* s.; **Looketh,** *imp. pl.,* look. O.E. *lōcian*

Loore, s., learning, instruction. O.E. *lār*

Looth, adj., loath, hateful; **Ful looth were hym,** it would be very hateful to him. O.E. *lāþ*

Lordinges, s. *pl.,* sirs, gentlemen. O.E. *hlāford* (lord) + *-ing*

Lorn(e), *p.p.,* lost. **See Lese(n)**

Losengour, s., flatterer. O.Fr. *losengeor;* Germ. *lausinga* (lie). Cf. E. *leasing*

Losten, *p.t. pl.,* lost; **Lost,** *p.p.* Cf. O.E. *los* (loss), *losian* (to be lost)

Loude, adv., loudly. O.E. *hlūde*

Lough, *p.t.* s., laughed. **See Laughe**

Lovedayes, s. *pl.,* days for settling disputes by arbitration, conferences

Loveknotte, s., interlaced knot or bow

Lovyere, s., lover. Cf. O.E. *lufiend* (loving)

Low(e), adj., low; Prol. 107, either: cut close, or weak (feathers). O.N. *lágr*

Lowly, adj., humble

Luce, s., pike, a fish. O.Fr. *lus,* LL. *lūcius*

Lucre, s., profit; **Lucre of vileynye,** filthy lucre. L. *lucrum* (gain)

Lust, s., desire; joy, delight. O.E. *lust* (desire)

Lusty, adj., lusty; jolly, happy

Luxurie, s., the sin of luxury, lust. L. *luxuria* (extravagance)

Lye(n) (1), v., to lie, be; **Lyth,** 3 *pr.* s., lies, is; **Lay,** *p.t.* s., lay, was stayed. O.E. *licgan, ligð; læg*

Lye(n) (2), v., to lie, tell lies; **Lyed,** *p.t.* s., lied. O.E. *lēogan*

Lyf, s., life; **Lyve,** *dat.* s.; **al hir lyve,** all her life; **this lyf present,** this present life. O.E. *līf*

Lyght, s., light, divine illumination. O.E. *lēoht, līht*

Lyk, adj., prep., like; **him lyk,** like him. O.E. *ge-līc*

Lyke, v., *impers.,* to please; **lyketh,** *pr.* s., it pleases; **you lyketh alle,** it pleases you all. O.E. *līcian*

Lyking, *s.*, pleasure. O.E.
līcung

Lyklihed, *s.*, likelihood

Lykne(n), *v.*, compare; **Lykned**,
p.p., compared

Lyned, *p.p.*, lined. Cf. O.E.
līnen (linen)

Lyte, *adj.*, *adv.*, little. O.E.
lȳt

Lyth, *pr. s.*, lies. See **Lye(n)** (1)

Lyve, *s. dat.*, life. See **Lyf**

Maad, *p.p.*, made, paid, arranged

Maden, *p.t. pl.*, made. See
Make(n)

Magyk, *s.*, magic; **magyk
natureel**, astrology. L. *(ars)
magica* (magic art), Gk. *magos*
(Persian priest, magician)

Maister, *s.*, master, one in
authority; master of arts.
O.Fr. *maistre*, L. *magister*

Maistow, 2 *pr. s.*, mayest thou.
See **May**

Maistrye, *s.*, mastery; **a fair
for the maistrye**, fine in the
highest degree, an exceedingly fine one. O.Fr. *maistrie*

Make(n), *v.*, make; cause;
Maketh, 3 *pr. s.*, makes;
Maken, *pr. pl.*, make; **Maked**,
Made, **Maad**, *p.t. s.*, made;
Maden, *p.t.*, *pl.*, made;
Maked, **Ymaked**, **Maad**, *p.p.*,
made; **maked of**, written
concerning. O.E. *macian*;
macode; *gemacod*

Maladye, *s.*, malady. O.Fr.
maladie, from *malade* (ill).
LL. *male habitus*

Male, *s.*, bag. O.Fr. *male*, Fr.
malle. Germ.

Malencolye, *s.*, melancholy,
gloom, sadness. Originally
a medical term denoting the
symptoms of internal ulcer.
O.Fr. *melancolie*, Gk. *melas*
(black) + *kholē* (bile)

Man, *s.*, man; **Men**, *pl.* O.E.
mann; **Man**, *indef. pron.*, *s.*,
one; **As man that is drecched
sore**, like one that is sorely
troubled; **Men**, *indef. pron.*,
s. (weakened form), one;
men clepeth Deeth, that one
calls Death, called Death; **if
men smoot it**, if one hit it, if
it were struck; **men moot**,
one ought (to). O.E. *man*
(one)

Maner(e), **Maneer**, *s.*, manner,
way; behaviour. The word
is frequently used in apposition: *e.g.*, **a maner deye**, a
kind of dairywoman; **everich
maner doctrine**, every kind
of teaching; **oother maner
pley**, another sort of amusement. O.Fr. *manière*, LL.
manu-āria (skill). Cf. *manus*
(hand)

Manhed, *s.*, manliness

Mankynde, *s.*, mankind. O.E.
mancynn

Mantel, *s.*, mantle, cloak. L.
mantellum

Many, *adj.*, many; **many oon**,
many a one. O.E. *manig*

Marbul, *s.*, marble. O.Fr.
marbre, L. *marmor*

Marchant, *s.*, merchant. O.Fr.
marchant, one frequenting a
marché, L. *mercātus* (market)

Mark, *s.*, the value of 13s. 4d.;
Mark, *pl.* O.E. *marc*

Marshal, *s.*, marshal, master of
ceremonies. O.Fr. *mareschal*
(chief groom), Germ. *marah-
skalk* (horse-servant)

Martir, *s.*, martyr. Gk. *martur*
(witness)

Martirdom, *s.*, martyrdom,
being a martyr

Mary, *s.*, marrow; **Mary-bones**,
s. pl., marrow-bones. O.E.
mearg

Matere, **Mateer**, *s.*, matter,

business. O.Fr. *matière*, L. *materia*

Maugree, *prep.*, in spite of, despite; maugree your heed, in spite of all you can do. O.Fr., *maugré*, L. *malo grāto* (with ill-favour)

Maunciple, *s.*, manciple, servant who purchases food for a college or inn of court. Cf. L. *manceps, mancipem* (buyer)

May, *pr. s.*, may, can; what may, how can; Maystow, 2 *pr. s.*, mayest thou; Mowe(n), *pr. pl.*, can; Myghte, *p.t.*, might. O.E. *mæg, magon* (*pl.*); *mihte*

Maze, *s.*, bewilderment, delusion

Medlee, *adj.*, of different colours, motley. O.Fr. *medlée* or *meslée* (mixed), LL. *misculātus*. Cf. L. *miscēre* (to mix)

Meede (1), *s.*, mead, meadow. O.E. *mēd*

Meede (2), *s.*, reward. O.E. *mēd*

Meel, *s.*, meal. O.E. *melu*

Meete(n), *v.*, meet, meet together; Mette, *p.t.*, met. O.E. *mētan*

Mene(n), *v.*, mean, intend; Mente, *p.t. s.*, meant. O.E. *mǣnan*

Mercenarie, *s.*, mercenary, one who works merely for gain. L. *mercenarius*. Cf. L. *mercēs* (salary)

Merciable, *adj.*, merciful. O.Fr. *merciable*

Mercy, *s.*, thanks; compassion. O.Fr. *merci* (pity), L. *mercēs, mercēdem* (payment)

Mere, *s.*, mare. O.E. *mere*

Mermayde, *s.*, mermaid, siren. O.E. *mere* (sea)+*mægden* (maiden)

Mervaille, *s.*, marvel, wonder.

O.Fr. *merveille*, L. *mirabilia* (wonderful things)

Merveillous, *adj.*, marvellous. O.Fr. *merveillos*. See Mervaille

Mery(e), Merie, *adj.*, merry, lively; pleasant; ther mery is, where it is pleasant. O.E. *myrige*, Kent. *merige*

Meschaunce, *s.*, mischance, ill-luck. O.Fr. *mescheance*. Cf. L. *cadere* (to fall)

Meschief, *s.*, misfortune, trouble. O.Fr. *meschief*. Cf. L. *caput* (head)

Messedayes, *s. pl.*, mass-days, festivals

Mesurable, *adj.*, moderate, reasonable. O.Fr. *mesurable*, L. *mensura* (measure) + *abilis*

Met, *p.p.*, dreamt. See Mete(n)

Mete, *s.*, meat, food; meal-time. O.E. *mete*

Mete(n), *v.*, *impers.*, dream; Mette, *p.t. s.*, dreamt; me mette, I dreamt; him mette, he dreamt; Met, *p.p.*, dreamt. O.E. *mǣtan*

Meynee, *s.*, household, followers. O.Fr. *maisniée*. Cf. Fr. *maison*, L. *mansio-nem* (mansion)

Ministres, *s. pl.*, magistrates. L. *minister*

Miracle, *s.*, legend, life of a saint. O.Fr. *miracle*, L. *miraculum* (marvel)

Mirie, *adj.*, *adv.*, merry; pleasantly. See Mery(e)

Mirthe, *s.*, mirth, pleasure; amusement. O.E. *myrgð*, *myrð*

Miscarie, *v.*, go amiss, fail

Mischaunce, *s.*, mischance, ill-luck. See Meschaunce

Mister, *s.*, trade. O.Fr. *mestier*, L. *ministerium*

Mistriste, *v.*, mistrust

Mitayn, *s.*, mitten, glove. Fr. *mitaine*

Mo, *adj.*, more (in number); **na mo,** no more. O.E. *mā* (*adv.*)

Mooder, *s.*, mother; **Moodres,** *poss.*, mother's. O.E. *mōdor*

Moone, *s.*, moon, position of the moon. O.E. *mōna*

Moore, *adj.*, *adv.*, more, greater; **withouten moore speche,** without further objection; **moore and lasse,** great and small; **never shal he moore,** never again will he. O.E. *māra*

Moost,Moste,*adj.*,most,greatest. O.E. *mǣst, mǎst*

Moot, *v.*, *pr. s.*, may, ought to; **men moot,** one ought (to); **so moot I go,** may I have the power to walk; **so moot I thee(n),** as I hope to thrive; **As ever mote I,** as sure as ever I hope; **Moote(n),** *pr. pl.*, must; **Moste,** *p.t. s.*, must; **Mosten,** *p.t.,pl.*, must. O.E. *mōt; mōste* (*p.t.*)

Moralitee, *s.*, moral. L. *moralitas*

Mordre, *s.*, murder; **mordre wol out,** murder shall be revealed. O.E. *morðor*. Cf. O.Fr. *murdre*

Mordre, *v.*, to murder. O.Fr. *murdrir*, Germ. *murdrian*

Mordrour, *s.*, murderer. O.Fr. *mordreour*

Mormal, *s.*, inflamed sore. O.Fr. *mortmal* (gangrene), LL. *mortuum malum* (dead evil)

Morne, *s.*, morning; **morne milk,** morning milk. O.E. *morgen, morgenne* (*dat. s.*)

Mortal,*adj.*,deadly. L.*mortalis*. Cf. *mors* (death)

Mortreux, *s. pl.*, meat prepared by pounding in a mortar, stews. For *mortrewes*; Cf. O.Fr. *mortier* (mortar)

Morwe, *s.*, morrow, morning; **by the morwe,** in the morning; **in the morwe tyde,** in the morning; **morwe-song,** morning song. O.E. *morgen*

Morwening, *s.*, morning, beginning of day

Moste(n), *p.t.*, must. See **Moot**

Mote, *v.*, *pr. s.*, may. See **Moot**

Motteley, *s.*, spotted cloth, motley

Mountance, *s.*, value, amount. O.Fr. *montance*

Mowe(n), *pr. pl.*, can. See **May**

Moyste, *adj.*, moist, soft; fresh, new. O.Fr. *moiste*, L. *mustus* or *musteus* (fresh, new wine)

Muche(l), *adj.*, *adv.*, much, many; great; greatly; **ful muchel,** very greatly, largely; **in as muche as,** in so far as. O.E. *mycel*

Mulier est hominis confusio = woman is man's confusion

Multiplye, *v.*, to make populous, increase. L. *multiplicare* (to make manifold)

Murie, Mury, *adj.*, merry. O.E. *myrige*. A Southern form

Murily, *adj.*, merrily

Muwe, *s.*, cage, mew; **in muwe,** fattening in coops. Fr. *mue*. Cf. L. *mutare* (change, moult)

My, Myn, *poss. pron.*, my; **Myselven,** myself. O.E. *mīn*; *me selfan* (dat.)

Myght, *s.*, might, power. O.E. *miht*

Myghte, *p.t.*, might. See **May**

Myghty, *adj.*, mighty, huge. O.E. *mihtig*

Mynde, *s.*, mind, reason; **in mynde,** remembered. O.E. (*ge-*)*mynd*

Myre, *s.*, mire. O.N. *mýrr*

N', *adv.*, not; shortened from Ne, before auxiliary verbs beginning with vowels, etc.; n' I wol not, I will not; nis, is not; nas, was not; nath, hath not; nolde, would not; noot, know not. O.E. *ne*

Nacion, *s.*, nation; rank. O.Fr. *nacion*, L. *natiō-nem*

Nadde, *p.t. s.*, had not. See N', Have

Namely, *adv.*, especially. O.E. *nama* (name) +*lice*

Namo, *s.*, no more (in number). O.E. *na mā*

Namoore, *adv.*, no more. O.E. *na māre*

N'arette, *v.*, account not. See Arette(n)

Narwe, *adj.*, narrow, small. O.E. *nearu*

Nas, *p.t. s.*, was not; nas but, was only. See N', Be

Nat, *adv.*, not; nat-but, only. Unemphatic form of O.E. *nāht*. See Nought, Noght

Nathele(e)s, *adv.*, nevertheless. O.E. *nā-þe-lǣs*

Natureel, *adj.*, natural; concerning nature. L. *naturalis*

Naught, *adv.*, not; *s.*, nothing. O.E. *nā-wiht* or *nāht*

Nayl, *s.*, nail; spur of a cock. O.E. *nægel*

Ne, *adv.*, not; *conj.*, nor; ne ... ne, neither ... nor; ne as by, nor by. O.E. *ne*

Necessitee, *s.*, necessity, compulsion; necessitee condicioneel, limited compulsion, conditional predestination. L. *necessitas*, *necessitātem*

Necligent, *adj.*, negligent. L. *negligentem* (neglecting)

Nede(n), *v. impers.*, to need, be necessary; Nedeth, *pr. s.*, there needs; therof nedeth not to speke, there is no need to speak of it; what nedeth, what is the need of; ther nedeth make, there is no need to make; Nedede, *p.t. s.*, there needed; hir nedede, she needed. O.E. *nēodian*

Nedely, *adv.*, necessarily

Nedes, *adv.*, needs, of necessity. O.E. *nīedes* or *nēdes*

Need, *s.*, need; as *adj.*, necessary. O.E. *nīed* or *nēd*

Neer, **Ner**, *adv.*, *comp.* of Ny (nigh), nearer. O.E. *nēar*

Neet, *s.*, cattle. O.E. *nēat*

Neighebor, *s.*, neighbour. O.E. *nēahgebūr*

Nekke, *s.*, neck; Nekke-boon, bone in the neck, spine. O.E. *hnecca*

Nere, *p.t. pl.*, were not; *p.t. s. subj.*, were it not. See N', Be

Never(e), *adv.*, never; I noot nevere what, what it was I don't know; never-a-deel, not a bit. O.E. *næfre* (ne ever)

Newe, *adj.*, *adv.*, new; newly, freshly; newe to beginne, newly begun. O.E. *nīwe*

Next, *adj.*, *superl.* of Ny (nigh), nearest; *prep.*, next. O.E. *nīehsta* or *nexta*

Nigard, *s.*, niggard, miser

Nis, *pr. s.*, is not. See N', Be

Noble, *s.*, gold coin worth 6s. 8d.; *adj.*, noble, magnificent. L. *nobilis*

Noght, *s.*, nothing; Noght, Nought, *adv.*, not. Emphatic form of O.E. *nāht*

Nolde, *p.t. s.*, would not. See N', Wol

Nombre, *s.*, number. O.Fr. *nombre*, L. *numerus*

Nones, **Nonis**, *s.*, once, present occasion; for the nones, a wrong division of M.E. *for then ones*, O.E. *for þæm ānum*, for the nonce

Nonne, *s.,* nun. L. *nonna*

Noon, No, *adv.* and *pron.,* no, none; is noon, there is none. O.E. *nān*

Noot, 1 *pr. s.,* (I) know not. O.E. *ne wāt* or *nāt*

Norice, *s.,* nurse. O.Fr. *norice,* L. *nutrix*

Norissyng, *s.,* nutriment

Nosethirles, *s. pl.,* nostrils. O.E. *nos(u)ðyrel (lit.* nosehole)

Notabilitee, *s.,* thing worthy of note

Notable, *adj.,* worthy of note. L. *notabilis*

Not-heed, *s.,* crop-head, head with hair cropped

Nothyng, *adv.,* in no respect, not at all; *s.,* nothing, nought

Nought, *adv.,* not, naught. Emphatic form of O.E. *nāht.* See Nat

Nouthe, *adv.,* now; as nouthe, just now, at present. O.E. *nū þā (lit.* now then)

Nowher, *adv.,* nowhere. O.E. *nāhwēr*

Noyse, *s.,* clamour, outcry. O.Fr. *noise,* L. *nausea* (seasickness)

Ny, *adv.,* nigh; closely; as ny as, as close as; wel ny, almost. O.E. *nēah, nēh*

Nyce, *adj.,* foolish, scrupulous. O.Fr. *nice,* L. *nescius* (ignorant)

Nyght, *s.,* night. O.E. *niht*

Nyghtertale, *s.,* night-time. O.N. *náttarþel* (the dark of night)

Nyghtingale, *s.,* nightingale. O.E. *nihtegale*

Nyne, *adj.,* nine. O.E. *nigon*

O, *adj.* (before a consonant), one. See Oon

O Alma Redemptoris Mater, O gentle Mother of the Redeemer (a Latin hymn)

Observe, *v.,* respect, favour. L. *observare*

Of, *prep.,* of, from; concerning, about; for; by, with; of hir propretee, from their nature; of Achilles, by Achilles; of swich mateere, with such matters; pale of drede, pale for fear. O.E. *of*

Office, *s.,* office; secular employment such as an appointment as chancellor or secretary. L. *officium* (service, duty)

Offre(n), *v.,* give (as an offering); offreth, *imp. pl.* O.E. *offrian*

Offryng, *s.,* offering of alms, offertory

Off-taken, *p.p.,* taken away

Ofte, often, *adv.,* often; ofte(n)-tyme, often; ofte sythes, many times. O.E. *oft*

Ofter, *adv.,* oftener

Oght, *s.,* aught, anything; *adv.,* ought, at all, in any way; wente oght forby, had passed by at all. O.E. *āwiht, ōwiht*

Oille, *s.,* oil; oille of tartre, cream of tartar. O.Fr. *oile,* L. *oleum* (olive oil)

On, *prep.,* on, at, against. O.E. *on*

Ones, *adv.,* once; of one (mind), united; at ones, at once. O.E. *ānes*

Onour, *s.,* honour. O.Fr. *onor,* L. *honōrem.* See Th'onour

Ook, *s.,* oak. O.E. *āc*

Oold, *adj.,* old. O.E. *eald* or *āld*

Oon, *adj., pron. (oon* before a vowel or finally: *o* before a consonant), one; after oon, according to one standard, the same; oon and oon, one by one; that one, the one

many oon, many a one. O.E. *ān*

Oonly, *adv.,* only. O.E. *ǣnlic* or *ānlic*

Ooth, *s.,* oath; **Othes,** *pl.* O.E. *āð*

Oother, *adj., pron.,* other; **Othere,** *pl.,* other; that **oother,** the other; **noon oother wayes,** not otherwise, in no other way. O.E. *ōðer* (second, other)

Ordre, *s.,* order, monastic order; as by **ordre,** in order. O.Fr. *ordre,* L. *ordo, ordinem*

Orgon, *s.,* music, part-song; **Organs,** *pl.,* organ. O.E. *organ* (song); *organan* (*pl.*) (organ), L.Gk. *organum, organa* (organ)

Original, *s.,* origin, source. L. *originālis*

Orlogge, *s.,* clock. O.Fr. *orloge,* L.Gk. *horologium*

Otes, *s. pl.,* oats. O.E. *āte, ātan* (*pl.*)

Othes, *s. pl.,* oaths. See **Ooth**

Oughte, *p.t. s.,* ought. See **Owen**

Ounce, *s.,* ounce; **by ounces,** in small bunches. O.Fr. *once,* L. *uncia* (inch, ounce)

Out, *adv.,* out; **was out of alle charitee,** had no love left, was not in a state of perfect charity; *int.* (come) out!; **Out! harrow!** help! help!; **out of,** without. O.E. *ūt*

Outcast, *p.p.,* cast out

Out-caughte, *p.t. s.,* drew out

Outcryeth, *pr. s.,* cries out

Outrageous, *adj.,* immoderate, violent. O.Fr. *outrageus* (excessive). Cf. L. *ultra* (beyond)

Outrely, *adj.,* utterly, completely. O.E. *ūterlic.* Cf. *ūtera* (outer)

Outrydere, *s.,* monk appointed to ride out on business, inspector

Outsterte, *p.t. pl.,* started out, rushed out

Over, *adj.,* upper; **Overlippe,** upper lip; **Overest,** *sup.,* uppermost, topmost; **Over,** *prep.,* above, beyond; **over hir might,** beyond their strength, to excess. O.E. *ofer*

Over-al, *adv.,* everywhere, wherever. O.E. *ofer all*

Oversprede(n), *v.,* spread over, cover; **overspradde,** *p.p.,* covered

Owe(n), *v.,* owe; own; **Oweth,** 3 *pr. s.,* owns, possesses; **Oughte,** *p.t. s.,* ought; **oughte us,** it behoved us, we ought; **Owene,** *p.p.* as *def. adj.,* own. O.E. *āgan; āhte* (*p.t.*); *āgena* (*adj.*)

Owher, *adv.,* anywhere. O.E. *ō-hwǣr*

Owle, *s.,* owl. O.E. *ūle*

Oxe, *s.,* ox; **Oxen,** *pl.* O.E. *oxa, oxan* (*pl.*)

Oynement, *s.,* ointment. O.Fr. *oignement.* Cf. L. *unguentum*

Oynon, *s.,* onion. Fr. *oignon,* L. *uniō-nem* (pearl)

Paas, *s.,* pace, walking pace; **goon a-paas,** walk at an easy pace. O.Fr. *pas,* L. *passus*

Pace(n), *v.,* pass, go; surpass. See **Passe(n)**

Pacience, *s.,* patience. L. *patientia*

Pacient, *s.,* patient, invalid; *adj.,* patient. L. *patiens, patientem* (suffering)

Page, *s.,* boy, attendant. O.Fr. *page*

Paire, *s.,* pair, couple, set. Fr. *paire,* L. *paria* (equal things)

Palmer, *s.*, pilgrim, *lit.* one who carried a palm-leaf as a token that he had visited the Holy Land

Paramour, *s.*, lover, mistress. O.Fr. *par amour* (by love)

Paraventure, *adv.*, peradventure, perhaps. O.Fr. *par aventure* (by chance)

Par cas: by chance. O.Fr. *par cas.* See Caas

Par chaunce: by chance, as luck would have it. O.Fr. *par chance*

Pardee, *interj.*, verily, by my troth. Fr. *par Dieu*

Pardoneer, *s.*, person licensed to sell indulgences

Pardoun, *s.*, pardon, forgiveness of sins; indulgences. O.Fr. *pardun.* Cf. LL. *perdonare* (forgive)

Parfit, Parfyt, *adj.*, perfect. O.Fr. *parfit*, L. *perfectus* (complete)

Parfourne, *v.*, perform; declare. O.Fr. *parfourner* or *parfournir* (furnish). Germ.

Parisshe, *s.*, parish. O.Fr. *paroche*, LL. *parochia* (parish). Cf. Gk. *oikia* (household)

Parisshen, *s.*, parishioner. O.Fr. *paroissien*

Parten, *v.* to part; depart. O.Fr. *partir*, L. *partire* (divide)

Partrich, *s.*, partridge. O.Fr. *perdriz*, L. *perdix*, *perdicem*

Parvys, *s.*, area before the west front of a cathedral. O.Fr. *parevis*, L.Gk. *paradīsus* (park)

Passe(n), *v.*, to pass, pass on; surpass; Passeth, 3 *pr. s.*, passes; that passeth heer forby, that is passing by this place; Passed, *p.t. s.*, passed; Passed, *p.p.*, passed, crossed over; Passe, *imp.*, pass;

passe over, pass it by, say no more about it. Cf. L. *passus* (footstep)

Pasture, *s.*, feeding. LL. *pastura*

Patente, *s.*, letters patent, papal or royal grant of a privilege. L. *patens*, *patentem* (open)

Patriarkes, *s. pl.*, patriarchs, heads of the church who rank above archbishops, and below the Pope.

Paye, *v.*, pay; Pay(e)de, *p.t.*, paid; Payd, *p.p.*, paid, satisfied. O.Fr. *payer*, L. *pacare* (satisfy). Cf. *pax* (peace)

Pecok, *s.*, peacock; pecokarwes, arrows with peacocks' feathers. O.E. *pēa*, L. *pavo* +*cok*, O.E. *cocc*

Peer, *s.*, equal (in rank). O.Fr. *per*, L. *par*

Pees, *s.*, peace; holde his pees, be silent. O.Fr. *pais*, L. *pax*, *pacem*

Peire, *s.*, set. See Paire

Pekke, *v.*, to peck; Pekke, *imp. s.*

Penaunce, *s.*, penance. O.Fr. *peneance*, L. *poenitentia* (repentance)

Peny, *s.*, penny; Pens, *pl.*, pence. O.E. *pening*

Peple, *s.*, people. O.Fr. *people*, L. *populus*

Perce(n), *v.*, pierce; Perced, *p.p.*, pierced. O.Fr. *percer*, LL. *pertusiare.* Cf. L. *pertūsus* (perforated)

Perchaunce, *adv.*, by chance, perhaps. O.Fr. *par chance*

Perche, *s.*, perch. Fr., L. *pertica* (pole)

Pers, *adj.*, blue-grey (cloth), perse. O.Fr. *pers*, L. *persus* (Persian ?)

Persévere, *v.*, continue; Persevereth, 3 *pr. s.*, lasts. L.

persevĕrare (persist). Cf.
sevĕrus (severe)

Person, *s.,* person ; **Persoun,**
s., parson, rector. O.Fr.
persone, L. *persona* (mask,
character in a play, person)

Pestilence, *s.,* plague ; this
pestilence, during this epi-
demic of the plague. L.
pestilentia

Peyne, *s.,* pain, torment. O.Fr.
peine, L. *poena* (penalty)

Peyne(n), *v.,* take pains, try ;
I peyne me, I take pains ;
Peyned, *p.t.* ; **peyned hir,** she
took pains, endeavoured

Philosophre, *s.,* philosopher,
alchemist

Philosophye, *s.,* philosophy.
L.Gk. *philosophia* (love of
knowledge)

Phisik, *s.,* physic, medicine.
L.Gk. *physica.* Cf. Gk. *phusis*
(nature)

Piled, *p.p.,* peeled, bald, stripped
of hair. L. *pĭlare* (make bald)

Pilwe-beer, *s.,* pillow-case. O.E.
pyle + *bĕr* (bier, litter)

Pinche(n), *v.,* pinch ; **pinche
at,** find fault with ; **Pinched,**
p.p., pleated. A.Fr. *pinchier.*
Cf. Fr. *pincer*

Pitaunce, *s.,* pittance, gift of
food ; gift. O.Fr. *pitance.*
Cf. L. *pietas* (pity)

Pitee, *s.,* pity. O.Fr. *pité,* L.
pietas, pietātem

Pitous, *adj.,* piteous, pitiful ;
tender. O.Fr. *pitos*

Plat, *adv.,* flat ; **al plat,** plainly.
O.Fr. *plat,* Gk. *platus*
(broad)

Plentee, *s.,* plenty, abundance.
O.Fr. *plenté,* L. *plēnitas,
plēnitātem.* Cf. *plēnus* (full)

Plentevous, *adj.,* plentiful. O.Fr.
plentivous

Plesaunce, *s.,* pleasure, pleasant-
ness. O.Fr. *plaisance*

Plesaunt, *adv.,* pleasant, pleas-
ing ; easy. O.Fr. *plaisant.*
L. *placens, placentem*

Plese(n), *v.,* please. O.Fr.
plaisir, L. *placēre*

Pleye(n), *v.,* play ; play music ;
amuse oneself, jest. O.E.
pleg(e)an

Pleyn (1), *adj., adv.,* full ,com-
plete ; fully, entirely. O.Fr.
plein, L. *plēnus* (full)

Pleyn (2), *adj., adv.,* plain,
plainly. O.Fr. *plain,* L.
plānus (flat)

Pleyne(n), *v.,* complain, lament ;
wel oughte us pleyne, much
ought we to complain. O.Fr.
plaindre, plaign(ant), L.
plangere (bewail)

Plighte(n), *s.,* plight, pledge ;
Plight, *p.p.,* pledged. O.E.
plihtan (to venture)

Plowman, *s.,* ploughman. O.E.
plōg + *mann*

Point, Poynt, *s.,* point ; **in good
point,** in good condition ;
every point, every detail.
O.Fr. *point,* L. *punctum*

Pokkes, *s. pl.,* spots, pimples.
O.E. *pocc*

Polcat, *s.,* polecat, kind of
weasel

Policye, *s.,* administration,
statecraft. O.Fr. *policie,*
L.Gk. *politeia* (citizenship)

Pomely, *adj.,* dappled. Fr. *pom-
melé*

Popet, *s.,* puppet, doll. O.Fr.
poupetta. Cf. L. *pŭpa* (doll)

Poraille, *s.,* poor people. O.Fr.
povraille, Italian *poveraglia.*
Cf. L. *pauper*

Port, *s.,* bearing, behaviour.
Cf. Fr. *porter,* L. *portare*
(carry)

Post, *s.,* post, pillar. O.E. *post,*
L. *postis* (door-post)

Potage, *s.,* soup, stew. Fr
potage (soup)

Pothecarie, *s.,* apothecary. LL. *apothecarius.* Cf. Gk. *apothēkē* (store-house)

Poudre marchaunt, *s.,* seasoning powder. O.Fr. *poudre marcheante*

Poure(n), *v.,* to pore, be absorbed

Poure, *adj.,* poor. O.Fr. *povre,* L. *pauper*

Povereste, *adj.,* poorest

Poverte, *s.,* poverty. O.Fr. *poverte,* L. *paupertas*

Poweer, *s.,* power. O.Fr. *pooir,* LL. *potĕre* (be able)

Powped, *p.t. pl.,* hooted

Poynaunt, *adj.,* pungent, spicy. O.Fr. *poignant* (pricking). Cf. *poindre,* L. *pungere*

Poyson, *s.,* poison. O.Fr. *puison,* L. *potiō-nem* (draught). Cf. L. *potus* (drunk)

Practisour, *s.,* practitioner. Cf. O.Fr. *pratiser* (to practise), LL. *practicare*

Preche(n), *v.,* preach. O.Fr. *prechier,* L. *prædicare* (proclaim)

Preching, *s.,* preaching, discourse

Predicacioun, *s.,* preaching, discourse. L. *prædicatiō-nem*

Preest, *s.,* priest. O.E. *prēost,* L.Gk. *presbuteros* (elder)

Preeve, *s.,* test, practical result. O.Fr. *prueve,* LL. *prŏba* (proof)

Prelat, Prelaat, *s.,* ecclesiastic, dignitary. O.Fr. *prélat,* L. *prælātus* (preferred)

Press, *s.,* press ; in presse, in a press ; out of the presse, out of the mould. Fr. *presse.* Cf. L. *pressare* (to press)

Preve(n), *v.,* prove ; Ypreved, *p.p.,* proved (to be so). O.Fr. *prueve,* accented stem of *prover,* L. *prŏbare* (test). See **Prove(n)**

Preye(n), *v.,* pray, ask ; Preye, Pray ; 1 *pr. s.,* pray ; Praye, *pr. pl.* ; Preyede, Preyde, *p.t. s.,* prayed ; Preyden, *p.t. pl.* ; Preye, *imp.* O.Fr. *preier,* L. *precari*

Preyere, *s.,* prayer. O.Fr. *preiere,* LL. *precăria* (prayer)

Prikasour, *s.,* one who spurs, hard rider

Prike(n), *v.,* prick, spur ; incite, excite ; Priketh, 2 *pr. s.* O.E. *prician*

Prikyng, *s.,* spurring, hard riding

Pris, Prys, *s.,* prize (A. 237) ; price (A. 815) ; praise, renown (A. 67). O.Fr. *pris,* L. *pretium* (money, reward)

Prisoun, *s.,* prison. O.Fr. *prison,* L. *prehensio,* (acc.) *prensiō-nem* (seizure)

Privee (1), *s.,* privy ; latrine. Fr. *privé,* L. *privātus* (private)

Privee (2), *adj.,* secret. O.F. *privé,* L. *privātus* (private)

Prively, *adv.,* secretly

Processioun, *s.,* religious procession. L. *processiō-nem*

Pronounce, *v.,* announce. O.Fr. *pronuncier,* LL. *pronuntiare.* Cf. *nuntius* (messenger)

Propre, *adj.,* own ; handsome (ironical). Fr. *propre,* L. *proprius* (one's own, special)

Proprely, *adv.,* naturally ; adequately

Propretee, *s.,* property, characteristic ; of hir propretee, from their natural properties. O.Fr. *proprieté,* L. *proprietas* (peculiarity)

Prove(n), *s.,* prove, test ; Proved, *p.t. s.,* showed (it). O.Fr. *prover,* L. *prŏbare* (test). See **Preve(n)**

Provost, *s.,* provost, chief magistrate. O.E. *profost*

Prow, *s.,* profit, advantage. O.Fr. *proud* or *preu*

Pryde, *s.*, pride. O.E. *prÿte* or *prÿde*

Pryme, *s.*, prime, from 6 a.m. to 9 a.m. L. *prīma (hora)*, the first hour

Prymer, *s.*, first reading-book. L. *prīmārius*

Prys, *s.* See **Pris**

Pulle(n), *v.*, pull ; pluck ; **Pulled,** *p.p.* ; a finch eek koude he **pulle,** he could also cheat a dupe ; a pulled hen, a plucked hen. O.E. *pullian*

Pulpet, *s.*, pulpit, portable desk. L. *pulpitum* (platform)

Pultrye, *s.*, poultry

Purchace(n), *v.*, purchase, acquire. O.Fr. *porchacier,* LL. *pro-captiare* (chase)

Purchas, *s.*, purchase, earnings, gain

Purchasyng, *s.*, purchasing ; getting of land or property otherwise than by inheritance

Purge(n), *v.*, purge. O.Fr. *purger,* L. *purgare*

Purs, *s.*, purse. O.E. *purs*

Purtreye(n), *v.*, portray, draw. O.Fr. *portraire,* L. *pro-trahere* (drag forth)

Putte(n), *v.*, put ; **Putte,** *p.t. s.* O.E. *putian*

Pye, *s.*, pie, pasty

Pyne(n), *v.*, torture ; **Pyned,** *p.p.*, tortured. O.E. *pīnian.* Cf. L. *pǣna* (punishment)

Quelle(n), *v.*, kill. O.E. *cwellan*

Questio quid juris, The question is, what is the law on the subject

Quicksilver, *s.*, mercurial ointment

Quik, *adj.*, alive, lively. O.E. *cwic*

Quod, *p.t. s.*, quoth, said. O.E. *cwæþ*

Quyte(n), *v.*, allow, repay ; quyte you your meede, grant you your reward. O.Fr. *quiter,* LL. *quiētare, quītare* (quieten)

Rad, *p.p.*, read. See **Rede(n)**

Radix malorum est cupiditas, Love of money is the root of all evil. Cf. I *Timothy* vi. 10

Rage, *s.*, rage, anger, frenzy. Fr. *rage,* L. *rabies* (rage)

Rage, *v.*, to frolic, behave riotously

Ram, *s.*, ram, the prize at a wrestling match ; Aries, the first sign of the Zodiac. O.E. *ramm*

Rather, *adv.*, earlier, sooner ; more willingly. O.E. *hraðor*

Rattes, *s. pl.*, rats. O.E. *ræt*

Raughte, *p.t. s.*, reached. See **Reche(n)**

Ravisshe, *v.*, ravish, carry away ; **Ravisedest,** 2 *p.t. s.*, didst attract. O.Fr. *ravir, ravissant,* L. *rapere* (seize)

Real, *adj.*, royal, kingly. O.Fr. *real,* L. *regalis.* Cf. *rex* (king). See **Roial**

Recche(n) (1), **Rekke(n),** *v.*, reck, care ; **Roughte,** *p.t. s.*, recked, cared ; **Rekke,** *imp. s.* O.E. *rēcean* or *rēcan ; rōhte* (*p.t.*)

Recche(n) (2), *v.*, relate, interpret ; recche aright, interpret favourably. O.E. *reccean*

Recchelees, *adj.*, reckless, negligent ; thoughtless. O.E. *rēcelēas*

Receyve, *v.*, receive. A.Fr. *receivre,* L. *recipere*

Reche(n), *v.*, reach, stretch out ; **Raughte,** *p.t. s.*, reached (forward). O.E. *rēcean ; rǣhte* (*p.t.*)

Recorde, *v.*, to record, set down for remembrance ; I it you **recorde,** I remind you of it

O.Fr. *recorder*, L. *recordari* (remember)

Rede(n), *v.*, read; advise, propose; Rad, *p.p.*, read; Rede, Reed, *imp. s.*; Redeth, *imp. pl.* O.E. *rǣdan* (advise)

Redily, *adv.*, readily, soon

Redy, *adj.*, ready O.E. (ge)*rǣde* +-*ig*

Reed (1), *s.*, advice, counsel; adviser. O.E. *rēd*

Reed (2), *adj.*, red, rosy; Rede, *def.*, red. O.E. *rēad*

Reed, *imp. s.*, read. See Rede(n)

Regioun, *s.*, region. L. *regiō-nem* (direction)

Reherce, *v.*, rehearse, repeat. O.Fr. *rehercier* (harrow again), Fr. *herse*, L. *hirpex* (harrow)

Rekene(n), *v.*, reckon, ascertain. O.E. *recenian*

Rekening, *s.*, reckoning, account

Rekke(n), *v.*, reck. See Recche(n) (1)

Religioun, *s.*, religion. L. *re-ligiō-nem*

Relik, *s.*, relic. Fr. *relique*, L. *reliquiae* (remains)

Reme, *s.*, realm. O.Fr. *reaume* or *reame*. LL.* *regalimen*. Cf. L. *regimen* (rule)

Remedie, *s.*, remedy; remedies of love, remedies for love, love-potions. L. *remedium*

Remembre, *v.*, remember; re-membringe on, calling to mind. O.Fr. *remembrer*, L. *re-memorare* (recall to mind)

Remenaunt, *s.*, remainder. O.Fr. *remanant*. Cf. O.Fr. *re-maindre*, L. *remanēre* (remain)

Rende(n), *v.*, rend; Rente, *p.t.*, tore. O.E. *rendan*

Renne(n), *v.*, run; Ran, *p.t. s.*, ran; Ronne(n), *p.t. pl.*, ran; Yronne, *p.p.* run. O.N. *renna*; *rann*; *runnum*; *runninn*

Renning, *s.*, running; at a renning, at a run, with one effort

Renoun, *s.*, renown. A.Fr. *renoun*. Cf. L. *nōmen* (name)

Rente, *s.*, revenue from farmed property, income. O.Fr. *rente*, LL. *rendita*, *p.p.* of *rendere*, L. *reddere* (give back)

Rente, *p.t.*, torn. See Rende(n)

Repaire, *v.*, return, resort. O.Fr. *repairer*, LL. *repatriare*. Cf. L. *patria* (native land)

Replecioun, *s.*, repletion, over-eating. LL. *replētiō-nem* (fullness). Cf. L. *replēre* (to fill up)

Repleet, *adj.*, full. L. *replētus*

Reporte, *v.*, tell, narrate. O.Fr. *reporter*, L. *reportare* (bring back [news])

Reportour, *s.*, spokesman, announcer, commentator

Repreeve, *s.*, shame, reproach. O.Fr. *re-prueve* (reproof). Cf. LL. *prōba* (proof)

Reprevable, *adj.*, reprovable, reprehensible

Reson, Resoun, *s.*, reason; statement, argument; Resons, *pl.*, arguments, opinions; by resoun, rightly. O.Fr. *raison*, L. *ratiō-nem* (account, reason)

Resonable, *adj.*, reasonable, fair

Reste, *s.*, rest; to reste, gone to his bed, set. O.E. *ræst* or *rest*

Restelees, *adj.*, restless

Rethor, *s.*, orator. L.Gk. *rhētor*

Reule, *s.*, rule. O.Fr. *rieule* or *reule*, L. *regula*

Reule(n), *v.*, rule; Reuled, *p.p.*, guided. O.Fr. *riuler*, L. *regulare*

Reve, *s.*, reeve, foreman of a manor, manager. O.E. (ge)-*rēfa*

Revel, *s.*, revelry, merriment. O.Fr. *revel* (riot). Cf. L. *rebellare* (revolt)

Reverence, s., honour, respect; in reverence, respectfully; of greet reverence, held in great honour; our lawe's reverence, the reverence which we feel for our law. L. *reverentia* (respect)

Revers, s., reverse, contrary. Fr. *revers*, L. *reversus* (turned back). Cf. L. *revertere*

Rewe(n), v., to rue, to be sorry; it reweth me, it repents me, I am sorry. O.E. *hrēowan*

Reyn, s., rain. O.E. *regn*

Reysed, p.p., served, gone a-soldiering. Cf. O.Fr. *reise* (raid), M.H.G. *reise* (military expedition)

Ribaudye, s., ribaldry, debauchery. O.Fr. *ribaudie*. Germ.

Right, adv., right; exactly, just; quite, really, very; right anon, immediately. O.E. *rihte*

Rightwisnesse, s., righteousness. O.E. *rihtwisnes*

Ringe(n), v., ring, resound; ring it out, speak with resonant voice; Rong, p.t. s., rang. O.E. *hringan*

Riot, s., debauchery, revelry; gambling. O.Fr. *riote*

Riotours, s. pl., revellers; gamblers

Roial, adj., royal. O.Fr. *roial*, L. *regalis*. See Real

Roialliche, adv., royally, regally

Rolle, s., cylinder of paper, document. O.Fr. *rolle*, L. *rotula*. Cf. L. *rota* (wheel)

Rolle(n), v., roll, revolve; Rollinge, pr. p., sparkling. O.Fr. *roller*, LL. *rotulare* (revolve)

Rome(n), v., roam; Romed, p.t. s.

Rong, p.t. s., rang. See Ringe(n)

Ronne, p.t. pl., ran. See Renne(n)

Rood, p.t. s., rode. See Ryde(n)

Roore(n), v., roar, cry out. O.E. *rārian*

Roos, p.t. s., rose. See Ryse(n)

Roost, s., roast meat. O.Fr. *rost*, M.H.G. *rost* (gridiron)

Root(e), s., root, source; Rote, dat. O.N. *rót*, cognate with O.E. *wyrt* (wort)

Roste(n), v., roast before a fire; Rosted, p.p., roasted

Rote, s., rote, a stringed instrument, fiddle; repetition, memory. O.Fr. *rote*, O.H.G. *hrotta*. Cf. Welsh *crwth* (a sort of fiddle); by rote, by heart

Roughte, p.t. s., cared. See Recchen (1)

Rouncy, s., cart-horse. O.Fr. *roncin*

Round, adj., adv., round; evenly, continuously; freely. O.Fr. *roönd*, L. *rotundus* (adj.)

Rounded, p.t. s., was round

Route, s., rout, company, band. O.Fr. *route* (road), L. *rupta* (broken)

Rude, adj., harsh. L. *rudis* (rough)

Rudeliche, adv., rudely

Ruste(n), v. to rust; Ruste, pr. s. subj., rust. O.E. *rustian*. Cf. O.E. *rust* (rust)

Ryde(n), v., ride; to ryden out, to go a-soldiering, to go to the wars; Rood, p.t. s., rode; Riden, p.t. pl., rode; Riden, p.p., ridden. O.E. *rīdan*; *rād, ridon; riden*

Rym, s., rhyme. O.Fr. *rime*, Gk. *rhuthmos* (rhythm)

Ryse(n), v., rise, get up; Roos, pt. s., rose; Rise, p.t. pl., rose. O.E. (a-)*rīsan; rās, rison; risen*

Ryve(n), v., rive; thrust, stab. O.N. *rífa*

Sacrement, *s.*, sacrament ; the mass. L. *sacrāmentum* (military oath). Cf. *sacer* (sacred)

Sacrifyse, *s.*, sacrifice ; they doon the devel sacrifyse, they sacrifice to the devil. L. *sacrificium*

Saffron, *s.*, saffron, the yellow stigmas of the Autumn Crocus used for flavouring in cookery ; to saffron with, for flavouring with, to flavour. Arabic

Saille(n), *v.*, sail. O.E. *seglian*, *seglan*

Salue, *v.*, salute, greet. O.Fr. *saluer*, L. *salūtare*

Sampsoun, *int.*, imitation of a snore

Sangwyn, *adj.*, *s.*, blood-red, rosy (cloth) ; the complexion in which blood predominates over bile and phlegm ; hence, rosy and happy, hopeful. L. *sanguineus*. Cf. *sanguis* (blood)

Sapience, *s.*, wisdom. L. *sapientia*

Saufly, *adv.*, safely, confidently. O.Fr. *sauf*, L. *salvus* (safe)

Saugh, *p.t. s.*, saw. See See(n)

Sautrye, *s.*, psaltery, musical instrument like a dulcimer. O.Fr. *sautier*, L.Gk. *psalterium* (lute). Cf. Gk. *psallo* (play a stringed instrument), whence ' psalm '

Save, *prep.*, except. O.Fr. *sauf*, L. *salvus* (safe)

Save(n), *s.*, save, keep ; so save, *pr. s. subj.*, may God save ; Savith, *pr. s.*, saves. O.Fr. *salver*, LL. *salvare*

Sawcefleem, *adj.*, pimpled, covered with white pimples. O.Fr. *sauce-fleume*, LL. *salsa phlegma* (salted inflammation)

Say, *p.t. s.*, saw. See See(n)

Sayn, Sayde. See Seye(n)

Scabbe, *s.*, scab, a skin disease

Scalled, *adj.*, scaly, scurfy. Cf. O.N. *skalli* (bald head)

Scarsly, *adv.*, frugally, sparingly. Cf. O.Fr. *eschars* (scarce)

Scathe, *s.*, scathe, harm ; a pity. O.N. *skaði*

Science, *s.*, theoretical knowledge, learned writing. L. *scientia* (knowledge). Cf. *scīre* (to know)

Sclendre, Sklendre, *adj.*, slender, slight. Cf. O.Dutch *slinder* (thin)

Scole, *s.*, school ; manner of speech ; in scole, in the universities ; to scoleward, towards school. L. *schola* (school), Gk. *skhole* (leisure)

Scoler, *s.*, scholar. O.Fr. *escoler* Cf. LL. *scholāris* from *schola*

Scoleye, *v.*, be a scholar, to study. O.Fr. *escoleier*

Scorne(n), *v.* to scorn, ridicule ; Scorned, *p.t. s.*, jested at ; scorned him ful faste, poured scorn on him. O.Fr. *escharnir* (mock) Germ.

Seche(n), *v.*, seek. See Seke(n)

Secree, *adj.*, discreet, trusty. O.Fr. *secré*, L. *secrētus*

See, *s.*, sea. O.E. *sǣ*

See(n), *v.*, see ; God you see, *pr. s. sing.*, may God look upon you, God bless you ; Seigh, Say, Saugh, *p.t. s.*, saw ; Syen, *p.t. pl.*, saw ; Seyn, *p.p.*, seen. O.E. *sēon* ; *seah, sæh* ; *sēgon* ; *segen*. See Y-sene, Sene

Seege, *s.*, siege. O.Fr. *siege*, LL. *sedium*. Cf. L. *sedēve* (sit)

Seel, *s.*, seal. O.Fr. *seel*, L. *sigillum*

Seint(e), *s.*, saint ; *adj.*, holy. O.Fr. *saint*, L. *sanctus* (holy)

Seke, *adj.*, sick, ill. O.E. *sēoc* or *sēc*

Seke(n), Seche(n), v., seek, search; **was not longe for to seche,** was easily found; **Soughte,** *p.t. s.,* sought; **Sought,** *p.p.* O.E. *sēcean; sōhte*

Selle(n), v., sell; **to selle, to sell,** for sale. O.E. *sellan*

Sely, *adj.,* happy; innocent; simple. O.E. *sǣlig, sēlig*

Seme(n), v., seem, appear; **Semeth,** *pr. s.,* seems; **Semed** *p.t. s.,* seemed; **it semed me,** it seemed to me, I thought. O.E. *sēman* (reconcile)

Semely, *adj., adv.,* seemly, comely; politely. O.N. *sœmiligr* (honourable)

Semicope, *s.,* short cape, tippet. See Cope

Semyng, *s.,* seeming; **to my seemyng,** as it seems to me, as I can see quite plainly

Senatour, *s.,* senator. L. *senator*

Sendal, *s.,* silk. O.Fr. *sendal.* Cf. Gk. *sindōn* (muslin)

Sende(n), v., send; **Sente,** *p.t.,* sent; **Sent,** *p.p.;* **Sendeth,** *imp. pl.,* send. O.E. *sendan*

Sene, Ysene, *adj.,* seen, apparent, visible. Not the *p.p.* of 'see(n),' but O.E. *adj. gesīene* or *gesēne* (visible)

Sentence, *s.,* opinion, meaning; instruction, morality; subject; sentiment, eloquence. O.Fr. *sentence,* L. *sententia* (opinion)

Sepulture, *s.,* grave, tomb. L. *sepultura* (burial)

Sergeaunt, *s.,* serjeant; sergeaunt of the lawe, barrister of high rank. O.Fr. *serjant* or *sergeant,* L. *servientem* (serving)

Sermone, v., to preach a sermon. Cf. L. *sermo-nem* (discourse)

Servant, *s.,* servant; **Servantz,** *pl.* O.Fr. *servir, servant,* *pr. p.,* L. *servire* (serve)

Servisable, *adv.,* serviceable, useful

Servise, *s.,* service; duty; religious service. O.Fr. *service,* L. *servitium*

Seson, Sesoun, *s.,* season. O.Fr. *seson,* L. *satiō-nem* (sowing)

Sessiouns, *s. pl.,* sessions, sittings of Justices of the Peace. L. *sessiō-nem* (a sitting)

Sethe(n), v., seethe, cook by boiling. O.E. *sēoðan*

Sette(n), v., set, place; **sette a soper,** lay, arrange a supper; **Sette,** *pr. s.,* set, value; **I sette nat a straw by,** I do not reckon as worth a straw; **Sette,** *p.t.,* set, put; **Sette hem,** sat down, seated themselves; **sette hir aller cappe,** made a fool of them all; **sette to hyre,** farmed out; **Set, Yset,** *p.p.,* set; **is doun yset,** has sat down; **were set hem,** were sitting. O.E. *settan*

Seuretee, *s.,* surety, security. O.Fr. *seurté,* L. *sēcūritas, sēcūritātem*

Sewe, v., pursue, follow; **Sewed,** *p.t. s.* O.Fr. *suir,* Fr. *suivre,* L. *sequere* for *sequi* (follow)

Seye(n), Sey(n), Sayn, v., say, speak; **soothly for to seye,** to speak truly, to tell the truth; **this is to seyn,** that is to say; **that is to seyn,** that is to say; **was to seye,** meant; **Seye,** 1 *pr. s.,* say; **I seye thee,** I tell thee; **Seith,** 3 *pr. s.,* says; **Seyn,** *pr. pl.,* say; **Seyde, Seide, Sayde,** *p.t.,* said; **Seyd, Sayd,** *p.p.,* said; **Sey,** *imp. s.* O.E. *secgan, segð; sægde; sægd*

Seyl, *s.,* sail. O.E. *segl*

Seyle(n), v., sail. O.E. *seglian*

Seyn, *p.p.,* seen. See See(n)

Seynd, *p.p.* of Senge (singe);
seynd bacon, toasted bacon.
O.E. *senged, sengd*

Seynt, *s.*, saint. See Seint(e)

Shake, *p.p.*, shaken. Cf.
Shake(n) (shake). O.E.
scacen

Shal, *pr. s.*, shall, ought to,
am (is) to; Shaltow, 2 *pr.s.*,
shalt thou; Shul, *pr. pl.*,
shall, must, will; Sholde,
p.t. s., should, ought to, was
(were) to; Sholde(n), *p.t. pl.*
O.E. *sceal, sculon (pr. pl.)*;
scolde

Shamfastnesse, *s.*, shyness,
modesty. O.E. *scamfæst-
ness*

Shape(n), *v.*, to shape, plan;
I wol shape me, I will prepare
myself; Shape(n), *pr. pl.*;
ye shapen you, you are preparing; Shoop, *p.t. s.*, shaped;
shoop him, (he) intended;
Shape, *p.p.*, shaped. O.E.
scieppan; *scōp-on*; *scapen*.
Cf. O.E. *(ge-)sceap, s.* (shape)

Shaply, *adj.*, formed, fit

Shave, *p.p.*, shaven, of Shave(n).
O.E. *scafen*

She, *pron.*, she; Hir, *acc. dat.*,
her; Hir, *poss.*, her

Sheef, *s.*, sheaf. O.E. *scēaf*

Sheeld, *s.*, shield, Sheeldes, *pl.*,
French *écus* or crowns, coins
worth 3s. 6d. O.E. *scield* or
sceld

Sheene, *adj.*, bright. O.E.
sciene or *scēne*

Sheep, *s.*, sheep. O.E. *scēap*

Shende(n), *v.*, harm, disgrace;
Shente, *p.t. s.*, injured; Shent,
p.p., scolded, punished. O.E.
sciendan or *scendan*

Shere(n), *v.*, shear, cut; Yshorn,
pp, shorn. O.E. *sceran*;
(ge-)scoren

Sherte, *s.*, shirt. O.E. *scyrte*,
Kent. *scerte*

Shewe(n), *v.*, show; Sheweth,
3 *pr. s.*, shows; Shewen, *pr.
pl.*, showed. O.E. *scēawian*
(look)

Shine, *s.*, shin. O.E. *scinu*

Shipman, *s.*, sailor. O.E. *scip-
mann*

Shirreve, *s.*, sheriff. O.E. *scīr-
(ge-)rēfa* (shire-reeve)

Shiten, *adj.*, befouled, filthy.
O.E. *sciten (p.p.)*

Sholde(n), *p.t. pl.*, should. See
Shal

Sholder-boon, *s.*, blade-bone

Shoo, *s.*, shoe. O.E. *scōh*

Shoon, *p.t. s.*, shone. See
Shyne(n)

Shoop,, *p.t. s.* shaped. See
Shape(n)

Short, *adj.*, short; Short-
sholdred, *adj.*, short-necked,
thick set. O.E. *sceort* or
scort

Shorte(n), *v.*, shorten; to shorte
with your weye, to shorten
your way therewith. O.E.
scortian

Shot, *s.*, missile, arrow. O.E.
(ge)scot

Shour, *s.*, shower. O.E. *scūr*

Shrewe, *s.*, scoundrel. O.E.
scrēawa (shrew-mouse)

Shrewe(n), *v.*, to curse

Shriken, *s.*, shriek, screech;
Shrighte, *p.t. s.*, shrieked,
screeched; Shriked, *p.t. pl.*,
shrieked. O.E.? Cf. O.N.
skrækja (screech)

Shryve(n), *v.*, to confess, hear
confession and give absolution; Yshrive(n), *p.p.*, shriven.
O.E. *scrīfan*

Shul, *pr. pl.*, shall. See Shal

Shulder, Sholder, *s.*, shoulder.
O.E. *sculdor*

Shyne(n), *v.*, shine; Shoon,
p.t. s., shone. O.E. *scīnan*;
scān

Signe, *s.*, sign, token; constellation. O.Fr. *signe*, L. *signum*

Significacioun, *s.*, sign, symbol. L. *significātiō-nem*

Significavit, *s.*, writ authorizing the arrest of an excommunicated person

Sik, *adj.*, ill; Sike, *pl.* O.E. *sēoc* or *sēc*

Siker, *adj.*, sure, trustworthy; also siker as, as sure as. O.E. *sicor*

Sikerer, *adj.*, *comp.*, surer

Sikerly, *adv.*, surely, certainly

Simple, *adj.*, of one kind, modest; simple necessitee, complete compulsion, predestination. O.Fr. *simple*, L. *simplex, simplicem* (onefold)

Singe(n), *s.*, sing; singe I moot certeyn, I needs must sing; Song, Soong, *p.t. s.*, sing; Songe, *p.p.*, sung; Singeth, *imp. pl.*, sing; Singynge, *pr. p.*, singing. O.E. *singan*; *sang*; *sungen*

Sinne, *s.*, sin. O.E. *synn*

Sire, *s.*, master. O.Fr. *sire*, L. *senior* (elder)

Sith, Sith that, *conj.*, since; Sith, *adv.*, afterwards, then. O.E. *siþþan*

Sitte(n), *v.*, sit; Sat, *p.t.*, set; Seten, *p.p.*, sat; Sittinge, *pr. p.*, sitting, being, which were. O.E. *sittan*; *sæt*; *seten* (*p.p.*)

Sklendre, Sclendre, *adj.*, slender, scanty

Slawe, *p.p.*, slain. See Slee(n)

Slee(n), *v.*, slay; Sleeth, *pr. s.*, slays; Slawe, Slayn, Yslawe, Yslayn, *p.p.*, slain. O.E. *slēan*; *slægen* (*p.p.*)

Sleighte, *s.*, sleight, cunning, trickery. O.N. *slǽgð*

Slepe(n), *v.*, sleep; Sleep, *p.t. s.*, slept. O.E. *slǽpan*; *slēp*

Slepere, *s.*, sleeper. O.E. *slǣpere*

Sleping, *s.*, sleep

Sleve, *s.*, sleeve. O.E. *slīefe* or *slēf*

Slough, *s.*, slough, bog; mire. O.E. *slōh*

Smal, *adj.*, small, slender; Smale, *pl.* O.E. *smæl*

Smerte, *adv.*, sharply. O.E. *smeart* (*adj.*) (sharp)

Smerte, *v.*, smart, grieve; Smerte, *p.t. s.*, it pained (him); Smerte, *p.t. s. subj.*, (it) might give him pain. O.E. *smeortan, smertan*

Smoot, *p.t. s.*, smote. See Smyte(n)

Smothe, *adj.*, *adv.*, smooth, smoothly. O.E. *smōþ(e)*

Smylyng, *pr. p.*, smiling

Smyte(n), *v.*, smite, strike; Smoot, *p.t. s.*, smote. O.E. *smītan* (smear), *smāt*

Snewe(n), *v.*, to snow, Snewed *p.t. s.*, snowed, abounded O.E. *snīwan*

Snibbe(n), *v.*, snub, reprove. Cf. O.N. *snubba* (snub)

Snowte, *s.*, snout, muzzle

So, *adv.*, so, in such a way; so as, just as, as far as. So is also used to introduce sentences expressing a hope or wish; So God you blesse, may God bless you; so moot I thee, may I prosper; so have I blis, may I have bliss, God grant me bliss; so save, may he save. O.E. *swā*

So, So that, *conj.*, provided that. O.E. *swā*

Sobre, *adj.*, serious, sad. O.Fr. *sobre*, L. *sōbrius* (sober)

Sobrely, *adv.*, serious, grave, sadly

Sobrenesse, *s.*, sobriety

Socour, *s.*, succour, help. O.Fr. *secors* or *socors*, L. *succursum* (helped)

Sodeyn, *adj.,* sudden. O.Fr. *soudain,* LL. *subitāneus.* Cf. L. *subito* (suddenly)

Softe, *adj., adv.,* soft, softly. O.E. *sōfte*

Softely, *adv.,* quietly

Solas, Solaas, *s.,* solace, consolation; pleasure; edification. O.Fr. *solas,* L. *sōlātium*

Solempne, *adj.,* solemn; pompous, important. O.Fr. *solempne,* L. *sollemnis*

Som, *adj., indef. pron.,* some. O.E. *sum*

Somdel, *adv.,* somewhat. O.E. *sume dǣle* (partly)

Somonour, *s.,* beadle, officer who summoned sinners before the archdeacon's court. O.Fr. *semoneor* or *somoneor,* L. *submonitor*

Somtyme, *adv.,* once; sometimes

Somwhat, *adv., indef. pron.,* something, somewhat

Sondry, *adj.,* sundry, various. Cf. O.E. *sundor* (*adv.*) (separately)

Sone, *s.,* son. O.E. *sunu*

Song, *p.t. s.,* sang; **Songe,** *p.p.,* sung. See Singe(n)

Sonne, *s.,* sun. O.E. *sunne*

Soond, *s.,* sand. O.E. *sand* or *sond*

Soone, *adv.,* soon. O.E. *sōna*

Soong, *p.t. s.,* sang. See Singe(n)

Soor, *s.,* sore, wound. O.E. *sār*

Soore, Sore, *adv.,* sorely, sadly; very. O.E. *sāre*

Soote, *adj.,* sweet. O.E. *swōte* (*adv.*) (sweetly)

Sooth, *adj., adv.,* true; truly, indeed. O.E. *sōþ*

Sooth, *s.,* truth. O.E. *sōþ*

Soothfastnesse, *s.,* truth. O.E. *sōðfæstnes*

Soothly, *adv.,* truly

Sop, *s.,* sop of soaked bread; sop in wyn, cake soaked in wine. O.E. *sopp*

Soper, *s.,* supper. O.Fr. *soper*

Sore, *adv.,* grievously, very. See Soore

Sort, *s.,* lot, chance. O.Fr. *sorte,* L. *sors, sortem*

Sorwe, *s.,* sorrow; with sorwe, with disastrous result. O.E. *sorg*

Sorweful, *adj.,* sorrowful, sad

Sory, *adj.,* woeful, sad; ill, unlucky; with sory grace, with ill-luck. O.E. *sārig*

Sought, *p.p.,* sought. See Seke(n)

Souke(n), *v.,* suck; **Soukinge,** *pres. p.,* sucking. O.E. *sūcan*

Soule, *s.,* soul. O.E. *sāwol*

Soun, *s.,* sound. O.Fr. *son,* L. *sonus*

Souple, *adj.,* supple, pliant. O.Fr. *souple,* L. *supplex, supplicem*

Sovereyn, Soverayn, *adj.,* sovran, supreme, highest. O.Fr. *soverain,* LL. *superānus* (supreme)

Sovereynly, *adv.,* above the rest

Sowded, *p.p.,* united, bound; devoted. Fr. *soudé* (soldered), L. *solidātus* (fastened together)

Sowe, *s.,* sow; pig. O.E. *sugu*

Sowe(n) (1), *v.,* sew; **Sowed,** *p.p.,* sewn. O.E. *sēowian* or *sīwian*

Sowe(n) (2), *v.,* to sow; **Sowen,** *p.p.,* sown. O.E. *sāwan*

Sowne(n), *v.,* sound, make music. O.Fr. *soner,* L. *sonāre*

Sowninge, *adj.,* resounding, talking loudly of; sowninge in, resounding in, full of, inclining to

Space, *s.,* space, space of time, course; heeld after the newe world the space, went his way according to the new style; withinne a litel space, in a short time. O.Fr. *espace*, L. *spatium*

Spanne, *s.*, span, distance stretched between tips of thumb and little finger, 9 inches. O.E. *spann*

Spare(n), *v.*, spare, refrain (from). O.E. *sparian*

Sparwe, *s.*, sparrow. O.E. *spearwa*

Speche, *s.*, speech, talk, discourse. O.E. *sp(r)ǣc*

Special, *adj.*, special; in special, especially. O.Fr. *especial*, L. *speciālis*

Spede(n), *v.*, speed, hasten, prosper; Speede, *pr. s. subj.*, prosper; God you speede, God prosper you; Sped, *p.p.*, made haste. O.E. *spēdan*

Speke(n), *v.*, speak; Spak, *p.t. s.*, spoke, spake; Spoke(n), *p.p.*, spoken. O.E. *sp(r)ecan*

Spende(n), *v.*, spend; Spente, *p.t. s.*, spent; Spent, *p.p.* O.E. *spendan*, L. *expendere* (weigh out)

Spere, *s.*, spear. O.E. *spere*

Spiced, *adj.*, flavoured, or preserved with spices; a spiced conscience, an assumed or artificial disposition, a hypocritical conscience. Cf. O.Fr. *espice* (spice), L. *species* (sort). See note on *Prol.* 526

Spicerye, *s.*, spices

Spitte(n), *v.*, spit. O.E. *spittan*

Spore, *s.*, spur. O.E. *spura* or *spora*

Sprede(n), *v.*, spread; Ysprad, *p.p.*, spread. O.E. *sprǣdan*

Spreynd, *p.p.* of Springen, sprinkled. O.E. *sprengd*; *sprengan* (*inf.*)

Springe(n), *v.*, spring, grow; dawn. O.E. *springan*

Squier, *s.*, esquire, attendant on a knight. O.Fr. *esquier*, L. *scūtārius* (shield-bearer)

Staat, *s.*, state; in good staat, with cash in hand. See Estaat

Staf, *s.*, staff, stick; Staves, *pl.* O.E. *stæf*

Stal, *p.t. s.*, betook. See Stelen

Stall, *s.*, stable, cow-house. O.E. *steall*, *stall*

Stampe(n), *v.* to pound (in a mortar). O.E.*stempan*(pound)

Stant, *pr. s.*, stands. See Stonde(n)

Stape, *p.p.* of Steppe(n), stepped, advanced. O.E. *stæpen* or *stapen*

Statut, *s.*, statute, law. L. *statūtum* (appointed)

Stede, *s.*, place; in stede of, instead of. O.E. *stede*

Stedefast, *adj.*, steadfast, constant. O.E. *stedefæst*

Steep, *adj.*, steep, prominent; Stepe, *pl.* O.E. *stēap*

Stele(n), *v.*, steal; Stal, *p.t. s.*, stole, went quietly. O.E. *stelan*, *stæl*

Steme(n), *v.*, steam; Stemed, *p.t. s.*, shone, gleamed. O.E. *stēman*

Stepe, *adj.*, *pl.*, prominent, bright. See Steep

Sterlynges, *s. pl.*, silver pence

Sterre, *s.*, star. O.E. *steorra*

Sterte(n), *v.*, start; Sterte, *p.t. s.*, started (up), jumped. O.E. *styrtan*, Kent. *stertan*. See Stirte(n)

Sterve(n), *v.*, die; dooth for to sterve, puts to death; Storven, *p.t. pl.*, died. O.E. *steorfen* (die); *storfen*

Stewe, *s.*, house of bad reputation. O.Fr. *estuve* (bath). Germ. Cf. Ger. *stube* (room)

Stif, *adj.*, stiff, strong, harsh. O.E. *stīf*

Stike(n), *s.*, stick ; Stiked, *p.p.*, stabbed ; a stiked swyn, a stuck pig. O.E. *stician*

Stikke, *s.*, stake, paling. O.E. *sticca*

Stille, *adv.*, still ; yet ; quietly ; lat . . . be stille, leave. O.E. *stille* (quiet)

Stinge(n), *v.*, sting. O.E. *stingan*

Stinte(n), *v.*, cease, end ; leave off, check ; stinte of, cease from. O.E. *styntan* (stupefy)

Stire(n), *v.*, stir. O.E. *styrian*

Stirte(n), *v.*, start, jump ; Stirte, *p.t.*, started, jumped. O.E. *styrtan*. See Sterte(n)

Stonde(n), *v.*, stand ; to stonden at my juggement, to agree to my decision ; Stondeth, Stant, 3 *pr. s.*, stands ; Stood, *p.t. s.*, stood ; Stonden, *p.p.*, stood. O.E. *standan* or *stondan* ; *stōd*, *p.t.* ; *standen* or *stonden* (*p.p.*)

Stoon, *s.*, stone ; precious stone ; Stones, *pl.* (precious) stones ; cristal stones, glasses, flasks. O.E. *stān*

Stoor, *s.*, store, stock ; telle no stoor, take no stock, think nothing (of). O.Fr. *estor*. Cf. L. *instaurare* (erect)

Storie, *s.*, history, life of a saint, tale. O.Fr. *estoire*. A.Fr. *estorie*, L. *historia*

Storven, *p.t., pl.*, died. See Sterve(n)

Stot, *s.*, pony. O.E. *stot*. Cf. O.N. *stútr* (stump)

Stout, *adj.*, brave, strong. O.Fr. *estout* (brave), L. *stultus* (foolish)

Straunge, *adj.*, strange, foreign. O.Fr. *estrange*, L. *extrāneus* (external)

Strecche(n), .,stretch ; Streight, *p.p.*, stretched. O.E. *streccan* ; *streht*

Streem, *s.*, stream, river. O.E. *strēam*

Streight, *adv.*, straightway. O.E. *streht* (*p.p.* of *streccan*)

Streit, *adj.*, strait, narrow ; scanty, strict ; Streite, *def.*, drawn (N.P.T. 587). O.Fr. *estreit*, L. *strictus* (drawn tight, unsheathed)

Streite, *adv.*, closely, tightly

Strenger, *adj.*, *comp.* stronger. O.E. *strengra*

Strengthe, *s.*, strength. O.E. *strengð*

Strete, *s.*, street. O.E. *strēt*, L. *strāta* (*via*), (paved way)

Streyne, *v.*, strain, constrain ; Streyne, *pr. pl.*, strain (through a sieve). O.Fr. *estreindre*, *estreignant*, L. *stringere* (draw tight)

Strike, *s.*, bunch of flax. Cf. O.E. *strica* (stroke, mark)

Strogel, *v.*, to struggle ; Strogelest, 2 *pers. s.*

Stronde, *s.*, strand, shore. O.E. *strand* or *strond*

Stryving, *s.*, strife. Cf. O.Fr. *estriver* (strive)

Studie, *s.*, study. L. *studium* (zeal, study)

Studie(n), *v.*, to study ; Studieth, *imp. pl.*, deliberate (on), consider

Stuwe, *s.*, fish-pond. O.Fr. *estui* (prison)

Styward, *s.*, steward. O.E. *stigweard* (house-warden)

Substaunce, *s.*, substance, wealth ; inner nature ; material (of a good listener). L. *substantia*

Subtilly, *adv.*, cunningly, craftily. Cf. L. *subtīlis* (slim)

Subtiltee, *s.*, subtlety, cunning. L. *subtilitas* (slimness)

Suffisaunce, *s.*, sufficiency, contentment

Suffisaunt, *adj.*, sufficient, capable

Suffise, *v.*, suffice. O.Fr. *suffise, suffisant*, L. *sufficere* (supply)

Suffre, *v.*, suffer, permit. O.Fr. *soufrir*, L. *sufferre* (endure)

Superfluitee, *s.*, superfluity, excess. LL. *superfluitas* (overflowing)

Surcote, *s.*, surcoat, outer coat. O.Fr. *surcote*

Suspecioun, *s.*, suspicion. L. *suspiciō-nem*

Susteene, *v.*, sustain, support; Sustened, *p.p.*, maintained. O.Fr. *sustenir*, L. *sustinēre* (support)

Suster, *s.*, sister; Sustres, *pl.* O.E. *sweostor* or *suster*

Swal, *p.t. s.*, swelled. See Swelle(n)

Swelle(n), *v.*, swell; Swal, *p.t. s.*; up-swal, was swollen with anger. O.E. *swellan*; *sweall*

Swerd, *s.*, sword. O.E. *sweord*

Swere(n), *s.*, swear; Swore, Sworn, *p.p.*, sworn. O.E. *swerian*; *sworen* (*p.p.*)

Swering, *s.*, swearing, perjury

Swete, Sweete, *adj.*, sweet; swete breeth, pleasant air. O.E. *swēte*. See Soote, Swoote

Swetely, *adv.*, pleasantly, indulgently

Sweven, *s.*, dream; Swevenes, Swevenis, *pl.* O.E. *swefn*

Swich, Such, *adj. pron.*, such; Swiche, *pl.*; swich thing, such a thing; swich licour, that liquid. O.E. *swylc* or *swulc*

Swink, *s.*, toil, labour. O.E. (*ge-*)*swinc*

Swinke(n), *v.*, toil, labour. O.E. *swincan*

Swinkere, *s.*, labourer

Swor(n)**e**, *p.p.*, sworn. See Swere(n)

Swoote, *adv.*, sweetly. O.E *swōte*

Swowne(n), *v.* swoon; Swowninge, *pr. p.* Cf. O.E. (*ge-*)*swōgen* (*adj.*) (inanimate)

Swyn, *s.*, swine. O.E. *swīn*

Swythe, *adv.*, quickly. O.E. *swīðe*

Syde, *s.*, side. O.E. *sīde*

Syen, *p.t., pl.*, saw. See See(n)

Syn, *adv., conj.*, since. O.E. *siþþan*. See Sith

Syth(e), *s.*, time; ofte sythes, often. O.E. *sīþ*

T', abbreviation of To before verbs beginning with a vowel, *e.g.*, t'allye, to ally

Taak, *imp. s.*, take. See Take(n)

Tabard, *s.*, smock; herald's coat; inn-sign of the Tabard. O.Fr. *tabart* or *tabarde*

Table, *s.*, table (of planks and trestles), table (of the law); table dormant, permanent table. O.Fr. *table*, L. *tabula* (board)

Taffata, *s.*, linen taffeta. Persian

Taille, *s.*, tally, reckoning kept on a notched stick; took by taille, bought on credit. O.Fr. *taillee*. Cf. L. *talea* (stick)

Take(n), *v.*, take, seize; Took, *p.t. s.*, took; took by taille, bought on credit; Tooken, *p.t. pl.*, took; Ytake, *p.p.*, taken; Taak, Tak, *imp. s.*, take; Taketh, *imp. pl.*, take; taak keep, take keep, take heed. O.N. *taka; tók, tókum; tekinn*

Takel, *s.*, tackle, gear; *e.g.*, arrows, etc.

Tale, *s.*, tale, story; telle I no longer tale, I will say no more; tale hath he told, account hath he taken. O.E. *talu*

Tale(n), *v.*, tell tales. O.E. *talian*

Talent, *s.*, desire, inclination. L. *talentum* (a measure of weight)

Tapicer, *s.*, weaver of tapestry. O.Fr. *tapisseur*. Cf. O.Fr. *tapiz*, L. *tapēte* (carpet, tapestry)

Tappestere, *s.*, barmaid. O.E. *tæppestre*. Cf. O.E. *tæppa* (tap)

Targe, *s.*, small round shield. O.Fr. *targue* or *targe*. O.N. *targa*

Tarie(n), *v.*, tarry, delay; Tarying, *pr. p.*, tarrying. O.E. *tergan* (annoy)

Tart, *adj.*, tart, sharp, pungent. O.E. *teart*

Tartre, *s.*, tartar; oille of tartre, cream of tartar. O.Fr. *tartre*. Arabic

Tavern, *s.*, inn; Taverneer, *s.*, innkeeper. O.Fr. *tavern*, L. *taberna* (hut)

Tayl, *s.*, tail. O.E. *tægl*

Teche(n), *v.*, teach, direct (to); Taughte, *p.t. s.*, taught; Taught, Ytaught, *p.p.*, taught. O.E. *tǣcan*; *tǣhte* or *tāhte*

Teer, *s.*, tear. O.E. *tēar*

Telle(n), *s.*, tell, relate; telle(n) tale, take account of; telle no stoor, set no store by, think nothing (of); Toolde, Tolde, *p.t. s.*, told; litel tale hath he toold, he has taken little account; Toold, *p.p.*, told. O.E. *tellan*; *tālde*; *tāld*

Temple, *s.*, inn of court. L. *templum* (temple)

Tendre, *adj.*, tender. O.Fr. *tendre*, L. *tener-um*

Terciane, *adj.*, (fever) whose fits occur every other day.

L. *tertiānus* (belonging to the third)

Terme, *s.*, term, period; mode of expression, phrase; in termes, in terme, in set terms, in precise phrases; accurately, precisely. O.Fr. *terme*, L. *terminus* (boundary)

Th', *adj.*, the. Th' is used before a vowel or before silent *h*; *pron.*, thee; the Goost that in th' alighte, the (Holy) Spirit that descended on thee

Than, Thanne, *adv.*, *conj.*, then, than. O.E. *þonne*, *þanne*

Thank, *s.*, thanks, gratitude. O.E. *þanc*

That, *adj.*, that, the; Tho, *pl.*, those. O.E. *þæt*, *þā* (*pl.*)

That, *conj.*, that, so that. That is redundant after Conjunctive Adverbs, e.g. *as* (*that*), *how* (*that*), *whan* (*that*), *if* (*that*); and also after Relative Adverbs, e.g., *wher* (*that*), *ther* (*that*). O.E. *þæt*, *þætte*

That, *pron.*, that, the; who, which; that that, what; that they, which; that oon, the one; that other, the other. O.E. *þæt*

Thee(n), *v.*, thrive, prosper; so theech = so thee ich, as I hope to thrive; God lat him never thee, God let him never prosper; so moot I thee, may I thrive, as I hope to prosper. O.E. *þēon*

Theef, *s.*, thief; Theves, *pl.*, thieves. O.E. *þēof*

Theer(e), *adv.*, there. O.E. *þǣr*, *þēr*

Theme, *s.*, text. L.Gk. *thema*

Thenke(n), Thinke(n), *v.*, think, imagine; Thoghte, *p.t. s.*, thought. O.E. *þencan*; *þōhte* (think). See Thinke(n)

Thennesforth, *adv.,* thenceforth

Ther, *adv.,* there; where, wherever; **ther he is now,** (there) where he now is; **Ther as,** there where, where. O.E. *þǣr, þēr*

Ther-biforn, *adv.,* before that, previously

Therby, *adv.,* by it, therewith

Therfore, *adv.,* for it, therefore, on that account

Therinne, *adv.,* in it, therein

Therof, *adv.,* of it, thereof, concerning that

Theron, *adv.,* on it, thereupon

Therto, *adv.,* moreover, in addition

Therupon, *adv.,* immediately

Therwith, *adv.,* with it, moreover, by means of it

Therwithal, *adv.,* with it, moreover, by means of it

Thikke, *adj.,* thick, plump. O.E. *þicce*

Thilke, *adj.,* that same, that. O.E. *þylc* or *þyllīc* (such), confused in meaning with *se ilca,* M.E. *the ilke, thilke* (the same)

Thing, Thyng, *s.,* thing, something; property, wealth; deed, legal document; **Thinges,** *pl.,* things, business; **for any thing,** in spite of anything, at all events; **in litel thing,** in little wealth, in a small income; **lette for to do my thinges,** delay doing my business. O.E. *þing*

Thinke(n), *v. impers.,* seem; **Thinketh,** 3 *pr. s.,* (it) seems; **it thinketh me,** it seems to me; **me thinketh,** it seems to me; **us thinketh,** it seems to us; **Thoughte,** *p.t. s.,* (it) seemed; **me thoughte, it thoughte me,** it seemed to me; **him thoughte,** it seemed

to him; **us thoughte, it** seemed to us; **hem thoughte,** it seemed to them. O.E. *þyncan, þūhte* (seem). See **Thenke(n)**

Thinne, *adj.,* thin. O.E. *þynne*

This, *adj.,* this, the; **Thise,** *pl.,* these. O.E. *þis*

Tho (1), *pl., adj.,* those. O.E. *þā (pron.)*

Tho (2), *adv.,* then. O.E. *þā (adv.)*

Thoght, Thought, *s.,* thought. O.E. *(ge-)þōht*

Thombe, *s.,* thumb. O.E. *þūma*

Thonder, *s.,* thunder. O.E. *þunor*

Th'onour, *s.,* the honour; **th'onour of God shal sprede,** reverence for God shall increase (thereby). O.Fr. *honeur* or *onor,* L. *honōr-em*

Though (that), *adv., conj.,* though, although; **As though,** as if. O.N. *þó,* O.E. *þēah*

Thoughte, *p.t. s. impers.,* it seemed. See **Thinke(n)**

Thresshe(n), *v.,* thresh. O.E. *þerscan*

Thridde, *adj.,* third. O.E. *þridda*

Thriftily, *adv.,* carefully, properly. Cf. O.N. *þrif* or *þrift* (thrift)

Thritty, *adj.,* thirty. O.E. *þrītig, þrittig*

Throte, *s.,* throat. O.E. *þrotu*

Throwe(n), *v.,* throw; **Threwe,** *p.t. pl.,* threw. O.E. *þrāwan* (twist); *þrēow*

Thryes, *adv.,* thrice, three times

Thurgh, *prep.,* through, by (means of). O.E. *þurh*

Thurghout, *prep.,* through

Thy, Thyn, *poss. pron.,* thy. O.E. *þīn*

Thyng, *s.,* thing; **Thynges,** *pl.,* business. See **Thing**

Til, *prep.,* to; *conj.,* until; **til**

oother, to the others. O.E. (Cædmon) *til,* O.N. *til*

Tipet, *s.,* tippet, short cape. O.E. *tæpped* or *tæppet*

Tiptoon, *s. pl.,* tiptoes, the tips of the toes ; **on his tiptoon,** on tiptoe

To, *prep.,* to, for ; **to our doctrine,** for our edification ; **to . . . ward,** towards, going to. O.E. *to.* **Too,** *adv.,* too. O.E. *tō* (same word as to, *prep.*)

Toft, *s.,* tuft

To-geder, To-gider, To-gidres, Togidre, *adv.,* together. O.E. *tōgædere*

Tollen, *v.,* take toll, receive payment. Cf. O.E. *toll* (toll, payment)

Tombe, *s.,* tomb. Fr. *tombe,* LL. *tumba* (grave)

Tombesteres, *s. pl.,* dancing-girls ; acrobats, tumblers. O.E. *tumbestre.* Cf. O.E. *tumbian* (dance, tumble)

To-morwe, *adv.,* to-morrow. O.E. *tō-morgen*

Tong(e), *s.,* tongue. O.E. *tunge*

To-nyght, *adv.,* last night ; to-night

Too, *s.,* toe ; **Toon, Toos,** *pl.,* toes. O.E. *tā, tān (pl.)*

Tool, *s.,* tool, weapon. O.E. *tōl*

Toold, *p.t. s.,* told. See **Telle(n)**

Toon, Toos, *s. pl.,* toes. See **Too**

Top, *s.,* top (highest part) ; hair on crown of the head. O.E. *top*

To-rende(n), *v.,* rend asunder, tear in pieces ; **To-rente,** *p.t. s.,* rent in pieces. O.E. *to-rendan*

Torne(n), *v.,* turn. O.Fr. *torner,* L. *tornare*

To-tere(n), *v.,* tear asunder, tear in pieces. O.E. *tō-teran*

Touching, *prep.,* concerning.

Cf. O.Fr. *touchier* or *toucher* (touch). Germ.

Toun, *s.,* village, town. O.E. *tūn*

Tragedie, *s.,* tragic narrative, sad story. O.Fr. *tragedie,* L.Gk. *tragœdia* (dramatic tragedy)

Traison, Trayson, *s.,* treason, treachery. O.Fr. *traïson,* L. *traditiō-nem* (surrender)

Trappe, *s.,* trap. O.E. *treppe* or *træppe*

Traytour, *s.,* traitor ; *adj.,* traitorous. O.Fr. *traïtre* or *traïtor,* LL. *trăditor, traditor-em* (betrayer)

Trecherye, *s.,* treachery, trickery. O.Fr. *trecherie.* Cf. L. *trīcae* (wiles, tricks)

Trede(n), *v.,* tread ; **Troden,** *p.p.,* stepped. O.E. *tredan*

Tresor, *s.,* treasure. O.Fr. *trésor,* L.Gk. *thēsaurus*

Trespas, *s.,* wrong. O.Fr. *tres-pas,* LL. *trans-passus* (passing beyond)

Trespasse, *v.,* do wrong. O.Fr. *trespasser,* LL. *trans-passare* (go beyond)

Trete, *v.,* treat of, tell. O.Fr. *traiter,* L. *tractare* (handle)

Tretee, *s.,* treaty, agreement. O.Fr. *traité* (treated), L. *tractătus* (handled)

Tretis, *adj.,* long, well proportioned. O.Fr. *traitiz* or *tretis,* LL. *tract-itius* (drawn out)

Trewe, *adj.,* true, honest ; **ful trewe,** very true. O.E. *trēowe*

Trewely, *adv.,* truly, certainly

Treye, *adj.,* three. O.Fr. *trei(s)*

Triacle, *s.,* antidote (for poison) ; medicine, especially licorice. O.Fr. *triacle,* L.Gk. *thēriaca* (antidote)

Tribulacioun, *s.,* tribulation,

rub, suffering. **L.** *tribu-
lātiō-nem* (affliction)

Trikled, *p.t. pl.*, trickled

Trompe, *s.*, trumpet. **O.Fr.**
trompe (hunting horn),
O.H.G. *trumba* or *trumpa*

Trone, *s.*, throne. **O.Fr.** *trone*,
L.Gk. *thronus*

Trouthe, *s.*, troth, truth; faith,
fidelity; have heer my
trouthe, I promise thee, take
my word for it; by my
trowthe, truly. **O.E.** *trēowð*
(truth)

Trowe(n), *v.*, believe, think.
O.E. *trēowan, trūwian* (trust)

Trussed, *p.p.*, trussed, packed.
Cf. **Fr.** *trousse* (bundle)

Truste(n), *v.*, trust, rely;
truste wel, believe me

Tukked, *p.p.*, tucked up

Turn, *s.*, turn; doon a freendes
turn, done a good turn

Turne(n), *v.*, turn; Turneth,
imp. pl., turn. **O.E.** *turnian.*
Cf. **O.Fr.** *torner*, **L.** *tornare*

Twelf, *adj.*, twelve. **O.E.** *twelf*

Twelfmonth, *s.*, twelvemonth,
year. **O.E.** *twelf monaþ*

Tweye, *adj.*, two. **O.E.** *twēgen*
(*m.*)

Twinne(n), *v.* to separate, depart. Cf. **O.E.** *(ge-)twinne*
(double)

Twyes, *adv.*, twice. **O.E.** *twiga*
+*es*

Tyd(e), *s.*, time; Tydes, *pl.*,
tides. **O.E.** *tīd* (time)

Tyme, *s.*, time, hour, season.
O.E. *tīma*

Tythes, *s. pl.*, tithes, tax of
one-tenth of the produce of
the land. **O.E.** *tēoða* (tenth)

Unbokele, *v.*, to unbuckle. Cf.
O.Fr. *boucle* (buckle). **L.**
buccula (cheek)

Unbrent, *p.p.*, unburnt. See
Brenne(n)

Undergrowe(n), *adj.*, undersized

Understonde(n), *v.*, understand,
Understonde(n), *p.p.*, understood. **O.E.** *understandan*
or *understondan*

Undertake, *v.*, undertake; vow.
See Take

Undiscreet, *adj.*, indiscreet

Undren, Undern, *s.*, morning
from 9 a.m. to 12 noon.
O.E. *undern*

Unknowe(n), *adj.*, unknown

Unkynde, *adj.*, unnatural, hard-
hearted. **O.E.** *uncynde* (unnatural)

Unlyk, *adj.*, *prep.*, unlike. **O.E.**
ungelīc or *unlīc*

Unnethe, *adv.*, hardly, scarcely.
O.E. *un-ēaþe* (not easily)

Unstable, *adj.*, irresolute, fickle.
Cf. **O.Fr.** *estable*, **L.** *stabilis*
(firm)

Untrewe, *adv.*, untruly. **O.E.**
untrēowe

Up, *adv.*, up; up and down,
backwards and forwards.
O.E. *ūp*

Up, Upon, *prep.*, on, upon; up
peril, on peril; upon lond, in
the country; upon a day, in
one day. **O.E.** *uppan*

Upright, *adv.*, face upwards, on
his back. **O.E.** *ūprihte*

Up-swal, *p.t. s.*, swelled up. See
Swelle(n)

Uptaken, *p.p.*, taken up. See
Take

Urinals, *s. pl.*, medical vessels.
LL. *urīnālia*

Usage, *s.*, usage, use, habit;
was in usage, was in use,
was used; hadde in usage,
was accustomed. **O.Fr.** *usage*,
LL. *ūsaticum*

Use, *v.*, to use; Used, *p.p.* **O.Fr.**
user, **LL.** *ūsare* (use). Cf. **L.**
ūsus (use)

Usure, *s.*, usury, money-lending. **L.** *usūra* (interest)

Vanisshe, *v.*, vanish, waste away. O.Fr. *(es-)vanir, (es)vaniss-ant.* Cf. L. *evānescere*

Vanitee, *s.*, vanity, emptiness, unreality. O.Fr. *vanité,* L. *vānitātem* (emptiness). Cf. *vānus* (empty)

Vavasour, *s.*, vassal, *e.g.,* knight or squire. O.Fr. *vavassour,* LL. *vassus vassorum* (vassal of vassals)

Venerye, *s.*, hunting. O.Fr. *venerie.* Cf. L. *venari* (to hunt)

Venim, *s.*, venom, malice. O.Fr. *venim,* L. *venēnum*

Venimous, *adj.*, venomous, poisonous

Verdit, *s.*, verdict. A.Fr. *verdit,* L. *vere dictum* (truly said)

Vernicle, *s.*, cloth with picture of Christ's face; copy of St Veronica's handkerchief, which was so marked after wiping Christ's face as He carried His cross

Verraily, *adv.*, verily

Verray, *adj.*, fine, true; fine (ironical). O.Fr. *verai.* Cf. L. *vērus* (true). (Never an intensive adverb like modern 'very')

Vers, *s.*, verse; **Vers**, *pl.*, verses. O.E. *fers,* O.Fr. *vers,* L. *versus* (line)

Vertu, *s.*, virtue, power; **of** which **vertu**, from which (whose) power. O.Fr. *vertu,* L. *virtus, virtūtem* (power). Cf. L. *vir* (man)

Vertuous, *adj.*, virtuous, beneficent; capable

Veyl, *s.*, veil. A.Fr. *veile,* L. *vēlum* (sail, *curtain*)

Veyn, *adj.*, vain; in veyn, in vain. O.Fr. *vain,* L. *vānus* (empty)

Veyne, *s.*, vein; thread. O.Fr. *veine,* L. *vēna*

Veyne-glorie, *s.*, pretentious-ness, boastfulness. O.Fr. *vain,* L. *vānus* (empty) + O.Fr. *glorie,* L. *glōria* (glory)

Viage, *s.*, journey. O.Fr. *veage* or *viage,* L. *viāticum* (money for travel). Cf. *via* (road)

Vigilyes, *s. pl.*, vigils, wakes; assemblies at church on the eves of festivals, especially of patron saint of a guild. L. *vigilia* (watching)

Vileynye, *s.*, the conduct of a villain or slave, vile conduct, filthy language, rudeness; ill-breeding; **lucre of viley-nye**, filthy lucre. O.Fr. *vilenie,* LL. *villānia.* Cf. O.Fr. *vilein,* LL. *villānus* (farm servant), L. *villa* (farm)

Virginitee, *s.*, virginity; the life of the Blessed Virgin. L. *virginitas*

Visage, *s.*, face. O.Fr. *visage.* Cf. L. *visus* (look)

Vitaille, *s.*, victuals, provisions. O.Fr. *vitailles.* L. *victuālia* (provisions)

Vouchesauf, *v.*, vouchsafe, grant, agree. O.Fr. *vochier,* L. *vocāre* (call) + O.Fr. *sauf,* L. *salvus* (safe)

Voys, *s.*, voice. O.Fr. *vois,* L. *vōx, vōcem*

Vyne, *s.*, vine. L. *vīnea* (vine-yard)

Waast, *s.*, waist. Cf. O.E. *wæstm* (growth)

Waferers, *s. pl.*, makers of wafers, confectioners. Cf. A.Fr. *wafre,* Fr. *gaufre* (wafer). Germ.

Waite(n), *v.*, watch, look out; waited after, expected, waited for. A.Fr. *waitier,* Fr. *guetter.* Cf. O.H.G. *wahten* (watch)

Wake(n), *v.*, be awake; **Wook**, *p.t. s.*, awoke. O.E. *wacan,* *wōc* (arise); O.E. *wacian* (wake(n))

Wakene(n), *v.*, waken, cause to be awake. O.E. *wæcnan*

Walet, *s.*, wallet, bag, scrip

Walke(n), *v.*, walk, roam. O.E. *wealcan* (roll)

Wan, *p.t. s.*, gained. See Winne(n)

Wandring, *s.*, wandering, travelling. Cf. O.E. *wandrian* (wander)

Wantown, *adj.*, wanton, riotous, wild. O.E. *wan* (wanting) + *togen* (drawn, educated)

Wantownesse, *s.*, wantonness, affectation

War, *adj.*, wary, aware; prudent; I was war, I was aware; be war, beware; beth war, beware. O.E. *wær* (heedful)

Wardrobe, *s.*, wardrobe; privy. A.Fr. *warderobe*, O.Fr. *garderobe*. Germ.

Ware(n), *v.*, take heed; War, *pr. s. subj.*, beware; war him, let him beware; war you, beware, make way; Ware, *imp. pl.*, beware (lest). O.E. *warian*

Warente, *v.*, protect, authorize. A.Fr. *warantir*, O.Fr. *garantier*. Germ.

Warice, Warisshe, *v.*, heal, save, cure. A.Fr. *warir*, *wariss-ant*, O.Fr. *garir*, Fr. *guérir*. Cf. O.H.G. *warjan* (guard)

Warne(n), *v.*, warn, forbid. O.E. *wearnian* or *warnian*. Cf. O.E. *wearn* (obstacle)

Wasshe(n), *v.*, wash; Wasshe, *p.p.*, washed, dipped. O.E. *wascan*

Wast, *s.*, waste. A.Fr. *wast*, O.Fr. *gast*. Cf. L. *vastus* (*adj.*, waste)

Wastel-breed, *s.*, fine bread,

cake-bread. A.Fr. *wastel*, O.Fr. *gastel*. Cf. Fr. *gâteau* (cake)

Waterlees, *adj.*, out of water, without water. O.E. *wæter-lēas*

Wateryng, *s.*, watering (for houses), pond

Wayk, *adj.*, weak. O.N. *veikr*

Webbe, *s.*, weaver. O.E. *webba*

Wel, Weel, *adv.*, well, fully; much, about; wel was him therwith, it was a joy to him; ful wel, very well. O.E. *wel*

Welked, *adj.*, withered

Welle, *s.*, well, fountain. O.E. *wella*

Welthe, *s.*, wealth. O.E. *wela* (wealth) + *th* (abstract suffix)

Wenche, *s.*, wench, girl. O.E. *wencel* (maid)

Wende(n), *v.*, wend, go; Wente, *p.t. s.*, went; Went, *p.p.*, gone; been went, are gone. O.E. *wendan* (turn)

Wene(n), *v.*, ween, suppose, think; Weneth, 3 *pr. s.*, thinks, imagines; Weende, *p.t. s. subj.*, would have thought. O.E. *wēnan*

Wepe(n), *v.*, weep; Weep, *p.t. s.*, wept; Wepyng(e), *pr. p.*, weeping. O.E. *wēpan*; *wēop*

Werche(n), Werke(n), *v.*, work, do, cause; Wroughte, *p.t. s.*, worked, did, created; Wroght, Wrought, Y-wroght, *p.p.*, made, done. O.E. *wyrc(e)an*, Kent. *werc(e)an*; *worhte* (*p.t.*)

Were, *p.t. s. subj.*, were; ful looth were hym, he was very unwilling; but it were, but were there, but if there were; Were(n), *p.t. pl.*, were. O.E. *wǣre*, *wǣron*

Were(n), *v.*, wear ; **Werede, Wered**, *p.t. s.*, were. O.E. *werian*

Werk, *s.*, work, deed. O.E. *weorc* or *werc*

Werke(n), *s.*, do, cause. O.E. *wyrcan*, Kent. *wercan*. See **Werche(n)**

Werre, *s.*, war. A.Fr. *werre*, O.Fr. *guerre*, O.H.G. *werra* (strife)

Werte, *s.*, wart. O.E. *wearte*

Wete(n), *v.*, wet ; **Wette**, *p.t. s.*, wetted. Cf. O.E. *wǣtan* (moisten), *wǣt* (*adj.*, wet)

Wex, *s.*, wax, beeswax. O.E. *weax*

Wexe(n), *v.*, wax, grow, become. O.E. *weaxan* (grow)

Wey, *s.*, way. O.E. *weg*

Weye(n), *v.*, weigh. O.E. *wegan*

Weylaway, *int.*, alas ! wellaway ! O.E. *wā la wā*

Whan (that), *adv.*, when. O.E. *hwænne* or *hwanne*

What, *interrog. pron.*, what, what sort of a ; *adv.*, why ? how ? ; **what that**, whatever ; **what so**, whatever. O.E. *hwæt*

Whelkes, *s. pl.*, pimples. Cf. O.E. *hwylca* (a boil)

Whelpe, *s.*, puppy, dog. O.E. *hwelp* (cub)

Whennes (that), *adv.*, whence

Wher (1), *adv.*, where. O.E. *hwēr*

Wher (2), *conj.*, whether ; **wher ye go or ride**, whether you walk or ride, however you go. O.E. *hwæðer*

Wheras, *adv.*, where

Wherewith, *adv.* (means) with which, wherewithal

Wherfore, *conj.*, for this (reason), therefore

Whete, *s.*, wheat. O.E. *hwǣte*

Whether (that), *conj.*, whether. O.E. *hwæðer*

Which, *pron.*, which ; who, whom ; what kind of ; **which that**, who, which ; **of which vertu**, from which (whose) power ; **Whiche**, *pl.* O.E. *hwilc*

Whil, *adv.*, whilst ; **the whiles that**, whilst. O.E. *hwīl* (while), *þā hwīle þe* (whilst)

Whilom, *adv.*, once. O.E. *hwīlum* (once)

Who, *pron.*, who ; **Whos**, *poss.*, whose ; **Whom**, *acc. dat.*, whom ; **Who-so**, *indef. pron.*, whoever, if anyone. O.E. *hwā, hwæs, hwām*

Why (that), *adv.*, why, for what reason. O.E. *hwȳ, hwī*

Whyl (that), *conj.*, whilst. O.E. (*þā*) *hwīle* (*þe*)

Whyle, *s.*, while, time. O.E. *hwīl*

Whyt, *adj.*, white ; **Whitter**, *comp.* whiter. O.E. *hwīt* ; *hwīttra* (*comp.*)

Widwe, a widow. O.E. *widwe*

Wight, *s.*, creature, person. O.E. *wiht*

Wikke, *adj.*, wicked, evil. Cf. O.E. *wicca* (wizard)

Wikkednesse, *s.*, wickedness, fault

Wilde, *adj.*, wild. O.E. *wilde*

Wilfully, *adv.*, willingly, deliberately

Wille, *s.*, will, desire. O.E. *willa*

Wille(n), *v.*, will, desire, wish, be ready (to) ; **Wil**, 1, 3 *pr. s.*, wish, desires ; **Wol(e)**, 1, 3 *pr. s.*, will, am (is) ready to ; **Wolt**, 2 *pr. s.*, wilt ; **woltow**, wilt thou ; **Wole**, *pr. pl.*, will ; **Wold, Wolde**, *p.t. s.*, would ; **Woldestow**, 2 *pr. s*, wouldst thou ; **Wolden**, *p.t. pl.*, would, were minded to. O.E. *willan* ; *wolde*

Wimpel, *s.*, wimple, kerchief of

linen arranged in folds about the head and pleated under the chin. O.E. *wimpel*

Winke(n), *v.*, blink, close the eyes. O.E. *wincian*

Winne(n), *v.*, win; profit; conquer; Wan, *p.t. s.*, won, gained; Wonne(n), *p.p.*, won; koude on him winne, could get the better of him. O.E. *(ge)-winnan*; *wan*; *wunnen*

Winning, *s.*, gain, profit

Wis, *adv.*, verily, surely; as wis, as sure (as). O.E. *gewiss* (*adj.*) (sure)

Wiste, *p.t. s.*, knew. See Wite(n)

Wit, *s.*, wit, judgment, mental power. O.E. *witt*

Wite(n), *v.*, know; Woot, 1, 3 *pr. s.*, wot, know, knows; God woot, God knows; ye woot, you know; Woost, 2 *pr. s.*, knowest; Witen, *pr. pl.*, know; Wiste, *p.t.*, knew; wiste a man, if a man knew. O.E. *witan*; *wāt*, *wāst* (2 *pr.*), *witon* (*pr. pl.*), *wiste* (*p.t.*)

With, *prep.*, with, by. O.E. *wiþ* (against), *mid* (with)

Withalle, *adv.*, withal, moreover. O.E. *mid alle*

Withholde(n), *v.*, retain; Withholde(n), *p.p.*, retained. O.E. *with-healdan*

Withinne, *adv.*, within, inside. O.E. *wiþinnan*

Withoute(n), *adv.*, *prep.*, without, on the outside. O.E. *wiþūtan*

Withseye(n), *v.*, contradict, gainsay. O.E. *wiþsecgan*

Witing, *s.*, fore-knowledge, knowledge

Witnesse, *v.*, testify, take to witness; witnesse on, see; witnesse on hym that any parfit clerk is, take any man to witness that is learned. Cf. O.E. *witnes* (testimony)

Wlatsom, *adj.*, disgusting, loathsome. Cf. O.E. *wlātian* (loathe)

Wo, *s.*, woe, misery; that werken . . . ful wo, that cause much distress; wo was, alas for. O.E. *wā*

Wo, *adj.*, unhappy, sad. O.E. *w(e)ā*; Wo was, alas for

Wode, *s.*, wood. O.E. *wudu*

Woful, *adj.*, unhappy

Wol(e), Wolt, Wolde. See Wille(n)

Wolle, *s.*, wool. O.E. *wull*

Wombe, *s.*, belly, stomach. O.E. *wǎmb* or *wǒmb*

Womman, *s.*, woman; Wommen, *pl.*, women. O.E. *wīf-mann*

Wonder, *s.*, wonder, marvel; *adj.*, wonderful, marvellous; wonder was to see, it was wonderful to see; *adv.*, wondrously, marvellously. O.E. *wundor* (*s.*)

Wonderly, *adv.*, wondrously. O.E. *wundorlice*

Wondre(n), *v.*, to wonder, marvel. O.E. *wundrian*

Wone, *s.* wont, habit, custom. O.E. *(ge)-wuna*

Wone(n), *v.*, dwell, be accustomed; Woned, Wont, *p.p.*, dwelt, accustomed; Woninge, *pr. p.*, dwelling. O.E. *wunian*

Wonne(n), *p.p.*, won. See Winne(n)

Wood, *adj.*, mad; but if he were wood, unless he were a fool. O.E. *wōd*

Woodecraft, *s.*, hunting

Woodnesse, *s.*, madness

Wook, *s.*, awoke. See Wake(n)

Woot, Woost, *pr. s.*, know, knows(t). See Wite(n)

Worm, *s.*, worm, snake. O.E. *wyrm* or *wurm* (reptile, worm)

Worshipe, *v.*, adore, pay honour

to. Cf. O.E. *weorþscipe* or *wurþscipe* (worship)

Worsted, *s.*, woollen cloth [of Worstead, Norfolk]

Worte, *s.*, vegetable, herb. O.E. *wyrt* or *wurt*

Worth, *adj.*, worth, worth while. O.E. *weorþe, wurþe*

Worthe(n), *v.*, be, become. O.E. *weorþan* or *wurþan*

Worthinesse, *s.*, bravery, moral excellence

Worthy, *adj.*, worthy, brave; excellent, pious. O.E. *weorþig* or *wurþig*

Wrappe, *v.*, wrap (in)

Wrastle(n), *v.*, wrestle. O.E. *wrǣstlian*

Wrecche, *s.*, wretch, unhappy man. O.E. *wrecca*

Wrecchednesse, *s.*, wretchedness, misery

Wreke(n), *v.*, wreak, avenge. O.E. *wrecan* (banish)

Wrighte, *s.*, workman, carpenter. O.E. *wyrhta*

Writ, *s.*, writing; hooly writ, the Bible. O.E. *writ*

Writ, *p.t.* *s.*, wrote. See Wryte(n)

Writyng, *s.*, writing, drafting

Wroght, Wrought, *p.p.*, made, done; wrought ful clene and weel, fashioned finely and skilfully. See Werche(n)

Wroot, *p.t.* *s.*, wrote. See Wryte(n)

Wrooth, *adj.*, wroth, angry. O.E. *wrāþ*

Wryte(n), write; **Wroot, Writ**, *p.t.* *s.*, wrote; **Write(n)**, **Ywrite**, *p.p.*, written. O.E. *writan; wrāt, writon (p.t. pl.); writen*

Wyd, *adj.*, wide, roomy. O.E. *wid*

Wyf, *s.*, woman, wife; **Wyves**, *pl.*, women, wives. O.E. *wīf*

Wyke, *s.*, week. O.E. *wice*

Wyn, *s.*, wine; **wyn-yevyng**, wine-giving. O.E. *wīn*, L *vīnum*

Wynd, *s.*, wind. O.E. *wind*

Wype(n), *v.*, wipe; **Wyped**, *p.t.* wiped. O.E. *wīpian*

Wys, *adj.*, wise, prudent; to make it wys, to discuss it. O.E. *wīs*

Wyse, *s.*, way, manner, fashion. O.E. *wīse*

Y-, prefix, frequently indicating the *p.p.* O.E. *ge-*

Yaf, *p.t.* *s.*, gave. See Yeve(n)

Y-been, *p.p.*, been. See Be, Been

Y-bore(n), *p.p.*, borne, carried. See Bere(n)

Y-bounde, *p.p.*, bound. O.E. *gebunden*

Y-caried, *p.p.*, carried. See Carie(n)

Y-cleped, *p.p.*, called, named. See Clepe(n)

Y-come (n), *p.p.*, come. See Come

Y-coyned, *p.p.*, coined. O.Fr. *coignier.* Cf. L. *cuneus* (wedge)

Y-crammed, *p.p.*, crammed, filled. O.E. *crammian (inf.)*

Ydel, *adj.*, idle, vain; in ydel, in vain. O.E. *īdel*

Ydelly, *adv.*, idly, in vain

Y-doon, *p.p.*, done. See Do, Doon

Y-drawe(n), *p.p.*, drawn. See Drawe(n)

Ye (1), *pron. nom.*, you; **You**, *acc.*, you; **Your**, *poss.*, your. O.E. *gē; ēow; ēower*

Ye (2), *adv.*, yea, yes. O.E. *gēa*

Yeddinges, *s. pl.*, ballads, tales. O.E. *giddung* (saying, song)

Yeer, *s.*, year ; **Yeer, Yeres,** *pl.*, years ; yeer by yeer, year after year. O.E. *gēar*

Yeerd, Yerd, *s.*, yard, garden. O.E. *geard*

Yeldhalle, *s.*, guild-hall. O.E. *gield* (guild) + *heall* (hall)

Yelding, *s.*, yielding ; produce, yield. Cf. O.E. *gieldan* (to yield)

Yellen, *v.*, yell ; **Yelleden,** *p.t. pl.*, yelled. O.E. *giellan*

Yeman, *s.*, yeoman

Yemanly, *adv.*, like a yeoman, smartly

Yerd, *s.*, rod, stick. O.E. *gierd* or *gerd* (yard, rod)

Yerne, *adv.*, eagerly, briskly. O.E. *georne*

Yeve(n), Yive, *v.*, give ; **Yaf,** *p.t. s.*, gave ; yaf in hir thought, suggested to her mind ; **Yaf, Yaven,** *p.t., pl.*, gave ; **Yeven,** *p.p.*, given. O.E. *giefan* or *gefan* ; *geaf* or *gæf* ; *gēafon* or *gēfon* ; *giefen* or *gefen*

Y-falle(n), *p.p.*, fallen, befallen, happened. See **Falle(n)**

Y-founde(n), *p.p.*, found. See **Fynde(n)**

Y-go, Y-gon, Y-goon, *p.p.*, gone. See **Goon, Gon**

Y-graunted, *p.p.*, granted. See **Graunte(n)**

Y-hent, *p.p.*, seized, taken. See **Hente(n)**

Y-holde, *p.p.*, held ; esteemed, considered. See **Holde(n), Hoolde(n)**

Yift, *s.*, gift. O.E., O.N. *gift*

Yis, *adv.*, yes. O.E. *gīse*

Yive, *v.*, give. See **Yeve(n)**

Y-knowe, *p.p.*, known. See **Knowe(n)**

Y-korven, *p.p.*, cut. See **Kerve(n)**

Y-lad, *p.p.*, led. See **Lede(n)**

Y-logged, *p.p.*, lodged. See **Logge(n)**

Y-lyk, *adj.*, like. O.E. *gelīc*

Y-maked, *p.p.*, made. See **Make(n)**

Ynogh, *adj.*, enough ; **Ynough,** *adv.*, enough. O.E. *ge-nōh*

Yong, *adj.*, young ; **Yonge,** *def.* O.E. *geong*

Youthe, *s.*, youth. O.E. *geoguð*

Y-preved, *p.p.*, proved, shown (to be). See **Preve(n)**

Y-punisshed, *p.p.*, punished. Cf. O.Fr. *punir, punissant,* L. *punīre*

Y-purfiled, *p.p.*, purfled, bordered with a line, trimmed. Cf. O.Fr. *porfil* (edging) ; cf. L. *fīlum* (thread)

Y-ronne, *p.p.*, run. See **Renne(n)**

Y-sene, *adj.*, seen, visible. O.E. *gesīene, gesēne*

Y-set, *p.p.*, set, seated. See **Sette(n)**

Y-seyled, *p.p.*, sailed. See **Seyle(n)**

Y-shadwed, *p.p.*, overshadowed

Y-shave, *p.p.*, shaven. O.E. *ge-scafen*

Y-shorn, *p.p.*, shorn See **Shere(n)**

Y-shrive(n), *p.p.*, confessed, absolved. See **Shryve(n)**

Y-slawe, Y-slayn, *p.p.*, slain. See **Slee(n)**

Y-sprad, *p.p.*, spread. See **Sprede(n)**

Y-stonge, *p.p.*, stung. O.E. *gestungen*

Y-take, *p.p.*, taken. See **Take(n)**

Y-taught, *p.p.*, taught. See **Teche(n)**

Y-teyd, *p.p.*, tied (with laces), fastened. O.E. *ge-tieg(e)d*

Yvel, *s.*, evil, wrong. O.E. *yfel* (*s.*)

Yvel, *adj.*, evil, wicked. O.E. *yfel* (*adj.*)

Yvel(e), *adv.*, ill. O.E. *yfle*

Y-warned, *p.p.*, warned. See Warne(n)

Y-wimpled, *adj.*, wimpled, wearing a wimple. See Wimpel

Y-wis, *adv.*, certainly, truly. O.E. *ge-wis*

Y-write(n), *p.p.*, written. See Wryte(n)

Y-wroght, *p.p.*, wrought, made. See Werche(n), Werke(n)

Zephirus, *s.*, the west wind. L.Gk. *Zephyrus*